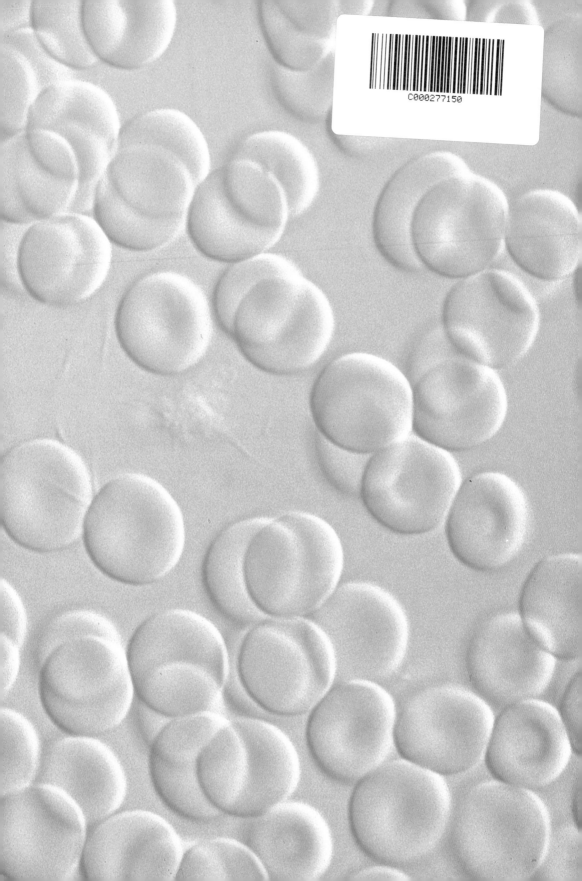

IN THE BLOOD

IN THE BLOOD

BLOOD

GOD, GENES AND DESTINY

STEVE JONES

HarperCollins*Publishers*

TO NORMA PERCY

HarperCollins*Publishers*
77 – 85 Fulham Palace Road,
Hammersmith, London W6 8JB

Published by HarperCollins*Publishers* 1996

1 3 5 7 9 8 6 4 2

Copyright © Steve Jones 1996

Steve Jones asserts the moral right to
be identified as the author of this work

A catalogue record for this book is available
from the British Library

ISBN 0 00 255511 5

Typeset in Linotype Janson by
HarperCollins*Publishers*

Printed and bound in Great Britain by
The Bath Press, Avon

CONTENTS

God, Genes and Destiny

For we wrestle not against flesh and blood,
but against principalities, against powers,
against the rulers of the darkness of this
world, against spiritual wickedness in
high places.

EPHESIANS 6:12

THIS BOOK WAS WRITTEN at Hitler's desk. Not, of course, the original – last seen in the hands of the Russians in 1945 – but a copy, a piece of stage furniture picked up cheap at the close of a play about the origins of the Second World War. It is a slightly embarrassing object to have to explain to visitors, but at thirty square feet is well suited for piling up books and even for banging in moments of frustration.

For a geneticist to use it as the plank for his opinions may strike some as appropriate. The bond between the study of human inheritance and Nazi ideology is well known: eugenics, the improvement of the human race by biological means, has always been close to political extremes on both left and right. Many are happy to use the history of genetics to berate its plans for the future. Those plans – designer babies, eugenic sterilization, racial classification – are more imagined than real. Most of those who study heredity are aware of the limitations of their subject and see no reason to defend it against outdated accusations. Genetics is, at last, like Germany, ready to stop apologizing for its past.

It is, though, facing a more subtle threat; that of public expectations far in advance of reality. One of the great moments in science fiction is when Flash Gordon, pursued by aliens, opens the boiler on his spacecraft and shouts to his crew: 'Throw on more uranium!' In the 1950s, uranium was wonderful stuff and space travel just around the corner. Obviously, space-ships would be superior versions of the *Flying Scotsman*. Nowadays, genes are in the same position: humans are based on DNA, they have social and medical problems, *ergo*, an understanding of DNA will soon cause those problems to disappear.

The title *In the Blood* turns on the widespread conviction that destiny is inborn. That belief began long before science. The term 'nature' itself derives from the Latin *natus*, that which is born, 'nation' from the same root. The Latin *sanguis* gave rise to the English 'sanguine'; hopeful and confident. Originally, though, it meant not just blood, but family, race and descent.

The idea of biology – blood – as essence is still very much alive. A 1995 article in *Wisden Cricketers' Almanack* claimed that the desire to play for England was a 'matter of biology' and that 'asians and negroes do not feel the same pride and identification with England as the white man'. The piece was entitled 'Is it in the blood?' Even for those without an overtly racial agenda, genes are more and more seen as responsible for fate. More and more, death seems to be programmed into our very being. Genes kill people; and two out every three readers of these pages will die for reasons connected with what they have inherited. Soon it may be possible to predict the probable date of a baby's death soon after its birth. Infectious disease may have been conquered, but is there any prospect of doing the same to afflictions that are inborn?

To some, all this threatens human autonomy. If everything is coded into DNA, what is left for free will? If man is but a glorified ape, where is the soul? Indeed, if society is no more than a mechanism for ensuring that genes are transmitted, what room is there for good and evil? Even those not interested in such abstract ideas are concerned that biology is removing the mystery from their own lives.

Because genetics is so often asked to test beliefs about what it means to be human, it is a science closer to moral and religious doctrine than any other. The Bible, the Torah and the Koran all explore the rules by which existence is governed: creation, inheritance, man's place in nature, good, evil, fate and salvation. The Old Testament was the first genetics text of all. It is largely a record of separation: of who is among the chosen. The idea of universal relatedness, a common humanity, is restricted to the New. Like most religious writings, both are codes for regulating society. Some people are labelled as inferior, others as born to rule. In biblical times, as now, human qualities were seen as innate and beyond control; the future, for good or ill, was set at birth. Kinship ruled those ancient lands and, in spite of the supposed tolerance of the times in which we live, it retains its power today.

At a time when three and a half million Americans claim to have been abducted by aliens and many more believe in the literal truth of the Book

A stirring image from 1930, the days when science seemed simple: the eugenics movement's view of the future.

ONLY *HEALTHY* SEED MUST BE SOWN!

CHECK THE SEEDS OF HEREDITARY DISEASE AND UNFITNESS BY EUGENICS

of Genesis there is need for rational analysis of such matters. Attitudes towards science when it tries to provide it mix fascination with distaste; a combination of sentiments similar to those held by many towards religion. Any discipline that sets out to explain the world, even in its own limited terms, comes inevitably into conflict with those whose beliefs are formed by faith rather than by evidence.

There have always been disputes between science and religion. Usually, it must be said, they are started by students of the latter (who tend to find science more interesting than scientists do theology). The war between the two is best seen as a battle between a shark and a tiger. On its own territory, each is invincible: but stray into the opponent's kingdom and the enemy is bound to prevail. Both tiger and shark, though, dominate their environment in a way that must make perfect sense to each. The ocean of ignorance that demands supernatural explanation is smaller than it was, but nobody knows when – if ever – it will dry up. The debate between belief and scepticism will run for a long time yet.

Although my own interest in matters religious is as amateur as that of most of my colleagues, it seems to me worth exploring the alternative accounts of existence if for no other reason than to point at their parallels. Because the questions posed by theology and by genetics are so similar *In the Blood* is, very loosely, structured around biblical themes: Adam and Eve, Original Sin, the Expulsion of the People of Israel, Resurrection, Armageddon, the Last Judgment and much more. By so doing one gets, remarkably quickly, from Genesis to DNA. Even if the ancient questions are not solved, at least they can now be asked in a new way.

By so doing, biology is in the same position as it was in 1858, when Charles Darwin and Alfred Russel Wallace presented their theory of evolution by natural selection to the Linnean Society of London. The idea that species – including our own – are not fixed but can change from one into another caused uproar in the religious establishment. It seemed to undermine the unique position of humankind and to destroy the relationship between man and God. Quite soon, at least in the eyes of enthusiasts, Darwinism emerged almost as a new religion: a system for justifying, or even organizing, the social order. Evolution entered the fabric of nineteenth-century intellectual life, and without at least a nodding acquaintance with it no-one could claim to be fully educated.

In the present century, genetics has succeeded in doing much the same thing. It has sold itself expertly to the public, which has been happy to pay the bill. A 1976 survey found that a third of British students had never heard of DNA, and that twice as many had no idea that it was a double helix. A poll twelve years later, though, found that eighty per cent of those questioned were able to answer quite sophisticated questions about inheritance – although two-thirds still thought that radioactive milk could be made safe by boiling. Geneticists have done a good job in educating society about what their subject can do. Certainly, its advances have been spectacular. Twenty years ago, only about a hundred genes had been located on human chromosomes. Now, around forty thousand have been placed in order along the twenty-three chromosome pairs.

They have, though, been more coy about what their subject has not achieved. Among the general public, one person in ten would be happy to accept gene manipulation to increase the intelligence of a child, or reduce the chance that it is born homosexual (the same proportion, incidentally, that would welcome a test to allow foetuses predisposed to homosexual behaviour to be aborted). These ambitions are, whatever their moral implications, scientifically quite unrealistic. Although the technology of ordering the letters in the DNA alphabet is well advanced, nothing is known about what most of it does. Working genes are, it seems, oases of sense in a desert of nonsense, with most of the inherited material having no apparent function.

Genetics has arrived at the same stage as the proud owner of a new video cassette recorder who tries to make sense of the instruction manual. To his dismay, half of it is missing and there is page after page of gibberish. Even worse, it is written in Japanese; the words are recognizably words, but that is all. Merely to set the clock is a matter of trial and error, just as if the manual had never been opened in the first place.

One of many attempts to parody Darwin: this one from a contemporary issue of *Punch* illustrates the nineteenth century's optimistic view that evolution means progress.

MAN·IS·BVT·A·WORM·

Design by Benjamin Waterhouse, architect of the Natural History Museum, illustrating Charles Darwin's *Descent of Man*.

When it comes to mending the machine should it go wrong, things are even worse. The instructions are useless as they give almost no hint of how what is clearly an impressive piece of equipment does its job. The promise of replacing damaged DNA has been just around the corner for a long time. The first claims of a breakthrough were made more than a decade ago. In 1996, there is not one case of a treatment whose success is unequivocally due to gene therapy. The rewards promised so confidently have not materialized and show few signs of so doing.

Nevertheless, and for reasons that have little to do with mundane matters of health, genetics is closer to the centre of public consciousness than it has ever been. In the 1960s, there was a retreat from the notion of biology as destiny. Everyone was, more or less, a free spirit, liberated from the restrictions of birth. That brief episode of emancipation is over. Now there is a new willingness to accept that life is constrained by biology. Even those who have long denied that genes say much about human existence are (often grudgingly) accepting that they can at least set the limits within which it is lived.

No-one disputes that social position is inherited: the chances of being in *Who's Who* are one in five for those whose father is included, but one in fifteen hundred for the general population. Some enthusiasts for the power of heredity feel that this is written into the DNA. William Bateson was the first Professor of Genetics at Cambridge. To him inheritance was central to the social order. In his 1912 book *Biological Fact and the Structure of Society* he wrote that 'The idea of social reform must not be to abolish class, but to ensure that each individual shall as far as possible get into the right class, stay there and usually his children after him.' Eighty years later, an American academic agreed: 'Success and failure in the American economy are increasingly a matter of the genes that people inherit . . . Programmes to expand opportunities for the disadvantaged are not going to make much difference.' Thus Charles Murray of Harvard. His 1994 bestseller *The Bell Curve* suggested that a biologically-deprived underclass had already emerged.

Sometimes, DNA is even seen as a burden of imperfection. It is becoming the court of last appeal. In a 1994 trial of a young American accused of murder the defence had a novel strategy to save their client from the electric chair. They used a supposed inborn predisposition to violence in a plea for mercy: 'You don't fault a blind person because he can't read the road signs, you don't fault a deaf person because he can't hear what you are saying . . . And if there is a biochemical basis . . . it's not justifying it, but it is mitigating.' The press, predictably, was outraged.

To others, the death sentence for the inherently imperfect is already being pronounced. According to Pope John Paul II, 'genetic screening is gravely opposed to the moral law when it is done with the thought of possibly inducing an abortion depending on the results. A diagnosis which shows the existence of a malformation or a hereditary illness must not be the equivalent of a death sentence.' In China, in contrast, the 1995 Law on Maternal and Infant Health Care makes prenatal testing compulsory; to be followed by termination if a disorder is found.

The idea that the dead live on and set rules for the living is uniquely human. No animal has a tradition beyond that learned from its parents or a social system that extends much beyond its own family. To ourselves, though, the past has always seemed part of the present. Genes bring the past alive. They show that all families and all nations are connected by an invisible web of kinship. To nationalists, shared blood is everything: for them, history is made in bed. Biology is the test of their ideas, and usually it proves them wrong.

DNA also contains the story of racial – and of human – history. Queen Victoria, on her first visit to London Zoo, thought the chimpanzees 'painfully and disagreeably human'. How would she have reacted to the discovery that we share ninety-eight per cent of our biological material with them and can no longer claim to be on some biological pinnacle, separate from the rest of creation? How, indeed, would she have coped with the finding that the differences among all European nations are less than those between adjacent African tribes under the control of a single member of her colonial administration? The theory of evolution, together with an understanding of the nature of inheritance, puts views about the inherent superiority or inferiority of ethnic groups into a new and powerful light.

All this might seem alarming. Genetics may indeed – as many non-scientists say – be so close to political and even to moral questions as to threaten the relationship between the natural and the spiritual. There is, though, a lesson from the past, when Darwinism seemed to do the same. It is that mankind has an infinite capacity not to be surprised. Only thirty-five years before the Darwin-Wallace lecture, the first fossil ever to be identified as human had been found in a cave on the Gower Peninsula, in South Wales. William Buckland, its discoverer (and Professor of Geology at Oxford), was astonished by its antiquity. The 'Red Lady of Paviland' (as she was named after her ochre-stained bones) must, he thought, be immeasurably ancient – perhaps as old as the Roman occupation of Britain. To Buckland, a believer in the biblical Flood, that was as far as his imagination could take him. The public agreed.

Now the Paviland fossil (of a man, not a woman) is known to be not two but twenty-five thousand years old; scarcely different from ourselves, and dead for what seems to modern eyes only an instant of evolutionary time. The oldest fossil of a human ancestor to be found in Britain (Boxgrove Man, discovered in 1994) lived half a million years ago and is, quite clearly, a biologically distinct precursor of today's Britons. Apart from a brief effusion of national pride at being the home of the oldest European (soon quashed by the discovery of an ancient Spaniard three hundred thousand years older) the public greeted its discovery with indifference. The theory of evolution is now banal, accepted by almost everyone who bothers to think about it. In spite of the fears of the Victorians it poses no threat to philosophy or to religion. It is just another fact that can, for those who wish to do so, be incorporated into the Divine plan.

A still from the 1960 film *Inherit the Wind*, based (loosely) on the Scopes Trial of 1925, in Dayton, Tennessee. John T. Scopes was accused of breaking the Butler Act (not itself repealed until 1967) which forbade the teaching of evolution in public schools as it contradicted the biblical account of Creation. The Monkey Trial (as it was known) became celebrated for the attack by Clarence Darrow, an eminent lawyer, on the constitutionality of the law and by the disastrous failure of William Jennings Bryan, the former Secretary of State, to refute him. Scopes was convicted and fined $100, but this was overturned on appeal. 1996 legislation in the same state prohibits the teaching of evolution as a 'fact' rather than a mere 'theory'.

The universal acceptance of Darwinism has another lesson for those with high expectations for science. Those who fear biology and those who see it as salvation are united in certainty of its power to confirm or to deny ideas about the human condition. Science, though, has no ambition or competence to do so. Efforts to arrange society on a scientific basis (and there have been plenty) always fail. In the same way, as attempts to suppress the teaching of evolution show, bids to use moral codes to regulate what science can say never succeed.

They arise from a delusion about its province. Science has, at its centre, a search for explanations that transcend human affairs. On the title-page of *The Origin of Species*, William Whewell, the inventor of the word 'scientist', is quoted as saying: '. . . with regard to the material world, we can at least go so far as this – we can perceive that events are brought about not by insulated interpositions of Divine power, exerted in each particular case, but by the establishment of general laws'. Such laws go beyond moral and ethical concerns about our own place in nature. This means that in science it is not enough to search ancient texts or even modern philosophy for solutions: instead there has to be objective enquiry into rules that apply to all creatures, human or not. As ethical beliefs are themselves a human construct they cannot be studied in this way. In spite of the hopes of those searching for salvation in biology, the double helix has no moral content.

The Linnean Society still occupies the building in which Darwin and Wallace presented their ideas. Burlington House is now more famous as the home of the Royal Academy, which shares it with the biologists and the geologists. It was built in 1665 as the home of the Earl of Burlington. Its address in Piccadilly was then the most fashionable in London, within walking distance of Westminster Abbey and St James' Palace. Now the area is more notable for such worldly institutions as the Ritz Hotel and Messrs Fortnum and Mason.

One of the curious things about London is its street names (they include, as it happens, only one Jones – Jones Alley, an undistinguished byway off Berkeley Square). Piccadilly, though, is a uniquely peculiar label. What can it mean? A quick look at a tourist guide gives one answer; close, in its nature, to those happy to accept metaphysical explanations of the human condition. The boulevard is named after 'one Higgins, a tailor', who built the first house there and who 'got most of his Estate by Pickadills, collars which in the last age were much worn in England'. The guide moves on to the next street, its explanation complete. To solve a problem, at least to the extent needed to satisfy a tourist's appetite, it is enough to describe it in more detail.

But, surely, that misses the interesting question. Why call a collar a pickadill in the first place? The book, alas, is silent. A little research with a dictionary shows how much it missed. The famous collars were finely pierced and cut into patterns. They came to England from Spain; and the Spanish for pricked or pierced is *picado* – the same root, indeed, as pique, piquant and picket. *Picado*, in turn, is from the Latin *pica*, used for something sharp and pointed like a bird's beak (and the Latin name given by Linnaeus himself to the magpie specimen that now inhabits a case in Burlington House). In fact, there is no real end; even a trivial enquiry about a London street name ends in a deep investigation of the origin of language.

That is the mark of science. It differentiates it absolutely from beliefs that depend on faith: there is no limit to its enquiries, and no explanation is ever complete. Science differs from religion in that referring to authority, however eminent, is simply not enough. I hope that – at least where genetics is concerned – I have managed to show the contrast between the two modes of explanation in this book.

It accompanies the BBC Television series *In the Blood* (although it covers more ground than does the series itself: a word is worth a thousand pictures when they come as frames of film). It could not have been written without the skill and commitment of those from the BBC who took part: and in particular the producers, Robin Brightwell, Chris Hale, Tessa Livingstone and Dana Purvis. Judith Bunting and Rosalind Arden became expert at extracting surprising stories from unlikely people and succeeded in finding beliefs about genes, ancestry and fate more improbable than anything I foresaw. I should mention in particular Lucinda Jarrett who played an essential part in so doing, with undiminished energy and enthusiasm, in some of the less comfortable parts of the world.

Many people have read parts of the manuscript: Neil Bradman, Professor Norman Cantor, Dr David Cesarani, Andrew Cottom, Professor John Griffith, Christopher Huhne, Dr Laurence Hurst, Andrew Huxley, Philip Gwyn Jones of HarperCollins, Marek Kohn, Brian Lapping, Michael Morgan, Linda Partridge and Norma Percy. Each noticed errors of fact or interpretation: others, no doubt, have slipped through and are conventionally but entirely my own fault. The pictures were found by Frances Abraham. I thank her for unearthing so many images that illustrate science through works of art. Philip Lewis, the book's designer, turned it into a thing of beauty in its own right. Lastly I should acknowledge my colleagues at University College London who covered for me in my (unpaid) absence as the British university system sank still further into decline.

I have no illusions that this book will alter anyone's views about the meaning of life. It was not written with any expectation that it would. Science and religion have, in the end, rather little to do with each other. In 1529, the iconoclasts of Basel, fired by the Reformation to test the precepts of their faith, carried out a scientific test. They attacked a carving of Christ, crying 'If you are God, defend yourself: if man, bleed.'

The image did neither. Unlike scientists, though, the faithful were not moved to change their minds. God was still there; only his effigies were false. Their response resembled that of today's theologians when faced with new and uncomfortable truths: God is there, whatever science might say. Science has no means of, and no interest in, refuting that argument. The issues explored in this book can, no doubt, be accommodated into any system of belief. However, the facts of modern genetics are remarkable enough to stand, quite unabashed, on their own merits; with no concern for the opinions of those who study them.

IN THE BLOOD

In the Blood

'The voice of thy brother's blood crieth unto me.'
GENESIS 4:10

THE BLOOD IS A VERY SPECIAL FLUID. Goethe, who came up with that laconic phrase (it sounds even better in German), was not speaking, as he sometimes did, as a scientist; but as a poet. Faust has just made a bargain. In return for a life of knowledge and power, with a demon as his servant and the prospect of immortality thrown in, he has sold his soul to the devil. Mephistopheles, knowing full well the nature of the trans-action, asks for it to be signed in blood. Parchment, paper, marble, brass; stylus, chisel or pen are not enough. Only blood will do.

The pact returns to haunt Faust. His life is driven by what he sees as an inescapable fate. Goethe's hero accepts that, sooner or later, he will pay the price for yielding to his own nature by burning in hell.

Blood has become a much more singular fluid than Goethe could have imagined. A pact sealed in blood, though, is now no more than a symbol.

Faust signs his pact with Mephistopheles – in blood.

Blood feuds, blood brothers, blue blood, cold blood, bad blood – all have shifted from the orbit of science into that of metaphor. But change the language a little, replace 'blood' with 'gene', and suddenly we are in the modern world. There is a new era of belief in the power of biology and a new fear of what we may find out about ourselves.

Mephistopheles appears just as Faust, in his study, has decided to kill himself. He is surrounded by the trappings of a scientist – smoke, dust, books, bones and instruments. One of the temptations offered by the devil in the hope of gaining his soul is that of the serpent to Eve: 'Eritis sicut deus, scientes bonum et malum' – 'Ye shall be as gods, knowing good and evil'. In secret, Mephistopheles gloats over the dangers of granting such a gift to a mere mortal. Science, understanding, the demon conjured up by Faust, is still under control; but more and more there is concern that he will return to demand his share of the bargain.

Blood retains its power. Outside the Buddhist shrine on the sacred

A Japanese fortune-telling box based on blood groups. The four holes are for groups A, B, AB and O. The device uses genetics to predict the fate of those willing to invest a few yen.

island of Miyajima in Japan is a red box with four holes labelled A, B, AB and O.

Inside each are folded messages, bearing the fortunes of those of the appropriate blood group. Group O people are, they say, relaxed; they aspire to leadership, but are poor on details. B individuals are eccentric, A conservative and co-operative. ABs, given their internal contradictions, are moody and stand-offish. As and Bs should avoid each other, but either would be happy with an AB partner. Os should stick to their own type, and steer clear of Bs. Japanese couples planning to marry often ask each other their blood groups and there are attempts to organize matters to provide offices with the right mix, guaranteeing a harmonious working relationship.

The idea has, fortunately, been subjected to scientific test. The French anthropologist Leon Bourdel, in a series of meticulous experiments, studied the heart-rate of people of different blood group when listening to music. Group As, he found, were attracted by harmony, Bs by rhythm and Os by melody. ABs liked all three (and were particularly keen on Bach). They should eat fish and avoid tomatoes.

It is easy to laugh at the idea that blood group determines personality. It is, though, only an exaggerated version of a general belief about what genes can do. The conviction that man's fate is in some way inborn is an old and abiding one. Whether – and how – this may be true goes to the heart of religion, of philosophy and of science.

The blood as the essence of humanity is nothing new. Cave paintings show arrows pointed at a rough drawing of a heart. In the Roman arena, spectators fought for a drop of vital fluid from the victorious gladiators, in the belief that it was an elixir that would give them strength. Pogroms against Jews were sparked off by the claim that Christian children were being killed to provide blood to put in the Passover bread; a macabre declaration of the idea that it was the vehicle of youth, innocence and the very principle of being.

Blood has always been tied to religion. Its universal symbolism – menstruation taboos, the draining of the body fluids of slaughtered animals, the cutting of the flesh in religious ecstasy – suggests an ancient root. Circumcision, perhaps, is the remnant of a progress from child sacrifice to castration to an emblematic shedding of blood. Freud saw communion, the metaphorical drinking of the blood of Christ, as a relic of a cannibal ritual, the eating of a god. The sacred fluid has always been a potent symbol for Christians. It was purifying to believers, but polluting to those who refused to accept Christ's message. Female mystics had tears or sweat of blood, nose bleeds, or fragile skin that bled at the slightest touch.

St Catherine of Siena, who died at the age of thirty-three in 1380, took this obsession to an extreme. In her journal she speaks of reducing her body to almost nothing, flagellating it with iron chains and tickling her throat with a fennel sprig to bring on vomiting. She claimed to have bleeding stigmata showing the wounds of Christ and had visions of drinking his blood as a sort of supernatural milk. One of St Catherine's letters describes her leading a condemned man to execution: 'He rested his head upon my bosom. I sensed the joy and perfume of his blood and the odour of my own which I desired to spill for the Sweet Bridegroom Jesus. At the side of the condemned, I rested my head on the block . . . He bent with a great calm. I extended his head on the block, I leaned toward him, and I reminded him of the Blood of the Lamb. His mouth never ceased to murmur "Jesus-Catherine". It was while he was pronouncing these words that I received his head into my hands . . . Immediately I saw God and man, as one sees the brightness of the sun. The side of Jesus was open, and he received the blood of the tormented one . . . My soul rested in peace and quietude, in the scent of the blood. I could not persuade myself to wash off the drops that had spurted on to me.'

In the fifteenth century, the power of this myth led to attempts to rejuvenate the ailing Pope Innocent VIII with transfusions from young boys. Based as they were on superstition, they failed. By 1666, though, the physicist Robert Boyle was writing – in true scientific style – to his Royal Society colleague Dr Lower '. . . as to whether the blood of a mastiff, being frequently transfused into a bloodhound, or a spaniel, will not prejudice them in point of scent'. Just a year later, the French professor Denis was transfusing calf's blood to a M Mauroy, who suffered from an 'inveterate phrensy, occasioned by a disgrace he had received in some Amours'. It was hoped that 'The calf's blood by its mildness and freshness might possibly allay the heat and ebullition of his own'. The first two transfusions did seem to help (although M Mauroy passed black urine; in fact the remains of the destroyed calf blood). After the third, he died. A court decided that he had been poisoned by his wife, tired by the continuing amours. The fad (often involving a lamb rather than a calf) lasted for another two hundred years. It was said to demand three sheep – the lamb, the patient and the doctor.

The first successful transfusion was carried out by an American

Christ squeezed as
in a wine-press,
distributing his blood
to the faithful;
the symbol of
communion in this
fifteenth-century
German manuscript.

surgeon in 1818. He regarded it as a desperate last chance for a dying patient. One woman 'felt as if *life* were infused into her body'. She was lucky. Nothing was then known about blood groups and she had a one-in-three chance of the gift infusing not life but death had it not matched her own.

Science has given blood properties more remarkable than those imagined by any poet. Every adult contains about five litres – a gallon or so. It is, indeed, very special stuff. About half is made up of red cells. They are unique in having no DNA; their genetic instructions are jettisoned as they develop. There are also various kinds of white cells and a straw-coloured liquid, the plasma, within which they drift. Although it is not, as imagined by the ancients, the elixir of life, blood does extraordinary things.

There are about five million red cells in every cubic millimetre. Those in a single person spread out flat would cover 3800 square metres, almost a football pitch, two thousand times the surface area of the skin. Each red cell is packed with the protein haemoglobin which, like a sponge, soaks up oxygen where it is available to shed it in places where it is needed. On the return journey it transports carbon dioxide to the outside world.

The blood is the body's main defence. A cut is sealed by an instant plug, a clot which, simple though it looks, is the result of a tortuous series of chemical reactions. The plasma contains billions of fragments of cells, the platelets. Any damage and they stick to each other. The first small clot starts a cascade of reactions until the breach is sealed and, within an hour, the new clot reduces in size by half, using the same proteins as those causing muscles to contract. Sometimes, there are failures of clotting –

Two red cells, filled with haemoglobin, are surrounded by a group of white cells, lymphocytes, responsible for producing antibodies.

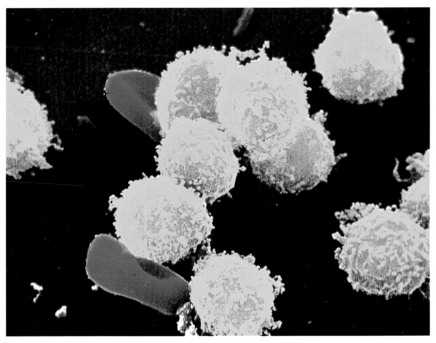

haemophilia. The genetic change – the mutation – involved was the occasion of the first observation of the laws of human inheritance. It is transmitted through females, but shows its effects more often in males. This was noticed as long ago as AD200 when Rabbi Judah the Patriarch exempted a third son from circumcision if two elder brothers had bled to death – and gave the same exemption to the boys' male cousins.

There is also a more subtle shield against invaders. White cells spend their time wandering between the circulation and the tissues. Their job is to fight infection. Some attack and destroy bacteria as they enter, punching holes in their walls and using powerful enzymes to liquidize them. Others, lymphocytes, make antibodies, proteins of exquisite specificity programmed to destroy intruders. They have a remarkable ability to tell foreign molecules – antigens – apart. Two proteins, each containing thousands of carbon atoms, can be distinguished even if they differ only in the precise tilt of a single one. Some lymphocytes retain the memory of past battles. Should an assailant attempt a second onslaught, a few of its opponents have been kept in reserve. They spring into action and pass on their inherited knowledge of the enemy's weaknesses to a new generation of lymphocytes that multiplies in number and overwhelms it. This is evolution – genetic change – within the body itself, as its cells adapt to deal with changing circumstances.

Blood cells bear cues of their own identity known as blood group antigens. Their existence was discovered in the first years of this century, long after the first transfusion, when blood from different people was mixed. Certain combinations combined perfectly well, but in others the red cells stuck together. This was due to an interaction between the antigens of one sample and the antibodies of the other. The antibodies trap the alien red cells and destroy them.

Although – as far as we know – blood groups do not affect personality or musical taste, they do alter susceptibility to disease. Some protect against specific illnesses, others give a wider resistance to infection. No doubt they have other functions as well. Most important, though, they gave the first insight into the uniqueness of the individual; of the existence of massive amounts of inherited diversity. Everyone knows about the ABO groups, but these are only one of many such systems. Their variation is such that even considering only antigens on the surfaces of blood cells, everyone alive today is unlike everyone else – and unlike anyone who ever has lived or ever will live.

Without difference there could be no genetics. Blood groups opened

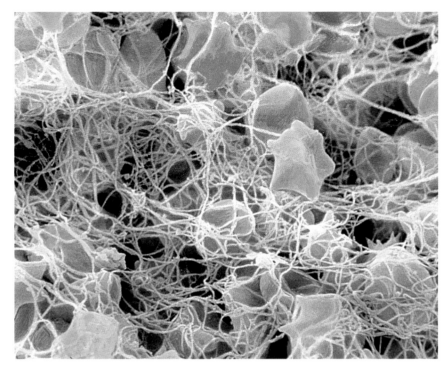

A clot being formed. The red cells have been trapped in a web of fibrin strands.

one of the great unanswered questions of biology – why is there so much variety? Is it just a series of accumulated genetic mistakes, or does all this uniqueness really mean something? For blood groups it probably does; but what is behind most of the diversity elsewhere in the DNA is quite unknown.

Even the plasma has specialized jobs of its own. As well as carrying antibodies, it moves the products of digestion from the gut. It contains proteins to control the flow of water into the tissues and prevent the body from drowning in its own juices. Other proteins do their humble job of helping to move iron, iodine, fats, and the everyday cargo of the body's economy from where it is made to where it is needed. The plasma is part of the body's information highway, moving its chemical controls, the hormones, from source to target. Hormones are made in specialized glands whose role mystified anatomists for many years. The thyroid gland in the neck was once, in a triumph of scientific reasoning, said to be designed to round out and beautify the neck by filling its vacant spaces, 'particularly in females to whom for this reason a larger gland has been assigned'.

The medical journal *Blood* (whose title reflects its contents as bluntly as does that of its stablemate *Gut*) produces more than nine thousand pages of solid research each year. Type its title into a database and, in a typical week, a thousand separate articles will appear on the screen. To read even a few of them would be a full-time job. Goethe was a great polymath: poet, philosopher, biologist (with ingenious – albeit faulty – theories of colour vision, embryology and the function of leaves). Now it is impossible to be a polymath even of blood alone.

Blood was long assumed to be the vehicle of inheritance. Pythagoras was the first to suggest that human life begins with a blend of male and female fluids, or semens, mixing to produce the next generation. According to Aristotle, these semens were in fact purified blood. In England there were some bizarre prohibitions of marriage that show how literally the idea was taken. Until 1907 it was forbidden for a widower to marry his deceased wife's sister. In the Bible, a man is referred to as being of 'one flesh' with his wife. They must therefore, it was supposed, share the same blood. Marriage with the wife's sister would be incest. It took forty-six parliamentary debates over sixty-five years before a bereaved husband was allowed to marry the woman most related to his previous spouse.

The idea of life as a mixture of fluids, each containing the essence of their begetter, was not disproved for more than two thousand years after Pythagoras. William Harvey (who discovered the workings of the heart and circulation) found that deer embryos are not in fact tinydeer but a small sphere, coming – he thought – from the egg, not from any liquid.

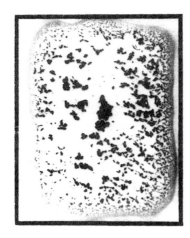 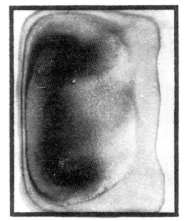

Blood from two people mixed together. On the left, incompatible blood groups; on the right, compatible. When incompatible bloods mix, their red cells form large clumps. In a transfusion, this is likely to prove fatal.

Inheritance – unlike, say, the workings of the gut – is a science about which it is impossible not to have opinions. Unfortunately, nearly all, passionately held though they may be, have proved to be mistaken. Today, most turn towards the importance or otherwise of genes in human affairs. For two thousand years, though, from Pythagoras onwards, the very mechanism of heredity was based only on conjecture. Often, the ideas put forward made (and make) perfect sense. Their only problem is that they are wrong. They show how, in science, common sense is often a false prophet. It may seem plain that when a fire burns something leaves it to make the flames; but this 'something' – phlogiston, as it was once called – does not exist and (whatever intuition might say) instead something else, oxygen, is consumed. The problem lies with what has been called 'the unnatural nature of science'; that what is obvious is usually not true.

As a result, and important though it is, the nature of inheritance was the last great area of knowledge to remain obscure. Confusion was almost complete until the beginning of this century. Darwin was aware that certain illnesses ran in families, but could make no sense of what was going on. Deafness, for example, turned up again and again in the same lineage, but there was no obvious pattern. He noticed the 'singular fact that, although several deaf-mutes often occur in the same family, and though their cousins and other relations are often in the same condition, yet their parents are rarely deaf-mutes . . . It is safer in the present state of our knowledge to look at the whole case as simply unintelligible.'

Whatever its cause, it was clear that deaf-mutism (the inability to speak arose because the child had no way to learn a language) was, like so many other attributes, inherited. Why this should be so remained a mystery. The puzzle of deafness and of thousands of other character-istics has – partly – been solved by the extraordinary developments of modern biology. The nineteenth century's confusion, though, has its modern equivalent: that genetics is today so well understood that it can answer all the ancient questions about what is inborn and what is not. This book is a testimony to how far this is from being correct; this chapter to how difficult it is understand even the mechanics of how traits are passed from one generation to the next.

Darwin believed that the blood was in some way the agent, the vital fluid of parents mixing in their children. He was also sufficiently impressed by the similarities of parents and offspring to propose his law of 'use and disuse'; that characters much utilized in one generation would be inherited by the next, while those not employed would slowly disappear.

Such beliefs are so persuasive that it seems almost unfair that they are wrong. Darwin's failed attempts to reconcile his notions about heredity with his theory of evolution led him into a morass from which he could not escape. The more he thought about the issue, the more he saw the problems that arose if inheritance was indeed based on the experiences of parents and the blood of their children. Nowadays, a discreet veil is usually drawn over the chapter in *The Origin of Species* on 'Laws of Variation' in which these thoughts are put forward. However, at the time they made sense; and hindsight shows that in fact many of the observations made by Darwin and his contemporaries are correct. They are, though, only exceptions to the great truth about the mechanism of inheritance, which is less obvious and more simple than anything they imagined.

The fatal flaw in the idea of blood as the bearer of qualities that mix as one generation succeeds the last was noticed not only by Darwin but by the British government when, in 1971, they set out to redefine the essence, the *sanguis*, of being British.

Once, British citizenship was an unequivocal thing. It depended only on 'birth within the dominions and allegiance' of the Crown. The 1971 Immigration and Nationality Act had an unspoken aim; to keep coloured immigrants out. There was, though, a problem, as a supposedly liberal society could not just discriminate on the basis of race. The authorities did not wish to exclude all Commonwealth citizens. White South Africans, Kenyans, or Australians would be enraged if they could not return to what many still saw as their homeland. What was needed was a way of designing a door to the British Isles that admitted only those who seemed to belong.

The solution was simple, cynical and ingenious. To establish a right to live in Britain, a new rule was made. It was based on a politically expedient model of inheritance. Having a passport was not enough. Instead, the idea of 'patriality' was born. This resided in the blood. British blood might be a rather special fluid, but it was defined as having a fatal weakness. Once watered down it lost its power.

The right to enter was made to depend on having the right proportion of the magic substance. Any Citizen of the United Kingdom and Colonies – and there were millions, from Uganda to Hong Kong – could gain patriality, the right of abode in the UK, only by birth in these islands or by having a native-born parent or grandparent. True Britishness, rendering its possessor eligible to live in Britain, was defined for the purpose of the act as having at least a quarter, one grandparent's worth, of blood inherited from someone born here. The rules for the citizens of independent Commonwealth countries (such as Canada or Australia) were even stricter. To be patrials they had to have a mother or father whose birthplace was in Britain.

Conveniently enough, most people in the British Isles around the time when the crucial grandparents or parents were born had white skins. In spite of their stiff blue passports, the millions of Africans and Asians who had been told to be proud of their link with the home of democracy found that the document had lost its value. For Canadians and Australians, things were – temporarily – not quite so bad; for a time, the law allowed the children of the many Britons who had emigrated after the War to return. Their grandchildren, though, need not apply.

Now, a generation after it was formulated, most have lost the right of residence. As time passes, the number of children born overseas who have the crucial connection gets smaller. The critical British-born individuals who conferred the freedom to live in the UK on their descendants no longer provide a large enough fraction of the child's heritage. As the years go on, fewer and fewer Commonwealth citizens will be able to claim the vital ratio of true British blood, passed down from a privileged parent or grandparent. In time, almost no-one born outside these islands will have the automatic right to dwell in them; this blessing has been thinned down until it means nothing.

The blending rule was applied in reverse in the United States. Any-one with a black ancestor, however distant, was defined as black. One drop of black blood was enough to pollute the line forever: the stain could never be lost. The rule originated as a way of enlarging the slave population with the illegitimate children of slaveholders. As recently as 1986 the Supreme Court refused to review a ruling that a light-skinned Louisiana woman whose black great-great-great-great-grandmother was the mistress of a French planter should be classified as black.

All this is the inevitable result of inheritance based on dilution. Sooner or later, if liquids mix, everyone becomes the same. Genetics is then based on an average, not on differences. Charles Darwin (like the British Government) had thought, when he wrote *The Origin of Species*, that inheritance involved the blending of bodily fluids. He too realized that, if it does work in this way, any advantageous character would soon become so thinned out that, like a small quantum of British blood, it would be

Julius Caesar's horse, represented as a unicorn with toes. Its feet were said to be almost like those of a human. It still had the genes for toes, although most horses had had their feet reduced to a single hoof for millions of years.

worthless. Evolution depends on the unfair distribution of benefit, with success given to those that have over those that have not. Any mechanism that automatically leads to equality will stop it in its tracks. Darwin never sorted out this problem.

Another oddity about inheritance that worried him because it did not fit the idea of the mingling of bloods was *atavism*. Now and again, an individual is born who looks not like the average of its parents but like a distant ancestor or relative. Most horses have but a single hoof on each foot, although they do possess small bones within the legs, the remnants of ancient toes. Both Julius Caesar's war horse and Bucephalus, the steed of Alexander the Great, had, though, toes that worked just as well as those of a dog or cat.

Whatever made them must have been hidden somewhere in the animal's heritage to reappear unchanged many generations later. The same happens in humans. A few people are born – just like dogs – with extra nipples; a very few (about fifty since the middle ages) like apes, with a thick coat of hair on face and body.

This did not fit at all with the idea of mixing of fluids. How could such characteristics remain distinct through thousands of generations if they were watered down each time someone lacking the trait mated with someone who had it?

The answer was simple but universally overlooked. It was discovered (unbeknownst to Darwin) in the 1860s by a monk, Gregor Mendel, the first biologist to count rather than to measure. Before Mendel there was nothing of any value in genetics. Unlike – say – chemistry, in which alchemy played an important part, the early history of the subject is empty. Mendel's contribution was to show that inheritance depends on particles passed unaltered from generation to generation. He made the crucial distinction between the message – the genes – and the medium, the individuals who propagate it. The message is what counts; the fate of those disseminating it more or less irrelevant. The idea of inherited information as encoded into distinct units, of genes as particles, means that a heritage, even from generations long dead, can reappear uncontaminated among distant descendants. Beyond this, the rest of genetics is details.

Mendel showed that inheritance resides not in liquid form in the blood or its semens, but as units of information passed on through sperm and egg. The most elusive, but most important, truth about genetics is that the life of the inherited message is separate from that of its carriers. Blood is a product of the genetic machinery and not the machinery itself. Characteristics acquired during an individual's lifetime are not inherited. To be more precise, they are not inherited through the biological machinery: nobody denies that education, wealth and social position – blue blood, indeed – are passed from generation to generation. Now, of

A Mexican lady with an 'atavistic' hairy face. Some of her descendants, with similarly hairy faces, are alive in Mexico today.

course, we know that Mendel's particles have a physical reality as a message written in millions of combinations of four separate chemical letters, coded into DNA and borne on chromosomes.

Darwin's failure to detach the fate of genes from those who bear them led to the greatest of his confusions, the idea of use and disuse, the inheritance of acquired characters. Now, of course, it is anathema to biologists, dismissed in the first lecture of every genetics course. The evidence against it seems compelling. One of the great unreadable books of the nineteenth century is William Paley's *Evidences of Creation*. Its first page is famous, with the discovery of a watch upon a heath and the evidence it must provide of the existence of a watchmaker – a proof, Paley said, of how the perfection of life is testimony of the existence of God as its designer. The rest of his book is less digestible, one phrase more than most as it is in Latin. It notes that Jewish children are born with foreskins, disproving the claim that traits obtained during life are passed to the next generation.

It is easy to mock the simplistic idea that the fate of children resides in the experiences of their parents. Clearly, Jewish boys are born un-mutilated; their foreskin, or their blood line, is not changed by anything in their father's environment. It is not as obvious, though, that characters like height, weight, intelligence or good health are immutably determined by biology. As science learns more, it is becoming more cautious about claims that characters inherited according to simple rules must be controlled by genes. Prince William, future King of England, will (perhaps) wear the crown because he receives it from his father. His ears will stick out for approximately the same reason. Ears, though, are coded in the genes in a way that crowns are not.

It is often not clear what is due to shared genes, shared environments, or both – or whether, indeed, the distinction means much. The argument has political and scientific implications that began before Mendel and are still not resolved. Left and Right join in common certainty in accepting or denying that human characteristics are inborn; but neither pauses for long to ask what that might mean.

Nowhere has the dispute between nurture and nature been more pointed than in the Soviet Union. Genetics came to a stop there for twenty-five years because of ideology. That some qualities are beyond human intervention because they are coded into biology could not be accepted by Marxists. In the whole of history, only two animals have been declared unfit for study; man during the Inquisition and the fruit fly in

Mendel had the luck to choose the right organisms: not humans, but garden peas. They have two great advantages. First, they exist as separate pure lines. Within every line, each plant is identical. Between them, though, they vary in characters such as colour or shape. Second, peas are hermaphrodite, bearing both male and female sex cells on the same individual and (unlike many of the creatures so blessed) can self-fertilize.

When pollen from a plant with yellow peas was used to fertilize the eggs of a plant with green peas, all the offspring were yellow. This was itself an important discovery, as they resembled just one parent and were not a blend of both.

When these first-generation plants with yellow peas were self-fertilized (that is, an egg was fertilized with pollen from the same plant) there was a surprise. Among the offspring, green peas reappeared. Whatever made them green had resurfaced after one generation of oblivion. This did not fit at all with the idea of blending inheritance.

Counting the peas said more. In this second generation there was a ratio of three plants with yellow peas to one with green. The same was true for other characters – round or wrinkled peas, for example. When plants differing in more than one attribute – green wrinkled peas versus yellow round, say – were crossed, patterns of inheritance for colour and shape were independent.

This suggested to Mendel that the outward form of the plant was disengaged from some internal and (to him) invisible element. It was the passage of information, not bodily material, between generations that was crucial. He proposed that pollen and egg carried one copy each of the instruction to produce a pea of a particular colour. The units of information (later called genes) came in two sorts. For some, dominants, only a single copy was needed to manifest its presence. For others, recessives,

Gregor Mendel, abbot, teacher and founder of genetics, portrayed in later life as spiritual and administrative leader of his monastery, his early experiments published but forgotten.

Mendel's garden at the monastery in Brno. Now a museum of his life and his science, the Mendelanium

two copies were necessary. The presence of a recessive is masked in a plant that also carries a dominant.

Thus, when these yellow plants from Mendel's first-generation were self-fertilized, each produced pollen and egg of two kinds, one bearing a gene for yellow, one for green. When these met there were three possible combinations – yellow with yellow (a quarter of the time), yellow with green (a half), and green with green (a quarter). As yellow is dominant to green, the first two classes produce yellow offspring, explaining his three to one ratio. The

same was true for other characters in peas – and in most other organisms, including humans. Mendel's work, crucial though it was, was lost from sight for thirty years, to be rediscovered only in the first year of the twentieth century.

BELOW: *The diagram that says it all. On the left, a male plant with two genes for yellow pea colour fertilizes a female with two genes for green. All their offspring have one copy of each gene, and are yellow. When they are self-fertilized, Mendel's ratio of three yellow to one green appears.*

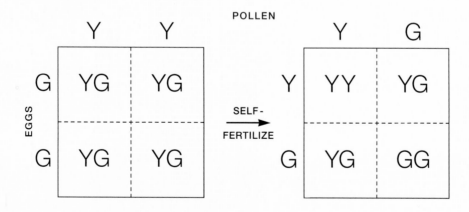

Stalin's time. The bigotry of the Soviets in declaring that genes could do nothing was (and is) matched only by their equivalents on the other end of the political spectrum who insist that they are all-important.

In the 1930s, genetics in Russia was thriving. It was, though, subject to constant review from a class position. Marx had insisted that man could be changed by altering society; once the revolution had succeeded a new and better humankind would emerge. This was, in itself, a theory about inheritance. The process of producing a new man – *Homo sovieticus* – had gone further in the Soviet Union than anywhere else. The masses had fulfilled the first five-year plan in four years, destroying millions of kulaks and intellectuals – wreckers and saboteurs – in the process. If traits acquired during life were indeed inherited, this huge collective effort should produce a joint change in consciousness which would be passed to the new generation. The idea that some qualities were fixed, whatever the political environment, was not acceptable. In 1938, under Stalin's influence, Trofim Denisovich Lysenko was appointed head of the All-Union Institute of Genetics and Selection in Odessa. He set out to apply Marxist ideology to genetics, in the end helping to destroy them both.

After the Second World War (and the disappearance of many Russian geneticists in the purges) the English biologist Julian Huxley visited Russia. He asked Lysenko to explain how, if there were no such things as genes, characters present in grandparents could reappear in grand-children after skipping a generation (the process of segregation, as it is known). Lysenko replied: 'You know my theory of fertilization. Fertilization is a process of mutual devouring. We know in our own persons that digestion is not complete. When that is so, what happens? We belch. Segregation is nature's belching: unassimilated hereditary material is belched out.' This gives a flavour of his science.

Chiffchaffs, Lysenko said, gave birth to cuckoos if they ate too many hairy caterpillars (thus displaying a certain ignorance of the natural history of cuckoos). His colleagues saw the implications of his ideas: '. . . Academician Lysenko will use these facts in the struggle with enemy ideology. If feed is capable of changing an organism's hereditary traits, then the theory of the gene ought to be abandoned.' The ideology – and the faked experiments – had disastrous effects. In 1942 Lysenko claimed that if winter wheat (which is cultivated in places with a climate mild enough to sustain it) were planted in Siberia among the stubble of spring wheat (which grows over the summer) it would be able to survive the

T. D. Lysenko
holding a spray of
wheat – allegedly
persuaded to grow
in Siberia through
the magic of the
inheritance of
acquired characters.

coldest winter. This 'vernalization of wheat' (which simply did not work) was imposed on farmers and led to famine.

In 1948, genetics in the USSR stopped. A purge was announced at a meeting of the Lenin All-Union Academy of Agricultural Sciences. Its *Proceedings, The Situation in Biological Science*, make painful reading today. What was causing hunger was not the collapse of the collective farms but geneticists: 'It is high time to realize that our Morganist-Mendelists are in effect making common cause with the international reactionary force of the bourgeois apologists not only for the immutability of genes but also for the immutability of the capitalist system . . . The formal geneticists have done us tremendous harm.' The inheritance of acquired characters had become law.

Well aware of the fate of dissidents, several geneticists read out a letter of apology: 'Glory to the Great Stalin, the leader of the people and the coryphaeus of progressive science!' Their retraction caused, according to the *Proceedings*, 'Stormy, prolonged and mounting applause and cheers. All rise.' Soviet genetics was dead. Much later, Khrushchev said to Lysenko: 'You and your experiments can go to the moon'; and, by the 1970s, genetics in the Soviet Union had rejoined the world of science.

Lysenko was the mirror of the view that held in Germany and elsewhere during the 1930s: that genes did everything. Hitler himself is known to have read a textbook on human genetics and many experts in 'race hygiene' (as the subject was then called) were involved in the extermination movement. Breeding from those with the finest genes and

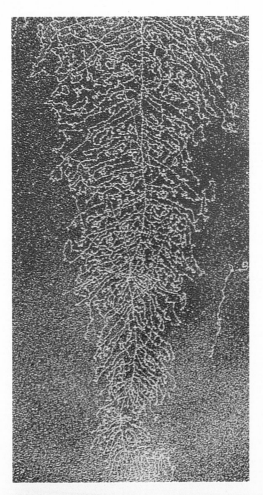

DNA: THE MEDIUM AND
THE MESSAGE

As was the steam engine for the nineteenth century, DNA is the image by which the twentieth century will be remembered. It is a means not only of transmitting information but of translating it into products called proteins via a complex series of intermediaries based on another kind of nucleic acid, RNA. This differs from DNA mainly in the sugars that make up part of the molecule.

LEFT: *DNA at work; the information being read from a DNA molecule through the medium of an intermediary molecule called messenger RNA. A string of messenger RNA molecules grows longer as it reads the DNA code before breaking away and carrying the information to the machinery of the cell.*

OPPOSITE: *A computer graphic of a DNA molecule showing the double helix surrounded by a cloud of water molecules (coloured green). The nucleotides are coloured blue and red; their supporting scaffold of phosphate bases purple and orange. The DNA's information is coded into nucleotides (or 'bases') of four types; A, G, C and T for short.*

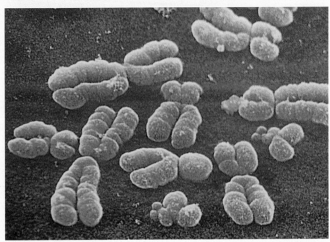

A group of human chromosomes. Each chromosome has its DNA coiled and coiled again until it is tightly packed onto a protein scaffold.

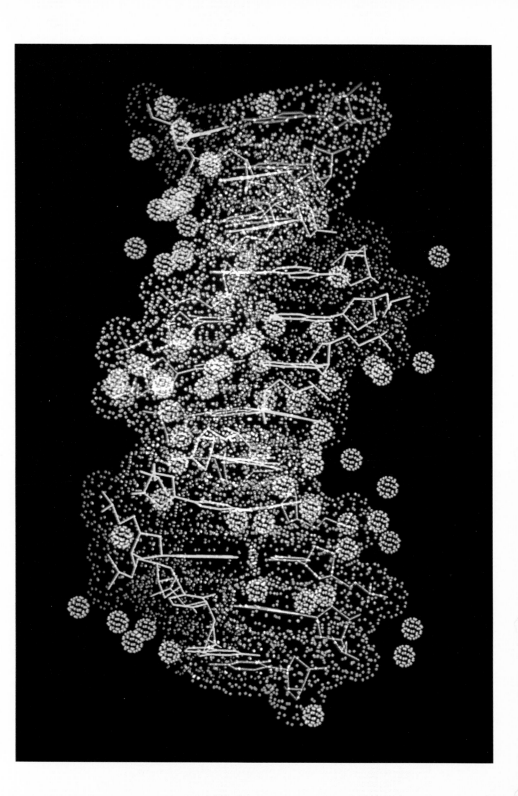

eradicating those with the worst was the only way to improve society. That idea, too, failed the test of history.

Now, of course, the separation of the biological message from what it makes – blood, bone or brain – appears a simple and universally acknowledged fact. No longer is it heresy to believe in a genetic blueprint, distinct from the organism it produces and passed from one generation to the next. This is the new orthodoxy of biology; and, as in Lysenko's time, anyone who dares to dispute it is in danger of being mocked.

It is, though, not the obvious solution to how heredity works. If anything, Lysenkoism makes more immediate sense. Acquired characters (wealth and social position included) can certainly be inherited. Often, children are the average of their parents for, say, height or weight and do not show the simple ratios discovered by Mendel. Even the detachment of the fate of genes from that of their carriers is less absolute than once appeared. Individuals change as they age; and it is natural to suppose that the same thing happens to their biological heritage.

The Japanese poet Ejima Kiseki, in his *Characters of Worldly Young Men* of 1715, spoke for the elderly everywhere when he observed that 'The shrewd observer of the modern scene will note that sons are altogether inferior to their fathers, and that the grandson rarely offers hope for improvement.' For those who believe that changes from one generation to the next are the same as those acting within a lifetime it is natural to suppose that acquired characters are inherited. Succeeding generations, each established on the blood of the last, must also face unavoidable decline.

In the days when it was believed that heredity is in the blood it seemed clear that should the magic fluid be polluted there was a danger that the contamination would be passed on. This was Darwin's 'use and disuse' taken to its logical conclusion. From this simple idea grew the fear of hereditary degeneration, that the sins of the fathers would pass irrevocably to their children.

The weakness of one generation could, it was thought, taint the heritage of those yet unborn. Gout came from drinking too much, but once in a family it became fixed and was difficult to eradicate even after generations of temperance. Alcoholics with their tremble, spasms and eroticism were liable to pass idiocy to their descendants. The blood, once defiled, was corrupted for ever. In the nineteenth century, this belief entered the folk imagination. Whole families were avoided because of a supposed taint. The concept is in the fiction of Wells, of Conan Doyle and of Conrad. Once, only the rich were seen to be damaging their heritage with over-indulgence. By the end of the century, though, there was concern that the future would be ruined by the universal excesses of the present. Anyone with an ancestral history of disease – a hereditary taint – went to great lengths to conceal it.

There was real reason for concern. In the fifteenth century, a devastating epidemic crossed Europe: 'In recent times . . . has crept in, from the western corners of Gaul, a disease which is so cruel, so distressing, so appalling, than until now nothing so horrifying, nothing more terrible or disgusting, has ever been known on this earth.' No-one wanted the responsibility of having been the originator of the 'Great Pox'.

The French called it the Italian disease; the Italians returned the compliment. The term 'syphilis' was coined by the Venetian poet Girolamo Fracastoro in 1530 in a ballad in which a shepherd of that name caught the disease. It was the source of the idea that tainted blood must, at all costs, be avoided and gave rise to a long-lasting confusion between infection and inheritance.

By the late nineteenth century, one Briton in ten was infected. The blame was placed squarely on females – on prostitutes, the source of contamination. The Contagious Diseases Act of 1864 sentenced them to prison if found to have the taint. Twenty thousand American women were quarantined during the First World War, and soldiers were told that 'A German Bullet is Cleaner than a Whore'.

Randolph Churchill caught syphilis in 1873, while at university. The initial symptoms were minor – a sore on the infection site and a fever. Then, things subsided. Many years later, Churchill began to behave oddly. He shouted obscenities at the Opposition in the House of Commons, and was observed squealing like a pig at a formal dinner. Twenty years later, he died insane, the disease having destroyed much of his brain.

Syphilis can pass from generation to generation, as a mother can infect her children while they are in the womb. Now we know that she passes the agent responsible – the spirochaete *Treponema pallidum* – to the foetus from her own bloodstream.

The pattern of transmission fits, quite precisely, the idea of hereditary degeneration: a parental weakness damns the children. Congenital syphilis leads to blindness, mental illness and – sometimes – death. Churchill's son, Winston, was lucky to escape as he was fathered a mere six months or so after Randolph had caught the disease – just after the

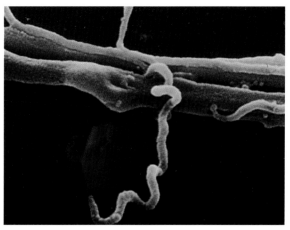

ABOVE: The infectious agents of syphilis, the spirochaete *Treponema pallidum*, attached to cells in the testis.

LEFT: An engraving, dated 1484, by Albrecht Dürer of a man suffering from syphilis – then a new and horrifying disease.

period when it is infective. His mother, Jennie Churchill (herself later the mistress of the Prince of Wales, who became Edward VII) remained healthy. The link between maternal contagion and childhood sickness suggested a wider connection between the diseases of parents and their offspring.

One symptom of congenital syphilis is profound deafness; passed, from the infected mother to her child. Deafness was itself the inherited trait described by Darwin as 'simply unintelligible'. He spoke, of course, with no knowledge of what genes are or how they work. Even that awareness has not always succeeded in making the inheritance of deafness much clearer. What appears to be obvious has, time and again, proved not to be so; and theories that are on first sight absurd turn out to contain some truth. Ideas about blending, degeneration and pollution of the blood all help explain what is going on. Its history is a warning to those who feel that genetics has all – or none – of the answers to the problems of medicine or society, and makes it easier to understand why the truth about inheritance remained so long obscure.

Science is always taught with the benefit of hindsight. From Mendel and the idea of genes as particles a genetics course proceeds inexorably to chromosomes and DNA, and to the way in which inherited information is transmitted as a four-letter code. From there it is a small step to describing how genetic diseases are due to coding errors – mutations – and to how (perhaps) it will become possible to correct them using the wonders of molecular biology. To the student it all seems straight-forward. How could previous generations have been so stupid? How could they have taken the ideas that human qualities reside in the blood and were open to modification by the environment quite so literally?

In fact, there was never any real prospect of uncovering the laws of genetics from what was known by Darwin and his fellows. Much of what was discussed – endlessly – by nineteenth-century biologists was based on human family patterns. Even now, though, a human genetics text is almost a catalogue of exceptions to Mendelism. Darwin's failure to find the genetical key – to deafness or anything else – is, with hindsight, perfectly understandable. Many of his observations can be explained in Mendelian terms. Others, though, cannot; both because of departures from the laws themselves, or because there are whole modes of inheritance that transcend DNA. The inevitable perversity of nature means that some of the most unlikely pre-Mendelian theories have their echoes in modern genetics. Even his most fundamental discovery – that the fate of the message is separate from that of its bearers – is not always correct. Darwin's confusion is easy to forgive.

Deafness has been known since antiquity. About one Briton in a thousand is born with defective hearing, most to parents with no sign of the disease. The Talmud restricts the rights of deaf people, and St Augustine argued that 'deafness from birth makes faith impossible, since he who was born deaf can neither hear the word nor learn it'. Many have argued that those born unable to hear should themselves not be allowed to reproduce. Alexander Graham Bell, the inventor of the telephone, spent most of his career working with the deaf. He was concerned that, because they often intermarried, the condition would become more common in future generations. In his *Memoir upon the Formation of a Deaf Variety of the Human Race* he recommended a ban on such marriages. In later years, following his advice, deaf people in some American states were sterilized to ensure that they had no children.

Many thought that parents with normal hearing produced a deaf child because they were themselves at fault. The first book in English on the

Mendel worked on peas; but his laws apply just as much to humans. He found that genes were particles, inherited independently. Every body cell had two particles (or genes) for each character; sperm and egg only one. There were two types of gene. For dominants, a single copy was enough. Whatever the other might be, those with a dominant always show the trait. For other characteristics, though, the gene responsible was recessive. To show its effects there had to be two copies: an individual inheriting one dominant and one recessive gene showed only the trait produced by the dominant one.

For a dominant, everyone with the condition has at least one parent who has it. The trait does not skip generations. For disease genes, the commonest type of marriage is between someone with a single copy of the dominant gene and an unaffected partner who has two copies of the normal, recessive, gene. In such families, about half the children are affected; if, for example, it is their father who carries the gene, half his sperm have the dominant and half the recessive, so that half the eggs he fertilizes – carrying a normal gene though they do – themselves receive the harmful dominant.

The pedigree below shows a family descending from one William Brown, a Scot living in eighteenth-century Virginia. Each horizontal line

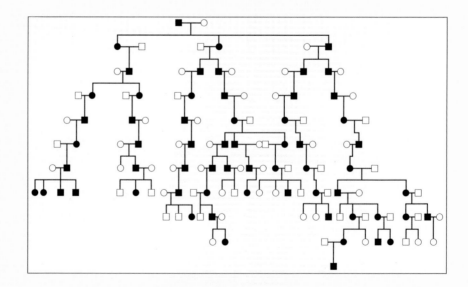

represents a generation and vertical lines join parents to children. Males are shown as squares, females as circles, and those affected with the condition are blacked in. Four hundred and sixty-five descendants of William Brown have been traced, but in the early generations only those affected and their spouses are shown.

The family carries a gene that damages bone growth. This does several things; for example, finger joints do not work and the ankles are stiff, and sometimes the toes are stuck together. Many are deaf because one of the tiny bones trans-mitting sound from the outside sticks to the inner part of the ear. The pedigree is a classic of dominant inheritance. All the patients have an affected parent, and the condition does not skip genera-tions. About one child in two in a family is affected. This is, of course, not always the exact ratio. Just like spinning a penny there are chance fluctuations.

Contrast this with the second pedigree; this time involving a recessive gene. Deafness skips generations, and deaf children are born to normal parents. This is because to show the condition one copy of the damaged gene must be inherited from each parent. Half the sperm of a carrier male carry the gene for deafness, as do half the eggs of his carrier partner. The chance of a sperm bearing the recessive gene for deafness meeting an egg carrying the same thing is a half multiplied by a half; which is a quarter. One child in four in affected families hence manifests the condition.

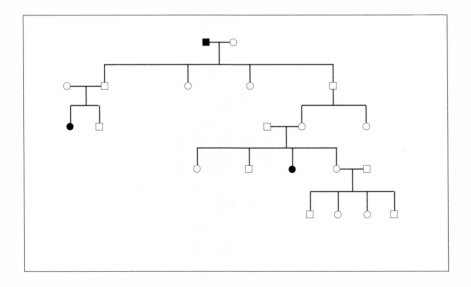

subject, published in 1648, gives a typical case: 'His mother being accused of stealing when she was with child with him, used such an imprecation that, if that which she was charged with was true, her Childe might never speak when it came to be in the world, but remain Dumbe all its life'. There were stories of pregnant women meeting those unable to hear and their child being born similarly afflicted. A French physician blamed the effects on pregnant mothers of 'the alarms sustained by the invasion of France by the allies in 1814 and 1815, and its subsequent occupation'. Soranus, though, 'affirmes that those who are borne in Ships at Sea, are by proprietie of their place of birth, like fishes, mute'. This all seemed proof of the inheritance of an acquired character.

In some places, the condition was common. In Derbyshire, in Switzerland, in Zaire and around the American Great Lakes many children were born without normal hearing. Marco Polo had noticed the same thing in Chinese Turkestan. Sometimes the problem reaches disastrous proportions: in parts of Zaire, one child in six is born profoundly deaf and often has severe mental impairment as well. One local cluster was on the island of Martha's Vineyard, off the coast of Massachusetts. In the middle of the nineteenth century, in the town of Chilmark, one person in twenty-five was born unable to hear.

What caused these patterns? Perhaps something in the environment was to blame. In 1883, Alexander Graham Bell decided to find out what was going on. He visited Martha's Vineyard and studied the pedigrees of the affected families. Like Darwin, he could make no sense of the affair. Perhaps, he thought, the condition had to do with the soil. Deaf people living on the island were clustered in places with a particular kind of clay. The idea came from a French physician who had studied villages in Switzerland with a high incidence of the condition. He saw a clear fit with geology and suggested an 'intoxicating principle' in the soil of Swiss mountains which, for unknown reasons, caused children to be born lacking this crucial sense. His book, though, was entitled 'A Treatise on Physical and Moral Degeneration' and in it he urged that the affected should be segregated to prevent their illness from spreading to the next generation.

Bell, too, believed that even though the cause might be environmental, there was danger to the bloodline. The disease would become more common unless something was done. He was quite unable to explain why the number of deaf children born on Martha's Vineyard had gone down (rather than increasing) during the course of the nineteenth century.

Indeed, the same thing was happening to the incidence of the disease in Switzerland.

Although the patterns of childhood deafness were similar in Switzerland and on Martha's Vineyard its causes were in fact quite different. In Derbyshire, Switzerland and many other places, local clusters of inborn deafness *were* due to something in the soil – or, to be more precise, something lacking from it. All are places where it rains constantly, or where the land has been submerged by floods or glaciers. In ancient times, salts were leached away and there is a great shortage of iodine, which is needed for the workings of the thyroid gland. Sometimes, the effect was sudden. In the remote Jimi valley of New Guinea a natural rock salt rich in iodine was replaced, in the 1950s, with commercial salt from shops. Soon, many children were born unable to hear.

The thyroid gland is not just, as the anatomists had thought, a means of filling out and beautifying the neck, but the source of the hormone that regulates the level at which the body's energy consumption is set. It also controls the development of part of the embryo. Many people in regions lacking iodine had an enlarged and defective thyroid, a condition some-times referred to as 'Derbyshire neck'. Their children were born with a thyroid deficiency which destroyed their hearing (and also caused pro-found mental impairment). The disease declined as people began to travel from their native villages to places with normal soil. They took in more iodine, and the incidence of deafness dropped. Switzerland began to put iodine into salt in the 1920s, and the illness was conquered.

In Zaire there really was an 'intoxicating principle'. The locals eat cassava. This must be soaked to remove poisons before it is edible. If the job is not done properly they remain and can damage the thyroid. Now, pregnant women there are treated with injections of iodine-containing oil to ensure that their foetus develops normally.

On Martha's Vineyard, in contrast, (and although many locals disputed it as they could seen no family pattern) deafness was genetic and had nothing to do with the environment. It was in the blood in a metaphorical rather than a literal sense. All those with the condition descended from a small group of families – the Luces, the Mayhews, the Smiths, the Allens and a few others – who had migrated to Massachusetts from Kent at the beginning of the seventeenth century. On the island, they were isolated, using pounds, shillings and pence (rather than dollars and cents) for a century after the Declaration of Independence. The population became inbred, and, by the 1700s, ninety-six per cent were married to a close relative. Almost everyone in Chilmark had Kentish names, showing a genetic connection to their English place of origin (itself then an isolated and inward-looking part of the British Isles). As it happened, they did live in a part of Martha's Vineyard with unusual soil, but this was a mere coincidence. What united them was shared genes, transmitted through the many generations of sperm and egg separating them from their ancestral home.

Deafness had been in the heritage of their English ancestors. The vital clue comes from Samuel Pepys who, in his account of the Great Fire of London, records a conversation with Sir George Downing (after whom Downing Street is named). He was well known as a Government spy who used a network of deaf informants who were not susceptible to revealing secrets, even under torture. Downing was able to communicate with them: 'There comes in that dumb boy . . . who is mightily acquainted here and with Downing; and he made strange signs of the fire, and how the King was abroad, and many things that they understood that I could not, which I wondered at, and discoursing with Downing about it. "Why", says he, "it is only a little use, and you will understand him and make him understand you, with as much ease as may be."' Downing had grown up in Kent in the 1630s – just at the time of the migration to New England. His ability to employ sign language suggests that deafness must have been common enough in his home village for it to be worthwhile for him to learn it as a youth. On Martha's Vineyard two hundred years later almost everyone, deaf or not, could sign.

The records of the Vineyard families show that the patterns of inheritance follow Mendel's laws for the transmission of a recessive gene. Indeed, hidden in Alexander Graham Bell's unpublished notebooks of the 1880s (twenty years before the rediscovery of Mendel's work) is a scribbled remark that, in families with hearing parents but deaf children, about one child in four was born with the condition. Bell had almost reinvented Mendelism, twenty years before his time.

The decrease in the incidence of deafness on the Vineyard that so puzzled him had a cause quite different from its equivalent in Switzerland. With more and more people coming to the island as it became the holiday playground of the eastern establishment, the locals were less liable to marry their relatives. The number of marriages in which both parents had a single copy of the damaged gene hence decreased, as did the number of deaf children born with two. The process has now gone so far that there is

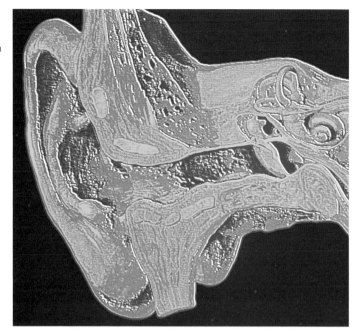

The ear; the organ of hearing and balance. The outer ear connects, through a wax-lined canal, with the middle ear via a membrane that vibrates in response to sound. The vibration passes through three bone levers into the inner ear. There, the spiral cochlea ('snail-shell') translates it into nerve impulses that pass to the brain. Above are three fluid-filled canals containing small particles that, by their pressure upon the nerve-endings on which they rest, give the body its sense of balance and acceleration.

no inherited deafness left on Martha's Vineyard. The last of those born unable to hear died in the nineteen fifties. No-one knows what gene was involved, and no affected relatives in Kent have ever been found.

Childhood deafness shows how the same condition can arise through the action of genes (as in Massachusetts) or of the environment (as in Switzerland). It has many other causes (including an infection with German measles during pregnancy, damaging the developing child). About half of inborn deafness is genetic. More than thirty distinct genes are involved, each affecting a different part of the hearing mechanism. As a result, when deaf people from different families marry, they are likely to have children with normal hearing; in only about one in six such marriages are any of the children affected. This is because such a child may well inherit a single copy of a damaged gene from each parent, but as each influences a separate section of the ear – and as two copies of the same gene are needed to show an effect – they are able to hear.

Mendel, no doubt, would have been equally puzzled (as was a whole generation of human geneticists until technology showed, more or less, what is going on). In the study of the inheritance of deafness almost every one of Darwin's ideas finds a place. Direct transmission through

THREE DEAF MICE – AND A CAT

Human genetics is done, more and more, on animals. We are, after all, related to other creatures. Genes reveal just how close that relationship may be. Hundreds of human genes (disease genes included) have equivalents in mice or other mammals. Even the arrangement of genes along chromosomes is conserved over millions of years of evolution: enough similarity remains among different mammals to make it worth making the map of mouse – or dog, or cat – genes in the hope of tracking down damaged genes in humans. As mice breed quickly and can be used in experiments that could not be done on ourselves, they play an increasing part in understanding inherited disease.

Darwin himself noted that white cats were often deaf. Now we know that this is because melanin – the pigment that gives skin, hair or fur its colour – is involved in the workings of sense organs. Albinos, and even people with an inherited white forelock may have poor hearing. The equivalent genes in mice also cause deafness. Mapping the mouse genes helped to find the human equivalent: and also showed that the problem arose early in development, when cells containing melanin fail to move into the ear and to do their – previously unknown – job of controlling the flow of electric currents into and out of the sense cells.

Some mouse mutants cause problems with both movement and hearing. The effects of the fidget movement are manifest from its name. The ear scarcely develops at all. A gene involved in the growth of the early

BELOW: *A mouse carrying the pallid mutation that removes pigment from the inner ear and makes its carriers deaf.*

RIGHT: *A white cat with blue eyes: also deaf.*

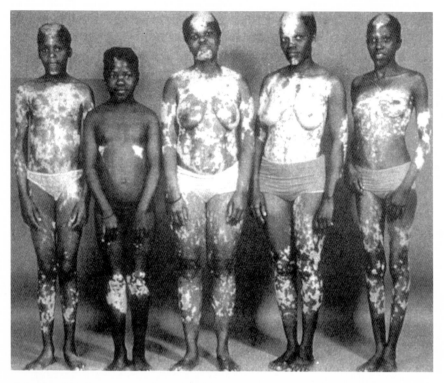

A family with white spotting of an otherwise black skin. In individuals in which a white spot covers the ear, there is deafness.

nervous system was involved. Searching for its equivalent in humans showed that, quite unexpectedly, the same gene was the cause of a human deafness called Wardenburg syndrome.

A few children are born who are both deaf and blind; something has gone wrong at the heart of the system for sensing signals - light or sound – from outside. The commonest form of deaf-blindness is known as Usher syndrome. Patients have abnormalities not only in the cells of eye and ear, but in the sperm. The gene itself was found by taking advantage of the fact that an ear mutant – shaker-1 – in mice has similarly damaged cells (although the animals are not blind).

This was mapped by making crosses, and the Usher syndrome gene found in the equivalent place on a human chromosome. What is more, the structure of the mouse gene suggests that it makes a protein related to the muscle protein myosin. Although there is as yet no prospect of treatment, it gives an essential clue about what has gone wrong in the human disease.

the blood (as in syphilis), the inheritance of acquired characters in places with a shortage of iodine, and atavism as relatives carrying a single copy of the same gene marry; all are involved in one form or another of inborn hearing loss. The message of deafness, for those willing to hear it, is that biology is filled with ambiguity. What seems to be a simple matter turns out, more often than not, to be complex, confused and full of uncertainty.

These terms are not often coupled in the public mind with science. Those with a profound attachment to any theory, political, religious or moral, are convinced that every new fact must fit. Scientists, in contrast, often disagree, sometimes about the very fundamentals of their subject. Surely, believers often say, science must therefore have lost the argument. In fact the opposite is true. Conviction kills the search for truth. Science is, above all, the art of the uncertain. All scientific disagreements can, in principle, be settled by observations with which all agree; but every one can be reopened if new evidence suggests that this was premature. Politics and religion, it is abundantly clear, are not like that.

Goethe, too, realized the dangers of conviction. He took sixty years to complete *Faust*. His theme came from a simple mediaeval tale of a Dr Faustus who had sold his soul to the devil and come to ruin. In Goethe's hands, a straightforward story of unfolding fate turns into a subtle account of the relationship between man and nature. It speaks of the promises and dangers of science, of defective blood and of men striving to be gods. Faust dies having renounced his search for immortality, but a mystery remains. Is he redeemed or does he pay the price? Goethe could not resolve the dispute between blood and free will and his poem remained, to both author and reader, profoundly ambiguous. It affirms that life's greatest danger lies in certainty. The history of genetics shows that a certainty based on science is the most dangerous of all.

CHAPTER I

The Paradox of Armageddon

*'I will multiply thy seed as the stars of
the heaven, and as the sand which is upon
the seashore.'*

GENESIS 22:17

ARMAGEDDON IS, GIVEN ITS REPUTATION, a slightly disappointing place to visit. It is easy to find: on the plain of Jezreel, in Northern Israel, lie the vestiges of the city of Megiddo. Its name, altered in translation, is synonymous with the Last Days. The ruins are an apt icon of destruction. In its four-thousand-year history Megiddo was devastated and rebuilt twenty times.

Armageddon from the air: the excavated city of Megiddo, with its walls and great grain pit, a reserve against siege. The ruins date from the city's beginnings six thousand years ago to its destruction by the Assyrians in 722 BC.

The city was founded by the Canaanites in about 4000BC. Two millennia later it was conquered by Tutmose III, King of Egypt. Soon, it was under siege by the people of Israel as they moved into the Promised Land. King David himself built the sixteenth city to appear on the ruins of the old and, at the time of Solomon, Megiddo was twice the size of Jerusalem.

Its downfall began with an invasion by the Assyrians. In 734BC, King Tiglath-pileser III conquered most of Israel, the kingdom north of Judaea. His successor finished the job by over-running the last enclave of the kingdom, Samaria, in 722BC. The following year, the next in line to the Assyrian throne, Sargon, destroyed many of the monuments of the Kingdom of Israel (Megiddo included) and, as he recorded in a triumphant inscription, deported its people to Babylon. Naturally, their descendants longed to return. That yearning became the dream of a gathering of the saved at Armageddon when the Messiah arrives.

It is a vision with a genetical theme, for it involves a link between generations, a meeting of those alive today with their ancestors. Then, all will have the chance to be accepted into a land where 'there shall be no more death, neither sorrow, nor crying, neither shall there be any more pain: for the former things are passed away'. The Last Judgment is, too, the final chance for evolution by natural selection; those without blemish will be saved and the imperfect cast, irreversibly, into darkness.

The fall of Megiddo was the first of many disasters to strike Israel. Each gave rise to a new vision of apocalypse. Ezekiel – himself among the exiles – wrote of a time when a valley of bones would join to form a great army, Daniel of four monsters with iron teeth and ten horns coming from the sea. John the Divine's Christian revelation has the star Worm-wood and a seven-sealed book. The followers of the Antichrist bear the number 666, the mark of the Beast.

Whatever the details of the plot, Armageddon is going to be an interesting event. Many have tried to predict when it might happen. In 1857, Fountain Pitts, a Tennessee Methodist, gave a sermon in the Capitol. For him, the timing was simple and depended only on that useful measure, the symbolic day (which could be adjusted to make those counted in Revelation fit any theory). Apocalypse – the end of history – had already arrived: 'The United States arose at the end of 1290 symbolic days from the destruction of Jerusalem . . . this reached from the burning of the Temple on the 189th day of the year 68AD to the 4th July 1776. Making the starting point at the occasion of the daily sacrifice, which

One vision of the Great Beast of Armageddon and his attendant devils, from a fifteenth-century French manuscript in the Bodleian Library.

happened, according to astronomy, at sunrise, three minutes past five o'clock AM on the day the Temple was burnt, the 1290 days run out at a quarter to three o'clock, PM, on the 4th day of July 1776; and, from the best sources of information, the Declaration of Independence was proclaimed at that hour on the Glorious Fourth.'

Few claim that the winnowing of the human seed in a final judgment has already been completed without anyone noticing. Instead, the day when the saved will be sorted from the damned is usually equated with crisis. In 1666, the year of the Great Fire of London, every clap of thunder was seen as a harbinger of the Last Days. In the United States during the Cold War there were watches giving the time only as 'one hour nearer the Lord's return' and since then there have been more than four hundred books, plays or films that deal with the end of the world. In 1988, according to Gallup, eight out of ten Americans believed that they would appear before the Lord on Judgment Day. The sense of an imminent end was strongest among those building the weapons of destruction that would, if ever used, lead to fire from heaven ('The elements shall melt with fervent heat, the earth also and the works that are therein shall be burned up'). Almost all the workers in the Pantex atomic bomb plant in Amarillo, Texas thought they were taking part in the preparations for the Second Coming.

Even now, there is evidence of imminent doom. Chernobyl means 'wormwood': the Star predicted for the Last Days is, perhaps, rising in the East. The proximity of Saddam Hussein's Baghdad to the site of Babylon also consoles those with a mind for the apocalypse. There is, though, still room for argument about who will pass the final test. The Alabama Baptists (the church to which Bill Clinton belongs) have, using the most modern methods, calculated that 46.1 per cent of the state's population will go to hell, but others dispute this figure.

Whenever the world might end, and whatever happens when it does, one prophecy is clear: all will be gathered together on the Plain of Armageddon. How many might be there? Certainly, there are plenty of candidates. Even in Britain, in the brief period since records of death began in 1837, eighty million people have died. With the methods of science, it should be possible to estimate the numbers lining up for judgment from the world's beginning to its end.

All true believers are certain that their own ancestors will spring from the grave on the Last Day. This modest assumption allows a simple but alarming calculation to be made. Perhaps – as the Millennarians say – the last trump will be heard in the year 2000. The exile from Megiddo was in 722 BC. That gives about 2700 years – around a hundred and thirty human generations – in which to accumulate predecessors who will gather at Armageddon. The basic rule of sexual reproduction is that two individuals co-operate to make one. Everyone has two parents, four grandparents, eight great-grandparents and so on back into history. Sex means that the number contributing to a pedigree doubles each generation. This, in its turn, implies that every sexual being has an enormous number of ancestors.

Taken literally, this first law of sex suggests that, at Armageddon, a

OPPOSITE: Armageddon: springing from the grave for judgment. A small part of the enormous crowd who will be there, shown in Hans Memling's 1472 altarpiece in Gdansk.

family reunion will involve two, multiplied by itself a hundred and thirty times, people; plus all those on the family tree between the living believer and that great assembly. The number is around ten thousand billion billion billion billion – ten with forty zeros after it. The Last Judgment is going to be a pretty crowded affair.

There is, though, a problem. The number is greater by far than the world's population. In fact, it is far more than the number of people who have ever lived on earth. The Registrar General of the Census Office in London once worked out that sixty billion people had died between 40,000BC and 1983, which itself makes Apocalypse a squeeze – but not an impossible one; they would, with some difficulty, all fit into Scotland. The simple law of multiplied ancestry, though, predicts a solid ball of resurrected corpses far larger than the Earth itself. That is the paradox of Armageddon – there will simply not be room for the faithful to gather together.

Its solution is simple but strikes at the heart of beliefs about ancestors, kinship and genes. There were, when Megiddo was rebuilt for the last time, fewer than a hundred million people on earth – compared to the untold billions needed if every individual alive today could follow a separate line of ancestry into the past. This has a simple and unavoidable conclusion; that every inhabitant of the modern world can trace a path of direct descent from everyone at the time of Megiddo who has left descendants. Of course, many people of that time have no posterity today: either they or their heirs had no children. However, all those whose family line did persist for the necessary three millennia or so, whoever they were and wherever they lived, have an unbroken link with everyone (or almost everyone) alive today. As a result, we all share ancestors with everyone else; we are all relatives. Trace any family back far enough, and it merges with all the others in a common stream of descent flowing from a surprisingly recent past.

There were just two kinds of people at the time of the first Armageddon; those who are the direct progenitors of all and those who – because they left no descendants – are the ancestors of none. A few distant people in a New Guinean valley or an African rainforest may escape the net of kinship; but a single indiscretion by an Arab trader or European explorer a few centuries ago would entangle thousands of his heirs, however remote, in its mesh today.

Christianity, in all its varieties, has always been more concerned with deciding who will be among the Chosen than in working out the number of candidates queuing up for the exam. It has, from the beginning, been eager to increase the number who pass by converting them to the true faith. Evangelists are still at work proclaiming the gospel to the world's six billion people. One church alone has taken the step – logical to any believer in resurrection – of preaching to the tenfold host of the dead. If the living can baptise their ancestors there will be a vast increase in the number who can pass the test of judgment day, as all those in a family tree leading back from a living believer will be among the elect. Salvation by hindsight is the doctrine of the most rapidly growing religion in the world, the Church of Jesus Christ of Latter-Day Saints – the Mormons.

Their creed brings together, in a quite unexpected way, modern science and mystical belief. It has made the Mormons into one of the world's great genetical laboratories. As part of their attempt to recruit members, the Mormons are building a pedigree for the human race. In so doing they are weaving a web of kinship that will, they hope, tie their church to the multitude of those who died long ago. On the way, they have mapped out their own genetical pathways into the past and – quite inadvertently – have become an essential part of biology's attempt to map the genetic material of the present.

Mormonism originates in the prophecies of one man, Joseph Smith. To some Americans, there has always been an inexplicable gap in the Bible, in that none of it happens in the United States. Joseph Smith, the first Prophet of the New World, did what he could to put this right. He was born in Vermont in 1805. The country was in a state of religious ferment. Joseph Smith himself was visited at the age of fourteen by God the Father and God the Son, both of whom warned him of the dangers of false prophets.

Smith was much interested in digging in Indian mounds in search of treasure. He could not believe that they had been built by the despised red man. Soon, he became acquainted with an angel, Moroni, who chose him to receive an extraordinary document, written in an unknown script on golden plates and buried in one of the mounds. It was accompanied by magic spectacles ('peepstones') made of three-cornered diamonds. For the unbeliever to look at the plates was death, but the chosen were able to translate the message using the spectacles. Over many nights, Joseph Smith dictated the contents of the plates to his astonished family.

Moroni had brought a missing book of the Bible, the Book of Mormon. It contained clues about the origins of the Americans. They

A painting by Arnold Friberg in Latter-Day Saints style, showing Lehi and his people arriving in the Americas.

were exiles from the Promised Land who had travelled long ago across the Atlantic and would forgather at the end of time at their very own Armageddon. The prophet Lehi, accompanied by his sons Nephi and Laman, had sailed from Jerusalem to America in 600BC.

In the New World there was a schism. It came to a climax near Smith's home in Palmyra, New York. In AD420 there was a battle at the Hill Cumorah (which Smith identified with a local Indian mound). The followers of Laman won, but fell into God's disfavour. Their complexions darkened and their descendants lived on as American Indians. Smith read, in some Egyptian inscriptions that came to his attention, that Christ himself had visited the New World, his presence remembered in the tale of Quetzalcoatl, the Plumed Serpent.

The truth about the mounds is more prosaic. They were built by farmers. In AD1250 one of them, Cahokia, now in a dingy suburb of St Louis, had twenty thousand inhabitants. It was a city bigger than London, and was not surpassed in North America until the growth of

Philadelphia in the eighteenth century. Cahokia has a volume greater than the Great Pyramid of Cheops. Those who built it died in the wave of disease brought by the white man to the continent. Their Armageddon was one not of battle but of pestilence.

In the context of his day, Smith's announcements – which led to his establishing the Church of Latter-Day Saints in 1830 as the declared successor of the Church founded by Christ himself – were not exceptional. New England was full of sects. The Adventists, themselves founded near Smith's home, made the tactical mistake of proclaiming the date of the second coming to be March 1843, placing them in an embarrassing position in April of that year. In such an atmosphere the narrative of Moroni was taken seriously. Even in Britain, mystical belief was in the air. The socialist Robert Owen thanked the spirit of Queen Victoria's father, Edward Duke of Kent, who 'informs me that there are no titles in the spiritual sphere into which he had entered'. Mormon missionaries – who were active in Wales and Liverpool, where they published a paper, the *Millennial Star* – persuaded thousands to come to America and to join the new Utopia. Robert Owen had already built his own, a society in which everyone was paid the same, in New Harmony, Indiana. It did not flourish.

As the Mormons awaited the arrival of an American Messiah their growing religion began to alarm the authorities. The sect moved on to Illinois, to Nauvoo, on the banks of the Mississippi, where they built a Temple. The first of many attacks on their beliefs – Philastus Hurlbut's book, *Mormonism Unvailed* – led to much hostility. Mormons began to feel that their future did not lie with the United States. They attempted to secede from Illinois and even hatched a plan to invade Texas. Scandal continued, much of it involving polygamy. Smith, who had forty-nine wives, went into hiding. Finally, he was arrested, lynched and shot.

In 1846 a whole people, under the leadership of Brigham Young, began to move West. Thousands trekked across the mountains, many hauling their belongings on handcarts. At last they reached the valley of a river they named the Jordan; flowing, like its namesake, from a freshwater lake into a salt. There, in Salt Lake City, the Mormons flourished, expanding into the huge organization of today – a church ten million strong, with a sixfold increase in numbers in thirty years and an annual income of ten billion dollars.

Like the people of the Old Testament the Mormons are obsessed by ancestry and, like those of the New, by the afterlife. Much of their ritual is concerned with binding – or 'sealing' – believers to their relatives and their ancestors. Every Mormon bride is sealed to her husband in an elaborate ceremony, stepping through a veil into a symbolic hereafter. For the rest of her life she wears a white undergarment (with a cut in the maritally appropriate place) representing the costume given by God to Eve. Those sealed make a special handshake – the 'sure sign of the nail'. Until a few years ago there was a gesture representing the cut throat reserved for anyone daring to reveal the secrets of the rite.

In 1847 the Utah Mormons consisted of Brigham Young and two thousand followers. Within three years there were five times as many, and by 1870 there were almost a hundred thousand Mormons in the state. Many had migrated from Britain and Scandinavia, but many more had been born in their new Zion. In the late nineteenth century each Mormon woman had, on the average, eight children. Their population boomed. Some of the pioneers have twelve thousand descendants alive today. Polygamy helped: after all, Brigham Young (about whom one contemporary humorist said 'In Utah the pretty girls mostly marry Young') himself had fifty-three children by nineteen of his twenty-seven wives – and in one memorable week nine of them gave birth. The tradition arose because of the excess of women in the early Mormon community. It is

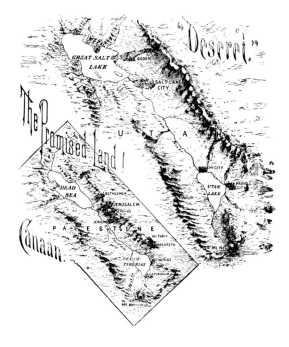

The Promised Land of Utah: showing the parallels between the Old Testament and the New World. A poster published by the Rio Grande Western Railroad in an attempt to tempt Mormon settlers to Salt Lake City.

An aerial view of Salt Lake City. The Mormon Temple (capped by a golden statue of the Angel Moroni) is in the foreground, the Mormon Tabernacle, home of their Choir, behind it. In the distance the highway stretches down the Valley of the Jordan towards the Great Salt Lake.

now extinct among the Mormons themselves, although some schismatic sects still insist on their right to it.

Whatever their marriage practices, all Latter-Day Saints have, from the very beginning, kept a family record. For many, it encompasses thousands of relatives. They often hold reunions, sometimes hiring a sports stadium to fit in those who belong. There is particular pride in being able to trace descent from the pioneers who trekked west and crossed the Wasatch Mountains into the valley of the Jordan. Those who can do so are the raw material of an ambitious operation by those interested in pedigrees for scientific, rather than spiritual, reasons.

The University of Utah sits on the edge of those mountains, overlooking the Mormon Temple. Once an insignificant State University emerging from a theocratic past it is now a world centre of human genetics. Its success depends on the Mormons and their compendium of human inheritance. The University has combined their genealogies with the medical registers of the State of Utah into what is known as the Utah Population Database. It contains the records of a million and a half living

A Mormon family of the 1870s. One husband, two wives, and nine children with – perhaps – ten thousand descendants alive today.

heirs of ten thousand of the earliest Mormon pioneers. They include some of the largest extended families in the world.

Such kindreds are useful in finding genetic patterns. One approach is to ask whether particular diseases are clustered within groups of relatives. If they are, then there is a good case that genes are involved. Among the Mormons, cancer of the testis and leukaemia are strongly associated with certain families. Their members may never have met and they may live very different lives, but for many their death has already been arranged because of their descent from a common ancestor. Bladder and liver cancer are less clustered and genes probably play a smaller part. Instead, smoking and exposure to chemicals are important.

The Mormons are also involved in genetics in a more fundamental way. The complete sequence of human DNA now being established by the scientists of the Human Genome Project will, when it is completed at the beginning of the next millennium, be to a great extent a map of Mormon genes. Many members of the church – children, parents and grandparents – have given blood to the gene mappers. It goes to the Centre des Etudes des Polymorphismes Humaines in Paris, where it is stored in a vast deep freeze, the Pantheon of the common man.

The French are doing to the human genome what the British did to the globe. Although the world's geography is anchored to Greenwich, its genes are going to be firmly based in Paris. The making of the biological map depends on the existence of inherited differences between individuals.

Humans are very good at telling one person from another, so much so that identical people – twins – are seen as disturbing. Faces are not just a statement of personal identity but a clue as to which family a person belongs to. The same is true of genes. There are about sixty thousand working genes in the human body. Polymorphism in perhaps a hundred of them is responsible for the variety in looks that allows everyone to recognize everyone else. Human diversity far transcends that shown in the face. A few technical tricks used for searching for small differences in the structure of DNA show that everyone is genetically unique.

Finding differences is the first step in looking for genes. The French have set themselves the necessary but tedious task of fulfilling, with enormous effort, the basic task of any map-maker; establishing fixed points against which the position of landmarks can be compared.

The Mormons are used to set up grid lines across the genetic map. Their DNA is examined for the position of particular variants. There are millions of these, some involving changes in single sequences of DNA, but most based on the pattern of two DNA bases, the letters C and A in the four-letter genetic alphabet. There are, scattered throughout the genetic material, repeats of CA; sometimes a few, sometimes many. They can be used as milestones in the journey along the genome. Each one is a clue about where more interesting parts of the genetic material are situated.

Already, thousands of reference points based on CA repeats and other markers have been set up along the three thousand million DNA letters in the human genome. They are the foundation of a 'physical map' – one based on the order of the DNA letters – of the genetic material. If a specific CA repeat tends to be found in consort with a particular working gene the two must be close to each other.

Unlike the map of the world, the chart of the genes changes with time. A child receives half its complement of DNA from its mother and half from its father so that, each generation, parents mix their genes in their children. By so doing, they alter the association of segments of the genetic message with each other. Rather like a hand of cards, parental genes are reshuffled in a child; a process known as recombination. If

CUTTING AND PASTING DNA

The structure of a restriction enzyme, the molecular scissors that cut DNA, visualized with X-ray crystallography. The view is end-on to the DNA chain, in the centre; the protein chains (in this computer model shown as coloured ribbons and strings) identify one very specific set of six DNA letters and attach themselves to it. The protein arms insert themselves into the grooves of the DNA, ready to slice through it. So exact is the match of restriction enzyme to target sequence that a change in one of the six letters in that sequence reduces binding by a million times. There are hundreds of different restriction enzymes, recognizing many distinct DNA arrangements. The precision of their attachment means that any change in the location of the target sequence from person to person produces a distinct pattern of cut DNA fragments. Restriction enzymes were the first clue to the extraordinary diversity in DNA. They are also important in medicine. A particular disease gene (perhaps one that has not yet itself been located) may travel down the generation in consort with a nearby variant in the DNA whose presence can be identified by a change in pattern when the DNA is cut. This can then be used in diagnosis.

Structure of a bacterial restriction enzyme, viewed end-on. The two interlocking protein helices that form the enzymes's 'scissors' are coloured green and purple; the DNA itself is orange.

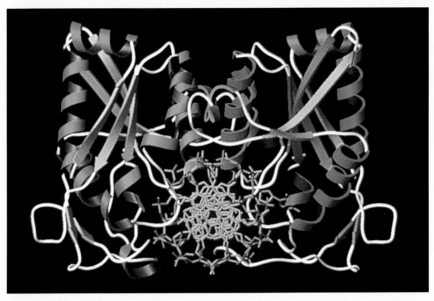

two genes (or two sets of CA repeats) are close to each other along the DNA, then they are less likely to reassort in children compared with parents. If they are far apart, the DNA chain between them will break and rejoin quite often and new arrangements will emerge each generation.

Checking the pattern of genes or of DNA segments in children compared with parents hence produces another kind of map: based not on chemical structure, but on the processes of genetics. It is built up by comparing the rate at which small groups of genes recombine. The process was completed long ago for fruit flies, but has scarcely begun in humans. The most surprising finding of modern genetics is that the physical and the biological maps are quite different because much of the DNA has no apparent function and simply separates the working genes. Its presence is scarcely noticed in a map based on recombination, but in the physical map this surplus DNA fills most of the landscape.

The families of Mormons are useful in making both kinds of map as they are so large. There are many relatives linked into a kindred of decreasing affinity, separated by more and more opportunities for a reshuffling of the genetic cards each time sperm or egg is formed.

Sometimes, a Mormon family has an inherited disease. If the location of the gene responsible is, by chance, close to one of the mapped sites then it will tend to accompany it down the generations. If it is very close to (or even within) the damaged gene nearly everyone with the disease will carry the appropriate marker. If (as is usually the case) it is further away, then the association between the gene and a mapped point nearby may be disrupted by recombination. Some people will then have the disease without the mapped segment. Even so, if there are enough patients an association between the two will emerge. To find roughly where the gene is, all that is needed is to see if those with the disease are more likely than others to carry the variant. Instead of searching blindly through the enormous span of the DNA, those using the French map have grid references for damaged genes. This approach has already led to some genetical triumphs.

Breast cancer causes many premature deaths. Usually it crops up sporadically, with no tendency to reappear within a particular family. Like many cancers, it is a group of diseases rather than a single disorder. There is, though, an inherited form of the illness. Those with an affected mother are, if they have received the damaged gene, in real danger of contracting the disease. A twenty year-old woman carrying the most

GENE MAPPING: THE ATLAS OF
AN UNKNOWN LAND

The map of the DNA has been made far more quickly than anyone expected. The complete sequence of the three thousand million human DNA units (or base pairs, the chemicals Adenine, Guanine, Cytosine and Thymine) should be ready soon after the year 2000. All kinds of technical tricks were used. Many utilize restriction enzymes used for cutting DNA at specific points.

First, a segment of human DNA is inserted into a virus, a bacterium or a yeast that multiplies it in number as it grows. Sometimes, multiple copies are made chemically instead. Then, a restriction enzyme is used to cut the DNA in a specific place. If this is done quickly enough in a tube containing many copies of the same DNA segment, there is only time for the enzyme to cut each one in a few places: a *partial digest*. Where the cut is made differs randomly from segment to segment, so that the DNA is sliced into a series of overlapping fragments, differing in size. These can be separated by electrophoresis (drawing the DNA into a filter with an electric field). By arranging the pieces by size, a computer can infer the patterns of overlap and hence the order in which they were arranged in the original molecule.

Byron, with his interests in sex and fate, questioned whether bloodshed was inevitable to man's condition. His poem *Don Juan* has been much dissected by literary theorists. A molecular biologist might deconstruct one

crucial phrase – 'And is this blood then formed but to be shed?' by cutting it into lengths wherever the letter H appears, in a partial digest. Several fragments would appear:

1) AND IS T (6)
   HIS BLOOD THEN FORMED BUT TO BE S (26)
   HED (3)

2) AND IS THIS BLOOD T (15)
   HEN FORMED BUT TO BE S (17)
   HED (3)

3) AND IS T (6)
   HIS BLOOD THEN FORMED BUT TO BE SHED (29)

4) AND IS THIS BLOOD T (15)
   HEN FORMED BUT TO BE SHED (20)

If they were separated by length (the number of letters is given for each in brackets), and read from top to bottom, the pattern emerging from each of the above after electrophoresis would be:

LENGTH IN LETTERS	DIGEST			
	1	2	3	4
3	—	—		
6	—		—	
15		—		—
17		—		
20				—
26	—			
29			—	

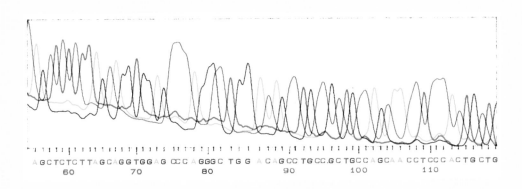

A GCTCTCTTAGCAGGTGGAG CCC AGGGC TG G A CAGCC TGCC.GC TGCC AGCA A CCTCCC ACTG CTG
60   70   80   90   100   110

Even without understanding the sense of the words, the sections could be arranged in order by looking for sequential and over-lapping fragments. Only one arrangement will produce the combination of lengths seen on the electrophoretic gel.

Once manageable sections have been ordered in this fashion, the next step is to read off the individual letters. One way of so doing for the four letters in the DNA alphabet is to attach a chemical tag to each, and to slice them off the fragment. Nowadays, this is done by machine. Its output shows the presence of a particular letter, A, G, C or T, as peaks in a coloured line. The section shown is a print-out of a piece of DNA near the gene for a disease called tuberous sclerosis.

Using these and other methods, it has been possible to map hundreds of human disease genes. Chromosome 1, carries, for example, the genes for Gaucher's Syndrome (a disease of the liver, spleen and nervous system), Usher Syndrome (a form of deaf-blindness) and Ehlers-Danlos Syndrome (a disease of connective tissue, leading to 'stretchy skin'). The X chromosome bears, among many others, those for Duchenne Muscular Dystrophy (muscle-wasting), Norrie Disease (an inherited eye tumour) and Haemophilia (a blood-clotting disorder).

The illustration shows some of those placed in position on just two of the twenty-three chromosomes. The vast majority of the information does not involve genes of known function at all: genes whose job has been identified are rare birds indeed.

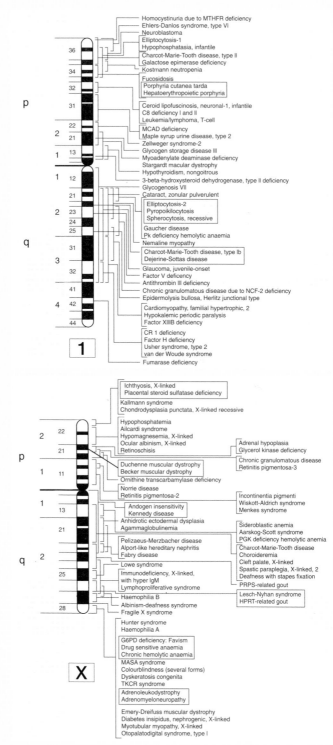

virulent form of the altered gene has the risk of contracting cancer of the breast increased by a hundred times.

The gene responsible for most cases of familial breast cancer was found by a group at the University of Utah. The first hint of its position came from a Mormon kindred with large numbers of affected individuals. It showed an association between the disease and a set of inherited variants already mapped to a particular chromosome, number seventeen. Within a few months, the gene itself had been found. There is now a test which tells women at risk whether or not they have inherited it, long before symptoms appear.

The test and the prospect of treatment means that Mormons at risk of the disease have gained from the attempts to connect the afflictions of the present to a legacy from the past. Mormon interest in making links with the dead, though, goes much further than the study of inborn disease.

In the decade that Salt Lake City was established, Nikolai Gogol published *Dead Souls*, one of the greatest of Russian novels. Its plot is ingenious. An unprincipled adventurer, Collegiate Councillor Chichikov, travels Russia buying from landowners the names of serfs who had died since the last assessment of taxes. These were valuable as they could be used as security for the purchase of live serfs – the 'dead souls' of the title were guarantees of the earthly fate of their living purchaser.

Joseph Smith, too, saw the material value of dead souls and, like Councillor Chichikov, used it to fulfil a natural desire to increase his own flock. His idea came from an otherwise enigmatic statement of St Paul: 'Else what shall they do which are baptised for the dead if the dead rise not at all. Why then are they baptised for the dead?' As Jesus had preached to the departed while he was in the tomb, why should not those anxious to recruit members to the Latter-Day Saints do the same thing? One of Smith's most remarkable revelations involved the baptism of the dead. As a result, billions of people – all of them deceased long ago – have gone through the sealing ceremony. Their posthumous welcome into the Church arises from Smith's vision of 'proxy ordinances'; by welcoming those who had died before Mormonism began it would be possible to recruit millions of souls. Unknown to him, his ingenious scheme was to give a new insight into human inheritance.

OPPOSITE: One of the more decorative documents used by Mormons to search out those to be saved. The sixteenth-century portion of the pedigree of the Hesketh family, of Rufford in Lancashire, shows portraits of family members. It continues, without portraits, up to the beginning of this century.

55

Breast cancer is a lamentably common illness, with about thirty thousand new cases per year in the UK. Most do not involve any inherited tendency towards the disease. However two genes – one, BRCA1, on chromosome 17 and one, BRCA2, on chromosome 13 – predispose to the familial form of the illness.

Women with a mutation in either of the two breast cancer genes are also at higher risk of getting ovarian cancer. In addition, both men and women with a mutation in the BRCA1 gene have their risk of colon cancer increased fourfold. Many families – some very large, and including several Mormon kindreds – with the BRCA1 gene have been studied. Nearly every one has its own unique change in the DNA. Well over a hundred different mutations are known, most confined to a single lineage; in other words members of families with the disease are themselves kin but are not linked genetically to most of the other affected families. Most of the mutations prevent the gene from producing its product, a protein. This suggest that in its normal, unmutated, form, BRCA1 may be a 'tumour suppressor gene', involved in stopping cells dividing at the wrong moment. When it loses its ability to do so cells multiply out of control and a tumour results.

Perhaps one person in five hundred – that is, about fifty thousand women in Britain – inherits a mutation in the BRCA1 gene. Many are likely to develop breast cancer, as the gene expresses its effects in more than eight out of ten of those who carry it. There are as yet no plans for a screening programme for the population as a whole, because of technical problems associated with the large number of mutations involved and the existence of harmless changes in the same gene. Among Ashkenazi Jews, one in a hundred carries a single BRCA1 mutation (which may be responsible for one case in six of breast cancer among Jewish women under fifty). This single mutation is more common among Ashkenazim than are all six hundred put together in the general population and may be the single most common serious single-gene yet found in any population. Although this defect is further evidence of common descent it is hard to know how to use the information. A screening programme would tell some people that they are at high risk; but one of the only treatments at present is to have a mastectomy before symptoms appear and it is not yet known whether this is effective.

Mutations in the breast cancer gene BRCA1. The gene is divided into more than twenty working segments and mutations have been found along its whole length. Some (those shown in green) are rare, found in only a single family. Others (shown in red) are more widespread. The common Jewish mutation is found in the second working section of the gene. The shapes of the symbols represent different kinds of mutations, some removing single amino acids (the building blocks of the protein chain), others changing one amino acid to another, and yet others altering the way the different parts of the protein molecule are spliced together.

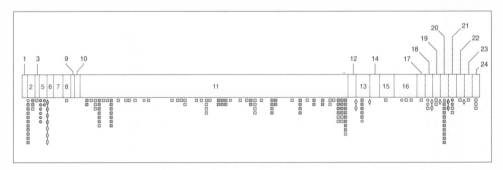

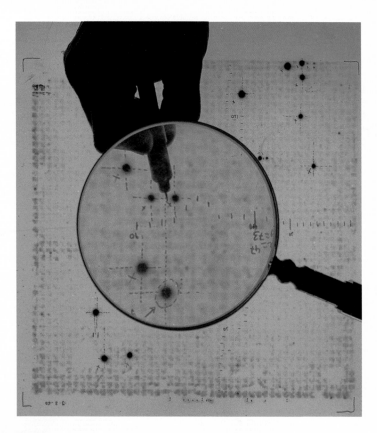

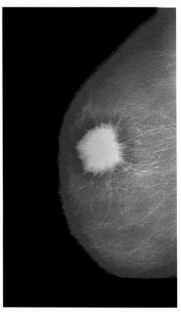

ABOVE: *A human chromosome, number seventeen in this case, has been cut into fragments, and the pieces arranged on a grid. The grid is carrying more than twenty thousand separate pieces of DNA, spotted onto filter paper. Radioactively labelled probes of known DNA sequence (which will attach themselves to their complementary sequences on the chromosome) are floated across the grid, and bind where they find their match. Black spots show up on an X-ray film, as here, and show where particular genes – including the breast cancer gene – are located.*

LEFT: *Cancer of the breast, early in its development.*

Holy men from Yunnan Province in China, each able to recite their pedigrees for more than a thousand years into the past.

The dead are in the spirit world. Although they can accept the Mormon message they cannot receive the ordinances themselves. Instead, a living Mormon briefly takes their name and goes through a sealing ceremony on their behalf. Some enthusiastic Latter-Day Saints have had a myriad identities during their lives, taking them on and shedding them as their original owners are recruited into the Church.

The process is based not on a general acceptance that the dead are linked to the living, but on the most painstaking genealogical research. It ties as far as possible every past member of the human race to a specific person alive today. Because many Mormons cannot trace their descent with any certainty the search includes everyone – Jew, Christian, or pagan. The Church insists that all it is doing is allowing the dead to make up their minds. They are free to reject the offer. This avoids the danger of other religions taking exception to the posthumous abduction of their ancestors. The Mormons are falling behind in their holy work. Sixty million people die each year, but only five million or so are posthumously baptised.

As part of their mission to the dead the Mormons have generated the most extensive collection of family records in the world. Their archives contain the names of almost ten billion people, most born after 1500. More than sixty billion individuals have had names of their own since humans – and language – evolved a hundred thousand years or so ago. One sixth of those names are already in the Mormon vaults. Sooner or later, all who bore them will be offered membership of the Latter-Day Saints.

Much of the information comes from censuses and records of births and deaths. The Church has poured tens of millions of dollars into microfilm. There are already two miles of it in their archive, and fifty million more exposures are made every year. Some of the evidence comes from oral tradition. The Hani people of Yunnan Province in south-west China can, it is said, recite their ancestry through fifty-eight generations.

Impressive though this is, past societies did even better. A tomb in Thebes dating from 664BC claims that its occupant, Aba, descends from another Aba who had lived two thousand years earlier. Akihito, Emperor of Japan, can trace his family for almost as long, with an uninterrupted descent of a hundred and twenty-five generations, starting in the third century AD. Mormon researchers travel to remote parts of the world in the hope of finding traditions about ancestry before they die.

Some of the records were located just in time. Those of Ceylon were filmed as the worms were eating them away. For others it is too late. The information from south-west England was destroyed in the wartime bombing of Exeter Cathedral. With the collapse of communism, huge

Inside Granite Mountain, the Mormon Archive. A small part of the hundreds of millions of names stored here, away from the eyes of the public – and the Flood due in the Last Days.

effort is being poured into Eastern Europe. Russia and China, too, are opening their registers.

The Mormon genealogical operation is housed in a vault dug deep into Granite Mountain, twenty miles from Salt Lake City. Up a side road distinguished only by a series of uncompromising 'Keep Out' notices is its entrance, a bomb-proof steel shutter set into a cliff.

The doors are hundreds of feet above the valley floor to escape the Flood predicted for the Last Days. On the plain below, in Salt Lake City itself – no doubt to be submerged when apocalypse arrives – there is the Family History Library. It contains a huge collection of maps and books of genealogy, and of records and documents on film. All the information is recorded on the computer as the International Genealogical Index, and much is linked into a vast pedigree known as the Ancestral File.

Rows of microfilm readers allow those in search of ancestors to find them in old censuses, military records or lists of ships' passengers. Once found, their connections can be chased down using the computers in the nearby Search Centre. The whole system is based on a computer network with links to such Centres across the world, a sort of Internet to the Dead. The operation has tens of thousands of users each year.

In what was once the Utah Hotel, now renovated to within an inch of its life and renamed the Joseph Smith Memorial Building, seekers sit in front of screens, communicating with the past. Given time, most people succeed in finding a forgotten ancestor. My own name, Jones, and that of my mother's line, Morgan, are so common that it is hard to be sure whether any Jones or Morgan, dead or not, is in fact a relative. However, I did find one of my great-great-great-great-grandfathers, David Morgan, who was baptised in 1759 in the church of Llanfihangel genau'r Glyn in Cardiganshire, just five miles from my own birthplace. The Mormons had got there first. He had been welcomed into the Latter-Day Saints in Provo, Utah in 1977, long after his death. Whether he accepted the doctrines of a Church founded after his own demise, nobody knows.

To find a lost ancestor is satisfying enough, but the real joy is in un-covering a link to some great figure in history. Many are astonished by just who turns up in their family tree. A typical day in the Family Search Centre will produce seekers who have found links with George Washington, with Henry I of England or – inevitably – with Adam him-self. Those proud of their descent from the nobility of Europe are following an old American tradition. On Huckleberry Finn's raft there

The gravestone of my ancestor, David Morgan; buried in Cardiganshire 1817, baptised in Provo, Utah 1977.

were, according to Mark Twain, both 'the rightful Duke of Bridgewater' and 'the poor disappointed Dauphin, Looey the Seventeenth'. Twain was mocking a common obsession of his day. His own mother was consumed with the desire to claim the Earldom of Durham on her son's behalf.

All explorers need a goal, however meaningless it may be. When fighting their way up a river, the obvious place to aim at is the fountain from which it springs. Those delighted to find an unexpected descent from a noble figure from the past are doing no more; as Speke believed during his exploration of the Nile, their journey is over as soon as they have found the great source from which their blood derives. Often, the motive for so doing is to claim an aristocratic descent denied to others.

A moment's reflection, though, shows that no river has a single origin. Instead, each has millions. The source, so-called, is just one, arbitrarily defined – as Speke himself found when, to his dismay, others claimed a different origin for the Nile. In the same way, geographers once argued about who had discovered the source of the Mississippi, down which Twain floated an English Duke and an unrecognized King of France. Now it is said to pour from Lake Itasca ([*Ver*]*itas Ca*[*put*], the True Head); neatly avoiding the question of what flows into Itasca and into what river, if not the Mississippi, the thousands of other local lakes drain. To be persuaded that a lineage is special because it has a root in some great personage is to make the same mistake; to follow one path upstream when in fact there are millions.

Aristocrats are fond of deluding themselves in this way. There are about three hundred families in Britain who feel special because they can trace an unbroken line of descent from William the Conqueror. In fact, their only distinction is that they have kept the documents; hundreds of thousands of other Britons could find their own path from William, if only they could negotiate their way through the genetic maze linking 1066 to the present.

To find a noble ancestor causes surprise and delight but if one goes far enough back it is almost unavoidable. The past is a country that can be reached in many ways. Patrician descent comes from the simple truths of genetics. Every seeker in the Utah Hotel is exploring a primal stream; a torrent of DNA pouring through history. The whole of biology is an attempt to trace its course. It has many tributaries. One joins each time a couple gets married. The further upstream, the less the river has been surveyed. Like any traveller, those in the Family Search Centre are inexorably drawn towards the tributaries that *have* been mapped. Quite soon – wherever they start, whoever they are – they find themselves following one descending from a King or a Queen.

Royalty keeps, as part of its reason for existence, a diary of its travels through the past. It was mapping the route of the genes long before genetics began. Prince Charles can trace three thousand distinct lines of descent from Edward III (who lived between 1312 and 1377). He also has a direct link with Mohammed, through that monarch's son, the Black Prince, Edward Prince of Wales, whose mother had Moorish blood. If Prince Charles has three thousand connections with a fourteenth-century English king it is not surprising that almost anyone who walks into the Family History Centre and has the energy to dig out the paperwork can find at least a single one.

Family trees pursued for a few centuries begin to gather unlikely historical figures simply because there is no room for them anywhere else. Trace one's lineage back far enough and it will, inevitably, coalesce with all the others. Soon, they all become branches on the universal pedigree that links everybody – William the Conqueror, Tutankhamun, Confucius, or any ancient icon who comes to mind – together into an extended family. Even a short journey upstream is almost guaranteed to unearth a magnificent ancestor. More or less everyone in the western world is descended from the Emperor Nero, rather fewer from William the Conqueror, and a mere few hundred thousand from George Washington.

This means, of course, that everyone is related to everyone else. The common ancestor of two randomly chosen people may be Nero, or William the Conqueror, but is more likely to be someone unknown to history. A little searching turns up surprising patterns of kinship even among those of lesser importance. Prime Ministers Margaret Thatcher and John Major both descend from John and Elizabeth Crust, who farmed in Leake, near Boston in Lincolnshire, in the eighteenth century; they are fifth cousins, once removed. The present Mr Crust, direct descendant of John of that ilk, is a much-married and much-tattooed seaman. He writes Country and Western songs. One, 'I've Burnt All the Bridges on the Road to No Return', has made it to the US charts.

His response to the news that he is a blood relative of two prime ministers is one of quiet resignation. His chagrin may be reduced by working out that something like a hundred thousand Britons are equally related to them, without knowing it.

If two people descend from the same individual, Crust or not, they have a chance of inheriting the same genes. Should they (unlikely though it seems in this particular instance) marry, their child may have two copies of the same gene from its parents' common ancestor. The copies are – to use the technical term – identical by descent. Prince William, future King of England, must have many. His parents share numerous genetic pathways through history. Prince Charles can trace his descent from Edward III along some three thousand different lines; but Princess Diana, his erstwhile wife (who does not on the face of it appear to be a particularly close relative) herself has around four thousand distinct lines of descent from the same person. Prince William and his younger brother

Geoffrey Crust, joint descendant, with Margaret Thatcher and John Major, from John and Elizabeth Crust, eighteenth-century Lincolnshire farmers: the web of kinship spreads widely.

have certainly inherited two copies of some of Edward III's genes, each pursuing a different route down the generations.

Identity by descent is not just a royal prerogative; it applies to everyone else too. The Mormons' Ancestral File proves that by going back far enough all family trees sooner or later coalesce, meeting in an individual who links them. Whenever this happens, two copies of the same gene will pass down separate routes from that focal person, however long ago he or she lived. Inevitably, some will meet in a man or woman alive today.

Usually this has no untoward effects and it is impossible to know the genes involved. Although segments of the Iron Lady are identical, by virtue of their descent from John Crust, with parts of her successor, there is no way of telling just how the two coincide. Sometimes, though, evidence of common descent is only too clear. Many genetic diseases show their effects in those inheriting two copies of the same gene. If an ancestor shared by a married couple carried it in single copy, they are each at risk of inheriting a copy of their own. As a result there is a greater than average chance of the children of relatives having two copies of their common gene and of being born with a genetic illness. The more recently the joint ancestor lived, the shorter the pathway – and the fewer chances for the gene to be lost from the lineage – from him or her to a child today.

Before genetics, the study of kinship depended – as the Mormons realized – on tracing patterns of descent in church or state documents. Now it is possible to search for relatedness by looking directly at genes themselves; the biological documents of ancestry. Two people carrying an identically damaged piece of DNA almost certainly have a common ancestor who was its source. Sometimes this is the first clue that they are indeed related.

In only one place in the world have both records and genes been studied in enough detail to compare the history written in each. In Finland, the Lutheran Church has kept a chronicle of births, marriages and deaths almost uninterrupted for three hundred years. Although Finland has endured war and starvation its people have been faithful to their roots: many families have lived in the same place for centuries. As a result, genes show the power of kinship more clearly there than almost anywhere else.

Because it is so isolated by language and by distance from the rest of Europe Finns have their own crop of genetic diseases. Thirty or so are unique to Finland or unduly common there. Some have been recorded in just a few parishes. One, which glories in the name 'variant late infantile neuronal ceroid lipofuscosis' (or vLINCL), is concentrated near the town of Lapua in the west of the country. It is a recessive: two copies of the gene, one from each parent, are needed to produce the disease. The illness is distressing. Affected children seem clumsy in their first few years, and as time goes on they suffer from seizures, go blind and become paralysed. Usually, they die in young adulthood. Twenty-one patients from eighteen families have been identified; for nearly all there was no known history of the condition in the family and the diagnosis came as a shock to their parents.

Church records (which go back to about 1600) showed that twenty-four of the thirty-six parents of the affected children were, without knowing it, related; sometimes in many different ways. The oldest recorded ancestor lived in the village of Kauhajoki at the beginning of the seventeenth century – thirteen generations before his affected descendants of today were born. For nearly four hundred years the gene passed through healthy people who carried only a single copy and were unaware of its existence. Finally, though, two streams of DNA met in a sick child; showing that its parents were indeed related.

Not all the recorded pedigrees converge in a single ancestor. No doubt, such an individual did exist, but the church records do not go back far enough to establish who he or she might have been. The vLINCL lineages fall into four groups that do not link up. However, as they all share almost the same set of DNA grid reference points around the damaged gene (which has not itself yet been found) they have all, almost certainly, inherited the same gene from the same person. He probably lived about six hundred years ago.

The disease shows how family trees can – quite unknown to those upon them – branch from a distant individual to meet again in people alive today. The tree of this particular family goes back only to the beginnings of Finland's recorded history. Others link Finns through diseases that have spread more widely to shared ancestors who lived much earlier. They show the power of kinship in determining the fate of people born many centuries after family lines diverge.

Shared genes can spread beyond a single nation to link people thousands of miles apart into a web of kinship. The most common inherited defect in Europe is cystic fibrosis. About one child in two thousand five hundred is born with the condition (and about one individual in twenty-five carries a single copy of the gene). Its effects are unpleasant. The lungs

A young Finnish boy with vLINCL, a severe genetic illness that affects nerve cells and is common only in his local area, with his mother and sister. Both his parents carry a single copy of the gene, and both – without knowing it – were descended from the same man who had lived in the parish more than three hundred years earlier.

and other tissues become clogged with mucus, and in spite of improved treatment most of those with the disease die young. The gene is a large one, and can be damaged in many different ways. The DNA of thousands of patients has been tested and more than four hundred separate genetic changes have been found. As each is distinct, each must descend from a different progenitor. Not all sufferers from cystic fibrosis are relatives.

Nearly all the damaged versions of the working gene, though, are rare. A single mutation, which removes three DNA bases, accounts for seven out of ten cases of the disease in western Europe. Most children with cystic fibrosis are indeed kin, descending from the long-dead individual within whom their shared mutation originated. As the gene is so widespread, with millions of copies around today, he or she must have lived many years ago; one guess is fifty thousand years before the present, long before the last Ice Age. The appearance of two copies of that ancient gene in a child today is the first unwelcome hint that its parents are members of an enormously extended family.

Cystic fibrosis is also found in Eastern Europe and the Middle East. Quite a different mutation is common there. Those who carry it descend not from the progenitor of most of the cases of the disease in Western Europe but from another ancestor. As a result, the screening tests used to search for carriers in England and France do not work well in Greece and Turkey.

FORGOTTEN KINSHIP IN FINLAND

Finnish history begins, according to the documents, a thousand years ago. The first people, though, arrived there at the end of the last Ice Age (much delayed in northern Europe); and farming began only two thousand years before Christ. There have never been many Finns and most have always lived in isolated communities of one or a few families. Because of wars between Sweden and Russia fought over their territory, and because of a succession of cold summers and repeated crop failures, its population dropped during the 'hunger years' from about six hundred thousand in 1690 to a quarter of a million forty years later. That disaster reduced many villages almost to extinction. Today's five million Finns descend from a small number of ancestors. In other words they consist of a few extended families. Some genetic

mutations present in those founders have, by accident, become more common today. Others, though, have been lost: there is no cystic fibrosis in Finland, perhaps because, by chance, nobody carrying the gene survived the population bottlenecks that were part of Finnish history.

More than thirty genetic diseases are either unique to or unduly common in Finland. Some are highly localized: vLINCL in Ostrobothnia in the west, a condition called amyloidosis in the south, and an inherited eye disease in the southwest. The pedigree is that of the young boy – Yussi Heikkila – shown on the opposite page. It shows how two copies of his damaged gene followed separate paths through history before coinciding in him. All reflect common descent – kinship – tracing back further and further into history.

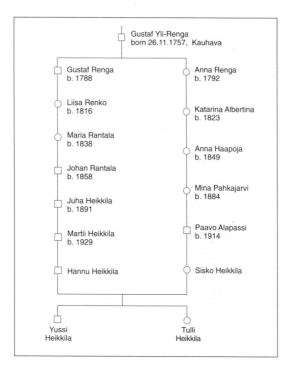

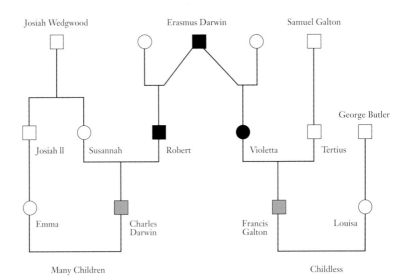

Josiah Wedgwood   Erasmus Darwin   Samuel Galton

George Butler

Josiah ll   Susannah   Robert   Violetta   Tertius

Emma   Charles
Darwin   Francis
Galton   Louisa

Many Children   Childless

A pedigree showing inbreeding: the relatedness of Charles Darwin, left, the founder of evolutionary biology, and Francis Galton, right, the progenitor of human genetics.

Damaged genes emerging in double copy in an affected child as family lines converge hence reveal previously unknown patterns of relatedness. This makes it possible, by looking at the genetic health of the children of parents whose degree of kinship is already known, to measure how many such genes must be hidden in their bloodline. The more recently a couple shared a common ancestor, the more likely they are to inherit the same gene. The rules are simple. A brother and sister share half their genes because they have the same parents. Should they have children (and sometimes they do) these offspring of incest would have a quarter (a half multiplied by a half) of their own genes identical by descent. When cousins marry, they share not parents but grandparents. The proportion of shared genes decreases as the last joint ancestor fades into the past.

Perhaps, for cousins, one of their two shared grandparents carried a single copy of a harmful recessive gene. Each child had a one in two chance of inheriting it; each grandchild – the cousins who decide to marry – a chance of one in four. There is, then, a one in sixteen chance (a quarter multiplied by a quarter) of *both* partners in this cousin marriage receiving a copy, identical because of shared descent, of their grandparent's damaged gene.

If both cousins are carriers there is then a one in four chance, based on the simple laws of genetics, of their child receiving two copies of the damaged gene and suffering from inborn disease. The children of cousins are hence expected to be less healthy than are those of people who marry outside the family. The more damaged genes are hidden in the population, the greater the effect of cousin marriage.

The children of close relatives are indeed less robust than average.

The coat of arms of the family of Lloyd of Stockton; a story of kinship and of shared descent. The three hundred and twenty-three separate quarterings each represent a link to a distinct family. Many of the symbols reappear more than once – that of the three crowns more than fifty times. The bearer of the arms had inherited them down more than one family line from the same source: in other words, the symbols are identical by descent. Lloyd of Stockton, proud though he might have been of his coat of arms, was displaying a document proving him to be considerably inbred. It also, it has to be said, displays considerable imagination: many of the links are disputed by modern heralds.

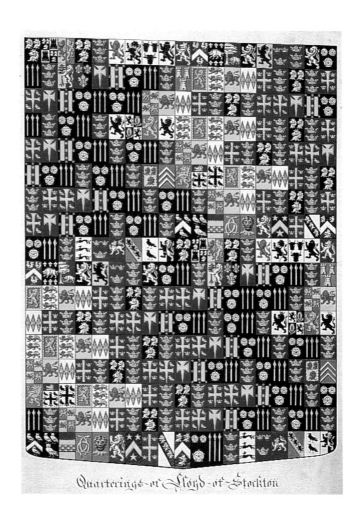

Quarterings of Lloyd of Stockton

Aristocrats are (or were) notorious for the marriage of kin. Sometimes this shows: as Bagehot put it, 'It has been said, not truly, but with a possible approximation to truth, that in 1802 every hereditary monarch was insane'. The French painter Henri de Toulouse-Lautrec was a dwarf. His two grandmothers were sisters, and his parents cousins. Toulouse-Lautrec's mother's brother married his father's sister. Four of their children suffered from inherited disorders of the skeleton. Toulouse-Lautrec himself blamed aristocratic inbreeding for his condition. Much of his art shows an obsession with deformity. He died, probably of alcoholic poisoning, at just thirty-seven.

The incidence of marriages between closely related people varies greatly from place to place. The chances of children receiving two copies of genes identical by virtue of descent down two pathways from a shared ancestor depends on what proportion of matings are among relatives. This can be calculated in several ways. One is to examine the pedigrees of married couples and see how recently any shared ancestors lived. A less efficient (but quicker) method is to ask how many marriages are between people with the same surname. As the name probably descends down two different family lines from their joint progenitor it is a clue about the extent of inbreeding.

In the mobile societies of the West, people rarely marry their close relations. Indeed, many scarcely know them. In today's France, husbands and wives are, on the average, approximately sixth cousins, sharing only a great-great-great-great-great-grandparent in common. Needless to say, most have no idea who their ancestor was, or even that they are related at

A self-caricature by Toulouse-Lautrec, emphasizing his unnaturally short limbs – and his red alcoholic's nose.

Maps showing the decrease in inbreeding in France. The density of the shading shows the extent to which husbands and wives share recent ancestors as measured by the incidence of cousin marriages. The increase in outbreeding between the 1920s and the 1950s has accelerated today.

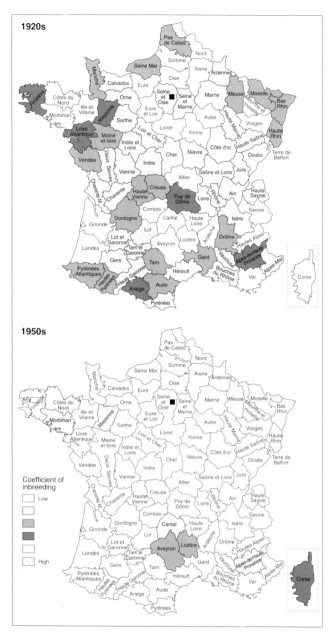

all. The chance of a French child receiving two copies of any particular gene identical by virtue of the shared descent of its parents is less than one in two thousand. Half a century ago, in the remote parts of Brittany or the uplands of the Aveyron, inbreeding was much more common. Now, with the spread of the *autoroute*, it is universally low.

Inbreeding in Britain, which has always been a shifting society with less of a stable peasant class than France, is lower still. Parts of the country often thought to be remote and inward-looking are not particularly so. Even in the smallest Norfolk villages individual surnames do not usually last more than about a century, showing that there has been movement of people – and genes – into and out of these supposedly isolated places.

In the West, kinship has lost much of its power. Society with its individualistic ways has long frowned on inbreeding. Ancient Roman law prohibited the matrimony even of second cousins. The emphasis on marrying out was picked up by the Church of Rome. The laws were made more and more stringent. In AD597 St Augustine asked Pope Gregory to establish rules about marriage. The Pope replied that 'sacred law forbids a man to uncover the nakedness of his kindred. Hence it is necessary that the faithful should only marry relations three or four times removed' – in other words, second or third cousins. By the eleventh century, these prohibitions had extended even to marriages to the seventh degree. There was a vast range of people – up to sixth cousins, sharing only a great-great-great-great-great grandparent – who could not marry without the church's dispensation. Should John Major and Margaret Thatcher have conceived an affection for each other they would have had to ask a bishop for approval by virtue of their descent from John Crust, who died two centuries before either was born.

Why the church was so keen on outbreeding is not known. Pope Gregory claimed that the children of close relatives did not thrive; but he could have seen no evidence of this in the offspring of distant cousins. The drastic restriction of the number of potential mates forced many into celibacy – and towards religion. In parts of Europe, a sixth of the population died never having married (giving rise to the proverb that 'Even the devil disapproves of unnatural vice, except in Alsace'). Often, the absence of heirs persuaded them to leave their property to the Church. Control over marriage gave the clergy power which they did not hesitate to use.

In Northern Scotland in the sixteenth century the Church was in conflict with the clans. A clan is itself, in a loose fashion, a kin group (although blood descent from the founder is carefully separated from inheritance of his wealth). The chiefs of the Clan Mackay had made a point of allying themselves with other noble families, but this was not enough to protect them from marriages within the prohibited degrees.

A detail from a mediaeval illuminated text showing the degrees of kinship prohibited from marriage by the Church.

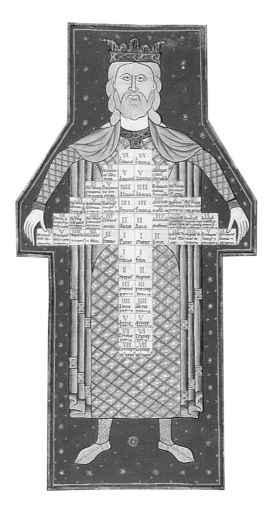

As the Church had little power in their remote domain they blithely ignored the rules. This was a mistake. In 1551 the Bishop of Orkney made a precept showing that Aodh Mackay's – the rightful heir's – grand-parents were not properly married as they had been too closely related. Aodh's father was hence illegitimate and Aodh could not inherit the estate. His lands passed to the Church. In a twist to the tale, the Bishop sold them back for the enormous sum of four thousand Merks Scots. Control over kinship can pay.

In England, a few years before, Henry VIII had reinterpreted the meaning of matrimony. His first attempt to do so rested on the biblical idea that a wife was of her husband's blood. His petition for divorce from

Catherine of Aragon turned on the fact that their marriage was incestuous and should be annulled, on the grounds that Catherine had been married to his elder brother Prince Arthur (who died young in 1502). The Pope's refusal to countenance this led to the Reformation, and to Henry's reducing prohibitions on marriage to allow even the union of cousins.

However, there remained social pressures against it. At a meeting of the American Association for the Advancement of Science in Providence, Rhode Island in 1855 the Reverend Charles Brooke demanded that science look urgently at the question: the 'safety and elevation of society' was at stake. Eight states soon passed laws making cousin marriage a criminal offence and thirty more declared it an infraction of civil law. Nowadays, only about one marriage in two hundred in the United States is of this kind. The practice is equally rare in most of Europe. In today's Britain nearly a third of births are outside marriage altogether, suggesting that the state's ability to control sexual behaviour has almost disappeared.

Elsewhere, inbreeding remains a formidable force. Alliances between relatives are the rule. Ancient Egypt took this to the extreme. Land was scarce, and inherited by both men and women. To keep it in the family, brother-sister marriages were common. The practice began with the deities Isis and Osiris. Ptolemy II married his sister Arsinoë (who took the name Philadelphus, or brother-lover). Of the next eleven kings of Egypt, seven married their sisters. For a brief period, in Roman times, a substantial minority of Egyptian marriages were between brother and sister (or half-sister). The high status of women, and the costly gifts made on marriage, encouraged the practice. Although the term incest is derived from *incasta*, unchaste, and although Freud saw a tabu against it as the very basis of social order, under some circumstances it is common.

Moses, on the flight from Egypt, laid down matrimony laws abominating the Egyptian pattern (notwithstanding his own status as the son of a marriage of a man to his own aunt). Nevertheless, later Jewish law favoured the union of relatives. Marriages between cousins were in some places the norm. Indeed, Joseph and Mary may themselves have been cousins (although their child had an unusual pattern of genetic relatedness to its earthly parents). In Germany as late as the 1920s one Jewish marriage in five was between those with grandparents in common.

As is true for the Finns, Jews have their own history of inborn disease.

Afflictions of the brain and nervous system are particularly common. Eight of the eleven inherited abnormalities common among Ashkenazi Jews (those originating in Eastern Europe) are of this kind. Inevitably, their incidence is higher among the offspring of close relatives. One group of Jews has developed a new way and ingenious way of reducing the number of such children. They use genetic testing not to terminate pregnancies, but to avoid the marriage of relatives carrying the same damaged gene.

Tay-Sachs disease is an inherited disorder of the central nervous system. It destroys the insulating sheath that covers many nerve cells, and leads to a progressive loss of movement and early death.

The condition is particularly common among Ashkenazim. As is the case in Finland, most carriers of the Tay-Sachs mutation are – unbeknownst to themselves – related: they carry an identically damaged copy of the gene and descend from a single common ancestor long ago. Many Jewish marriages are among people who know themselves to be kin: but the illness is a statement that many others take place between those who are relatives without being aware of it.

The gene has been found and now, for the first time, there is a test for carriers. Some Jews have used it to check their unborn child and to terminate pregnancies when necessary. The Orthodox community, though, is profoundly opposed to abortion: in their view all children, whatever their afflictions, are of equal value in the eyes of God and all have the right to be born.

Rabbi Joseph Ekstein is a member of the Lubavitcher community of Orthodox Jews in New York. Their best-known centre is in Crown Heights, in Brooklyn, but there are many other members in London and elsewhere. The Lubavitchers revere the memory of their founder, Rabbi Schneerson, who died in 1994. They follow the Orthodox tradition that insists that marriages are between families as muchas between individuals. Marriages are often arranged using a matchmaker, who takes into account the wealth, the interests, the traditions and – crucially – the health of a family before attempting to plan a wedding. A history of inborn disease is a reason for failing to make a match. Genetics makes the problem worse: if a young man or woman is known to carry a harmful gene then other families can scarcely be blamed for using the information when selecting a new member. Many potential marriages are stopped because of one impediment or another without those who might have become spouses knowing of each other's existence.

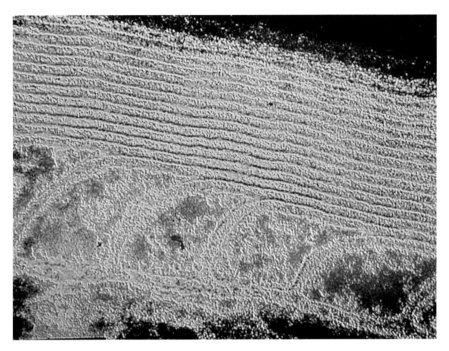

A cross section of a nerve cell, showing the sheath of fatty myelin that is wrapped round healthy nerves, but is destroyed in Tay-Sachs disease.

In the Crown Heights community, one person in sixteen is a carrier of a single copy of the Tay-Sachs gene, compared to one in three hundred in the American population as a whole. The disease has haunted Rabbi Ekstein's family. Four of his children died of it, and he speaks movingly of the anguish of seeing a healthy baby fade away. Because of the nature of the disease and because of the wide understanding of the laws of genetics in the community his brothers and sisters found it difficult to obtain partners.

After the discovery of the gene there was resistance by some Lubavitch youngsters to being tested. No-one wanted to be stigmatized; to be shown to be carrying an unsuspected defect and to be shunned in the marriage market. Rabbi Ekstein had a simple but brilliant idea. If people were tested anonymously, and the parents told that a particular marriage was undesirable should both of them be carriers, then only a few potential marriages – those between two carriers – would be negated. Neither partner need learn why; the parents might be told only that the marriage should not go ahead (although some might wish to know the truth). In the more frequent case of a marriage planned between a carrier and a person free of the Tay-Sachs gene there is no risk of an affected child and no impediment to marriage. The carrier need never learn his or her genetic status. In 1983 Rabbi Ekstein founded Dor Yeshorim, the 'Association for an Upright Generation'. Its plan is simple. Teenagers are – voluntarily – tested at school, before they are old enough to think of marrying. Each is given a number. They are not told the results of the test: only the Association knows that. The number, and the separately recorded status of the child – carrier or non-carrier – is held on a computer in New York. When a marriage is planned, a telephone call allows the appropriate numbers to be checked against the records. Should both partners be carriers, the idea is dropped.

The Association is, effectively, promoting outbreeding by preventing the marriage of relatives – those who share descent from an ancestor, recent or distant, who carried the Tay-Sachs gene – and allowing those between couples who do not have the gene in common. It has been very successful. Tens of thousands of tests have been carried out in Jewish communities all over the world and many potential marriages between carriers avoided. The birth of at least twenty afflicted children has been averted. This managed change in breeding structure has reduced the incidence of Tay-Sachs children born, without recourse to abortion. Rabbi Ekstein feels that his idea could be employed by non-Jews and for other diseases. Already, his community is using it to test for the cystic fibrosis gene.

Although Dor Yeshorim's approach is ingenious and may well be taken up more widely, it is unlikely to change mating patterns that have built up over centuries. In much of the world, the marriage of close kin is still routine. In Tamil Nadu, in southern India, for example, the average degree of relatedness among spouses is that of first cousins once removed. Many children are from even closer matings, uncle with niece being common.

Information from such places tests the influence of inbreeding on health as it is a measure of just how much hidden genetic damage exists. If there is almost none, then cousin marriage should have a negligible effect; although the children share many genes identical by descent, this does not matter as few do harm. If a population is full of damaged genes, harmless in single copy but showing themselves when a child inherits one from each parent, then the children of cousins will pay a high price.

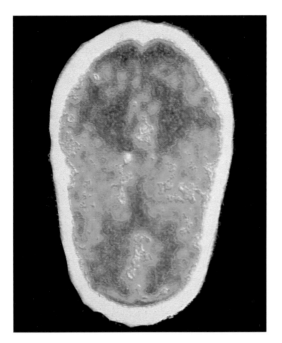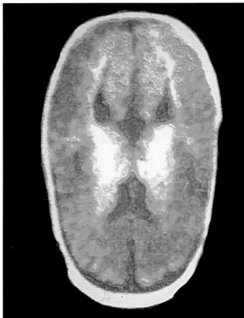

As the brain grows, connections form between nerve cells. Many nerves are covered with a thick layer of myelin, shown white in these brain scans (taken at birth, six months,

The earliest hint of the size of the effect came from the Mormons themselves. Their family tree has many links between its hundreds of thousands of branches as close relatives marry. Over the past century (a time when infant mortality was much higher than it is today) one child in five among first-cousin marriages died before the age of sixteen, compared to one in eight among the Mormon population as a whole. It took fifty years to find out whether the atom bombs had any genetic impact on the people of Hiroshima and Nagasaki; but the influence of cousin marriage showed itself much earlier. In the two cities, the children of cousins started walking – and talking – about two weeks later than did those of unrelated parents, revealing the existence of genes which, when inherited in double dose, reduce the rate of growth.

The most inbred group in Britain is the Pakistani community. More than half of all marriages are between cousins; and their incidence shows no sign of decreasing. The proportion of children born dead, or dying before they reach their first birthday – at around two per cent of all births – is twice the national average. Poverty, and a suspicion of western

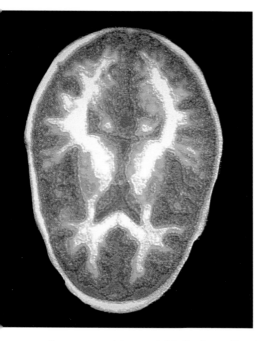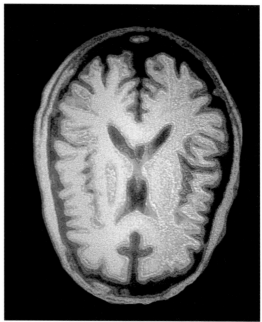

five years and in an adult). In demyelinating diseases such as Tay-Sachs, the layers of melanin fail to form correctly.

medicine, may play a part; but inbreeding is important as well. If the marriage of relatives were to stop, there would be a halving of the infant death rate among Britons of Pakistani origin.

The effect is consistent all over the world. Counting all deaths before the age of ten (including stillbirths and miscarriages) infant mortality ranges from one in thirty in Japan to one in three in Brazil. The increase in the death rate in the children of cousins is around four per cent in places as different as Japan, Brazil, France, India and Britain. The children of uncle-niece marriages (who share twice as many genes as do those of cousins) are ten per cent more likely to die than are those of unrelated parents.

A little mathematics shows that, to obtain such a increase in the mortality among the children of cousins, each of their grandparents must have carried, on the average, between one and two genetic 'lethal equivalents'; that is, between one and two copies of different recessive genes which, were they present in double dose, would kill them. The same is, presumably, true of everyone alive today.

Pursuing the genetical path into the past shows that humankind is full of genetic damage. The search for ancestors reveals, not the pure and noble lineage that everyone hopes for, but a tide of imperfection flowing through history and showing itself in the afflictions of the present. Why there should be so many harmful genes lurking unseen no-one knows. Some have arisen through genetic mistakes in the recent past and will soon disappear, but many more are so widespread that they may confer some unknown advantage on those who carry them.

The literal meaning of the Greek word 'Apocalypse' is 'the unveiling of that which is hidden'. For two thousand years there were attempts to interpret what was concealed in the Bible's message about the end of the world. Sir Isaac Newton spent years speculating about it (leading Voltaire to suggest that Newton 'wrote his comments on the Revelation to console mankind for the great superiority he had over them in other respects'). By dint of sophistry and credulity (much of it based on 666, the Number of the Beast, without which no-one could buy or sell) the Antichrist was identified with figures who might, perhaps, be agents of the devil – or even Mephistopheles himself.

Tolstoy, in *War and Peace*, points out that using the convention that A=1, B=2 and so on 'L'Empereur Napoléon' makes the magic number. The Pope ('Römischer Pabst') adds up to the same thing. With careful analysis, Oliver Cromwell, *Rex Oliver, Lord Protector*, fits the bill as well (all that is needed is to omit the 'L' from 'Lord'). Lovell, Anders and Berman, the crew of the Apollo 8 moon mission all had six-letter names; surely more than a coincidence. John F. Kennedy received 666 votes at the Democratic Convention that nominated him to the Presidency. To be safe, Ronald Reagan (in fact Ronald Wilson Reagan – six letters each; the man who once said that 'There's a sign that the day of Armageddon is not far off . . . Everything is falling into place, and it can't be long now') changed his house number from 666 to 668. And, of course, VI is six in Latin script, in Greek the letter S looks like a six, and there is a 'possibility' that the Babylonian letter A stood for six: giving, straight away, the credit card – VISA – without which it is almost impossible to buy anything.

The real genetic apocalypse – the unveiling of what is concealed in the DNA – is almost complete. It is revealing the secrets of how the genetic

OPPOSITE: One of many pedigrees showing the alleged link between Queen Elizabeth II of England and King David; proving, those who devise them say, her divine right to rule over much of the globe.

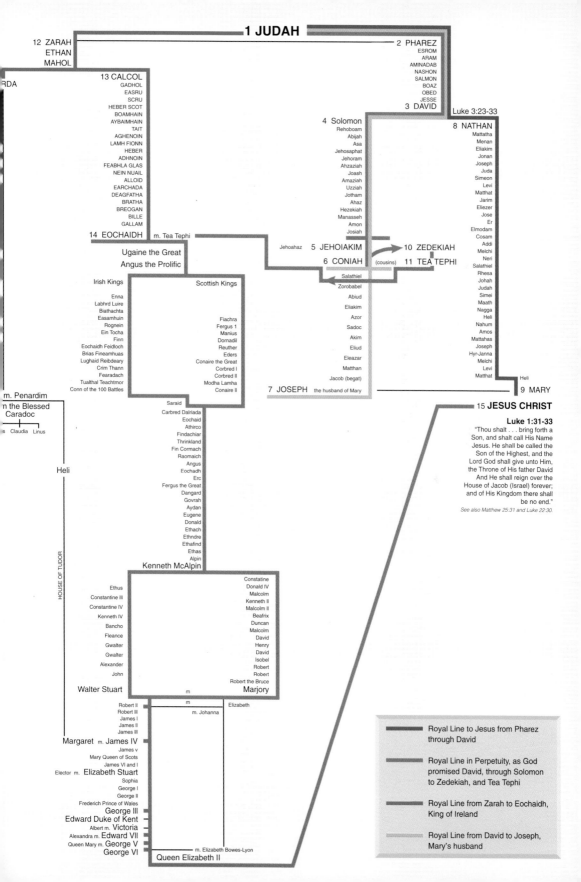

1 JUDAH

12 ZARAH
ETHAN
MAHOL

2 PHAREZ
ESROM
ARAM
AMINADAB
NASHON
SALMON
BOAZ
OBED
JESSE

3 DAVID

13 CALCOL
GADHOL
EASRU
SCRU
HEBER SCOT
BOAMHAIN
AYBAIMHAIN
TAIT
AGHENOIN
LAMH FIONN
HEBER
ADHNOIN
FEABHLA GLAS
NEIN NUAIL
ALLOID
EARCHADA
DEAGFATHA
BRATHA
BREOGAN
BILLE
GALLAM

4 Solomon
Rehoboam
Abijah
Asa
Jehosaphat
Jehoram
Ahzaziah
Joash
Amaziah
Uzziah
Jotham
Ahaz
Hezekiah
Manasseh
Amon
Josiah

Luke 3:23-33

8 NATHAN
Mattatha
Menan
Eliakim
Jonan
Joseph
Juda
Simeon
Levi
Matthat
Jarim
Eliezer
Jose
Er
Elmodam
Cosam
Addi
Melchi
Neri
Salathiel
Rhesa
Johah
Judah
Simei
Maath
Nagga
Heli
Nahum
Amos
Mattahas
Joseph
Hyr-Janna
Melchi
Levi
Matthat

14 EOCHAIDH m. Tea Tephi

Jehoahaz **5 JEHOIAKIM** → **10 ZEDEKIAH**

Ugaine the Great

Angus the Prolific

6 CONIAH (cousins) **11 TEA TEPHI**

Salathiel
Zorobabel
Abiud
Eliakim
Azor
Sadoc
Akim
Eliud
Eleazar
Matthan
Jacob (begat)

Heli

9 MARY

Irish Kings

Scottish Kings

Enna
Labhrd Luire
Biathachta
Easamhuin
Rognein
Ein Tocha
Finn
Eochaidh Feidloch
Brias Fineamhuas
Lughaid Reibdeary
Crim Thann
Fearadach
Tualthal Teachtmor
Conn of the 100 Battles

Fiachra
Fergus 1
Manius
Dornadil
Reuther
Eders
Conaire the Great
Corbred I
Corbred II
Modha Lamha
Conaire II

Saraid
Carbred Dalriada
Eochaid
Athirco
Findachiar
Thrinkland
Fin Cormach
Raomaich
Angus
Eochadh
Erc
Fergus the Great
Dangard
Govrah
Aydan
Eugene
Donald
Ethach
Ethndre
Ethafind
Ethas
Alpin

7 JOSEPH the husband of Mary

15 JESUS CHRIST

Luke 1:31-33
"Thou shalt . . . bring forth a
Son, and shalt call His Name
Jesus. He shall be called the
Son of the Highest, and the
Lord God shall give unto Him,
the Throne of His father David
And He shall reign over the
House of Jacob (Israel) forever;
and of His Kingdom there shall
be no end."
See also Matthew 25:31 and Luke 22:30.

m. Penardim

n the Blessed
Caradoc

s Claudia Linus

Heli

HOUSE OF TUDOR

Kenneth McAlpin

Ethus
Constantine III
Constantine IV
Kenneth IV
Bancho
Fleance
Gwalter
Gwalter
Alexander
John

Constatine
Donald IV
Malcolm
Kenneth II
Malcolm II
Beafrix
Duncan
Malcolm
David
Henry
David
Isobel
Robert
Robert
Robert the Bruce

Walter Stuart m **Marjory**

Robert II
Robert III m Elizabeth
James I m. Johanna
James II
James III

Margaret m. **James IV**
James v
Mary Queen of Scots
James VI and I
Elector m. **Elizabeth Stuart**
Sophia
George I
George II
Frederich Prince of Wales
George III
Edward Duke of Kent
Albert m. **Victoria**
Alexandra m. **Edward VII**
Queen Mary m. **George V**
George VI m. Elizabeth Bowes-Lyon
Queen Elizabeth II

Royal Line to Jesus from Pharez
through David

Royal Line in Perpetuity, as God
promised David, through Solomon
to Zedekiah, and Tea Tephi

Royal Line from Zarah to Eochaidh,
King of Ireland

Royal Line from David to Joseph,
Mary's husband

machine works. Most of all, though, it shows what the results of the last judgment will be.

First, everyone will find a place, simply by virtue of descent. It is easy to mock the royal pedigrees that join Queen Elizabeth II with the people of the Old Testament, passing as they do through such implausible figures as Conn of the Hundred Battles, King Lear and Angus the Prolific and, in biblical times, Amos, Jehosophat and Er. They depend on imagination, the indispensable tool of the amateur genealogist. However, it is a simple arithmetical fact that, although the details of the route through history are unknown, Elizabeth is almost guaranteed to have an uninterrupted descent from that greatest of all kings, David, and from his ancestors in Megiddo. We all share that honour; everyone has a heritage from the people of the destroyed city whose longing for their descendants to reunite in judgment led to the idea of Armageddon.

However, the gathering of those hoping for redemption will be not of the perfect but of the universally flawed. The apocalypse hidden in the genes unites us all, but on a journey down a stream of shared imperfection flowing through history.

CHAPTER II

Sex and Taxes

*'There is a strange charm in the thoughts of
a good legacy, or the hopes of an estate, which
wondrously alleviates the sorrow that men
would otherwise feel for the death of friends.'*
CERVANTES, *DON QUIXOTE*

GENETICS IS ALL ABOUT INHERITANCE, but inheritance is certainly not all about genetics. In fact, the rules that people care about most – those controlling how property is passed from one generation to the next – were formulated long before Mendel. What they are determines what the society that devises them will become; whether wealth accumulates in some hands or is spread among all. The struggle between political systems is, at its roots, an argument about the laws of succession. Who should receive the fruits of past labour, many or few?

The political debate is close to the disputes about ancestry that have taken place since society began. Like the argument over kinship, the issue turns on sex, the process that attaches everyone, however humble, to a pedigree that includes everyone else. Sex leads, each generation, to the mixing of the biological capital of two people and its dispersal among their children. Sex, not death, is the great leveller.

Taxes are an attempt to smooth out differences in wealth and to equalize the flow of income. They disperse the assets of individuals among the population as a whole. In some ways, they are an attempt to force money to behave sexually. In economics, the process is known as redistribution, in genetics as recombination.

Most people, of course, do not like equal sharing when money rather than genes is involved. As Colbert put it, the art of taxation is to pluck the goose so as to extract the maximum of feathers with the minimum of hissing. Everyone prefers to keep their financial feather-bed to themselves, or at least to their direct descendants. Asexual reproduction – of genes or of money – does so by ensuring that a parent's biological or financial capital is passed untouched to her offspring. It retains resources

WHAT SEX REALLY MEANS

Sex seems a straightforward thing. What determines whether an embryo develops into one sex or the other? As usual in biology, the answer seems simple but is in fact complicated. The easy explanation is that a sperm bearing a Y-chromosome makes an embryo male. How it does so, though, varies. Fruit flies use the balance between the number of sex chromosomes and that of the others to determine whether the animal is male or female. Humans do it in a less complicated way. A gene on the Y drives the developing embryo into the path of masculinity. It is a powerful thing. Sometimes, children are born with up to eight X chromosomes and a single Y. They suffer from severe symptoms in mind and body – but they are male.

The crucial gene was found in 1990, in patients who were male – but did not have an obvious Y. In fact, a tiny portion of the Y was stuck to an X: the first hint as to where the male-determining gene must be. Now it has been found and, by injecting it into mouse eggs, genetic females can be made to develop as males. The protein made by the crucial gene binds to the DNA molecule in specific places and causes it to bend sharply. Perhaps this regulates the action of other genes and causes the embryo to switch towards maleness.

Just what these additional genes do is not clear. Some cause cancer when they go wrong (suggesting that their normal role is to control cell division), others lead to abnormal sexual development. One causes male embryos to develop more rapidly than do embryos producing females – which is why men are taller than women. Yet more genes come into play later in development, providing males and females with their various sexual characters. Some genes do quite different jobs in the two sexes. The gene which, when inherited by males, causes them to become bald has a more serious effect in females as the women who carry it are liable to develop polycystic ovaries (which are less able to produce eggs and can cause unpleasant symptoms).

Chromosomes of a male treated with a fluorescent dye that binds only to the Y chromosome. This chromosome, carrying the crucial gene that turns the developing embryo into a male, stands out from the others.

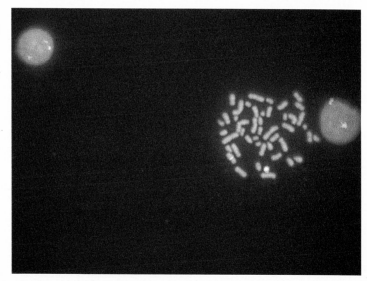

BELOW: *The code for masculinity. The string of letters within the box shows the length of DNA, with its four 'letters' A, G, C and T, that switches the early embryo to develop as male. The accompanying string of letters (D, R, V and so on) represent the amino acids, the building blocks of the protein that actually does the job of initiating the development of testes rather than ovaries. Those with an eye for coincidence may be interested to note that four of the amino acids listed in the second line within the box spell out, helpfully, M A L E.*

```
GAATATTCCCGCTCTCGGGAGAAGCTCTTCCTTCCTTTGCACTGAAAGCTGTAACTCTA        537
  N  I  P  A  L  P  R  S  S  S  F  L  C  T  E  S  C  N  S

AGTATCAGTGTGAAACGGGAGAAAACAGTAAAGGCAACGTCCAG GATAGAGTGAAGCGAC        597
  K  Y  Q  C  E  T  G  E  N  S  K  G  N  V  Q  D  R  V  K  R

CCATGAACGCATTCATCGTGTGGTCTCGCGATCAGAGGCGCAAGATGGCTCTAGAGAATC        657
  P  M  N  A  F  I  V  W  S  R  D  Q  R  R  K  M  A  L  E  N

CCAGAATGCGAAACTCAGAGATCAGCAAGCAGCTGGGATACCAGTGGAAAATGCTTACTG        717
  P  R  M  R  N  S  E  I  S  K  Q  L  G  Y  Q  W  K  M  L  T

AAGCCGAAAAATGGCCATTCTTCCAGGAGGCACAGAAATTACAGGCCATGCACAGAGAGA        777
  E  A  E  K  W  P  F  F  Q  E  A  Q  K  L  Q  A  M  H  R  E

AATACCCGAATTATAAGTATCGACCTCGTCGGAAGGCGAAGATC CTGCCGAAGAATTGCA        837
  K  Y  P  N  Y  K  Y  R  P  R  R  K  A  K  M  L  P  K  N  C
  N  T  R  I  I  S  I  D  L  V  G  R  R  R  C  C  R  R  I  A
```

within a lineage, mother to daughter and so on, rather than dissipating them through a group. Sexual reproduction redistributes. The battle between capitalism and socialism is, as a result, essentially an argument about sex. Although the contrast between the two modes of inheritance is less stark when it comes to money than when genes are involved the urge towards protecting cash from sexual reproduction is a powerful one.

Societies based on the asexual transmission of wealth and power inevitably produce inequality and, in time, political upheaval. The American Revolution, itself based on concerns about taxation, was directed towards sharing authority (if not capital) among everyone. As Tom Paine put it: 'All hereditary government is in its nature tyranny . . . To inherit a government is to inherit the people, as if they were flocks and herds.' Ironically enough, it is in the United States today that the systems of inheritance for genes, for money and for power come into closest conjunction. They do so for reasons which stretch back to the ideals of the Revolution and to the societies that preceded it.

Modern states all try, to a greater or lesser extent, to reduce the accumulation of wealth by taxing it. At what level taxes should be set, and who should pay them, is at the heart of politics. In general, sex and taxes bear more heavily on the rich (who have more of one and pay more of the other). Many politicians feel that their burden (at least when it comes to taxes) should be reduced.

In its early days, rulers applied taxes to those least able to avoid them – hence the tax on salt and the poll tax, which applied to rich and poor alike but took proportionately far more from the latter. Inheritance taxes in England were introduced long before income tax. Because it is hard to conceal property they were, for a time, an effective way of extracting resources from the well-off. Now, though, things have changed. Inheritance taxes account for less than half a percent of government revenue, and the present British Government was elected with an explicit, albeit undated, promise to get rid of them altogether. However, the proportion of national income taken in tax as a whole increased (from thirty-four per cent to thirty-seven per cent) in sixteen years of Conservative government between 1979 and 1995. In those years, the tax burden of the poorest fifth of the population shot up, while that of the most affluent fifth dropped.

Sex, like taxes, is an expensive business. There are endless arguments about why it evolved and (again like taxation) about who should indulge in it, how often, and when. Sex is costly because it needs one whole class

– the males – who are, in effect, unproductive. Not only do they fail to give birth to children of their own, they force the reproductive class, the females, to copy male genes without any direct benefit from so doing. The problem is an economic one. Why should females invest resources in producing males? There are parallels between the immediate advantages of reproducing without sex – conveying all one's biological capital undiminished and undiluted, to one's own offspring – and the attractions, shared by almost all families, of passing on economic assets in the same way.

If assets are – like genes – divided among all potential heirs (which, in a sexual system, means in the long term their dispersal through the whole population) there is, in time, equality; everyone receives more or less the same. If, though, they are transmitted asexually, as a unit down a single line of descent, a few can secure huge resources while others have almost nothing. It is a matter of simple arithmetic. In 1873 a Brazilian millionaire, Domingo Faustino Correa, left his estate to be divided equally among his descendants alive a hundred years after his death. The case is still not settled. There are nearly five thousand claimants, and although no doubt they will welcome their legacy, none will become rich. A single heir down the male line would have held the land intact and would be extremely wealthy.

The difference between the two modes of inheritance was noticed long ago by those who demand a special place in society as a birthright. Following genetic pathways into the past allows (as so many discover when they explore their pedigree) everyone to claim noble descent by finding a blue-blooded ancestor; but it does so only through benefit of sex. If a pedigree can be pursued in all its twists and turns, through men and through women, it will certainly lead, in time, to whatever grand precursor might be hoped for. In the same way, any aristocrat will inevitably produce, as the generations pass, a vast number of commoners among his descendants. To ensure exclusivity, the aristocracy invented a new rule of inheritance: only a single route through history counts.

In England, the inheritance of most titles avoids sex. They pass only through males – 'heirs male of the body lawfully begotten'. The Scottish system is more forgiving as it allows titles to be inherited through females – 'heirs male, whoever'. Among the three hundred English families who can trace descent from William the Conqueror only one is linked to him through the select (and asexual) male connection. The Bassett family are alone in following the patriline – son to father, to grandfather, and so on

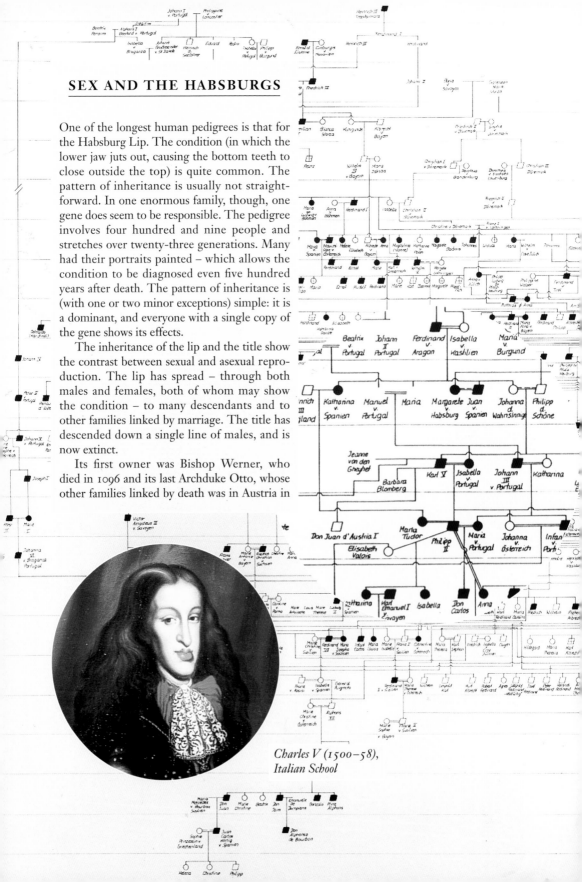

SEX AND THE HABSBURGS

One of the longest human pedigrees is that for the Habsburg Lip. The condition (in which the lower jaw juts out, causing the bottom teeth to close outside the top) is quite common. The pattern of inheritance is usually not straight-forward. In one enormous family, though, one gene does seem to be responsible. The pedigree involves four hundred and nine people and stretches over twenty-three generations. Many had their portraits painted – which allows the condition to be diagnosed even five hundred years after death. The pattern of inheritance is (with one or two minor exceptions) simple: it is a dominant, and everyone with a single copy of the gene shows its effects.

The inheritance of the lip and the title show the contrast between sexual and asexual repro-duction. The lip has spread – through both males and females, both of whom may show the condition – to many descendants and to other families linked by marriage. The title has descended down a single line of males, and is now extinct.

Its first owner was Bishop Werner, who died in 1096 and its last Archduke Otto, whose death was in Austria in

Charles V (1500–58),
Italian School

Bernard Strigel, Group Portrait of Emperor Maximilian and his Family (c.1515) The Habsburg Pedigree

1963. On the way it followed a single path, from father to son; passing through the rulers of Austria and of Spain, Italy, Hungary and parts of the Netherlands. This contrasts with the sexual inheritance of the lip. The gene became detached, through recombination, from the title and drifted off into the minor nobility of Europe.

Unfortunately for the symmetry of the argument, the direct male line of the Austrian Habsburgs ended with Charles VI in 1740 as he died leaving no sons. By declaring the Pragmatic Sanction of 1713 (a device denied to geneticists; and one so shocking to its day that it led to the War of the Austrian Succession) he bent the rules to allow his daughter Maria Theresa to inherit the title. She returned it to the male line with the birth of her son Joseph.

Maximilian I established the Habsburgs as a European power. He arranged the marriage of his son, Philip I, shown here as a young boy – with clear evidence of the family face – to Joanna the Mad, gaining by the match the whole of Spain. Their son, Charles V, the Holy Roman Emperor, was – in spite of his appearance – for a time the most powerful ruler in European history.

back to the Conqueror himself. The genetic highway pursued by the two hundred and ninety-nine other families who are so proud of their noble descent is forced to zigzag wildly through history, from fathers to mothers and back again, to make the link.

It is much easier to find the way to status if sex is allowed. Sex links John Crust, of Lincolnshire, to John Major and Margaret Thatcher; but it also explains why there are no eminent politicians called Crust. John Crust's surname, unlike his genes, was passed on asexually – it travelled just through males. As a result, being a Crust is a much more exclusive thing than being a fifth cousin of Mrs Thatcher. The disengagement of his name from his biological heritage emphasizes a fundamental truth about ancestry.

Sex is a democratic process as it allows everyone to join. Asexual reproduction, in contrast, is exclusive; so much so, indeed, that it means rapid extinction for nearly all those who indulge in it. In the case of the aristocracy, should any nobleman fail to have sons, his title will disappear. The romantically named Knight of Glin, Desmond John Villiers FitzGerald of Glin Castle, County Limerick, is the twenty-ninth successor to his noble station. He is, alas, the last Knight as all three of his children are daughters. The title will die with him.

The number of noble names is hence bound to decrease each generation: any sonless marriage kills the title. The average persistence of a title created in the middle ages was just three generations. All the five thousand feudal knighthoods recorded in the Domesday Book are extinct. Inheritance down a single line of descent opens all patrician names – and all genes – to the threat of instant death.

Two small segments of the human genome show the risks of following such an exclusive route through history. The Y chromosome passes – like a title – from fathers to sons. Every son receives his Y from his father, his grandfather, and so on back. All male Bassetts carry (forgetting the dangers of illegitimacy) William the Conqueror's Y chromosome. Genes on mitochondria are transferred only through the egg; that is, through females. Mothers pass on their mitochondrial genes to their daughters and sons, but only daughters transmit them. Mitochondria and Y chromosomes are just two tributaries of the genetic river, special only in that they do not drain into each other until their course reaches the sea of people alive today.

It is easy, in principle at least, to follow their fate. How many men alive at, say, the time of William the Conqueror have a direct line through sons

WHEN ADAM
MET EVE?

The diagram below shows the ancestry, through males, of ten men alive today; and (on the lower right) the same for ten females traced through the female line. There is much more variation in the mating success of males, some men having many children, some none. Most women, though, have roughly the same number of offspring. As a result, the last shared male ancestor lived long after the last shared female. In spite of the images (taken from a 1465 illustrated French translation of a work by Giovanni Boccaccio) of the Expulsion from the Garden of Eden, Adam almost certainly never met Eve.

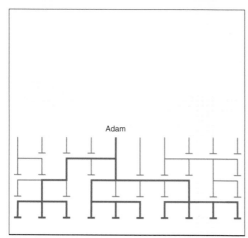

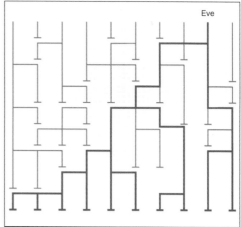

to a living male; and how many women an equivalent link through daughters to a female (or a male; a carrier but not a transmitter of mitochondria) alive today? Usually the records are not good enough to say – and even if they were the tendency of men to father children outside marriage means that the written and the genetic versions of history would soon diverge. For women, and their mitochondrial genes, the problem is less serious as in most cases a recorded link between mother and child can be depended on.

The French began to populate Québec in 1608. The explorer Samuel de Champlain – who once suggested to the King of France the idea of a canal across the Isthmus of Panama – set up his new colony at Stadaconda (later Québec City). In its first twenty years it attracted only seventy-eight immigrants. Soon, though, Cardinal Richelieu got involved and set up a commercial operation to found large farms or 'seigneuries', for those rich enough to buy them, along the St Lawrence River. About thirty thousand French people emigrated, but the harsh climate and the heredi-tary estates already established on the best land meant that only ten thousand stayed, many moving on to more remote parts of the province such as the valley of the Saguenay. In 1760, when the English took control, migration stopped.

The Saguenay has one of the best collections of family records in the world. It gives an insight into the fate of asexually transmitted genes. Only a quarter of the twenty thousand women who moved there before 1950 (most long before then) have contributed mitochondria to today's population. Just like the feudal knighthoods in the Domesday Book the other mitochondrial lineages that entered over the past three hundred years – only around fifteen generations – are extinct. Some of the original mothers have, purely by the accident of founding a lineage with lots of daughters, been very successful in passing on their mito-chondrial genes. One has five hundred descendants down the female line – in spite of the fact that three-quarters of her female contemporaries left none.

The same is certainly true for many of the Y chromosomes of the men who moved there. In fact, even fewer are likely to have survived. The variation in the number of children left by men is much greater than that of women. Some males are promiscuous and others do not find a partner at all. A few of the founding men in Saguenay left very many descendants, which means that many more left none at all and their Y chromosomes have disappeared.

MITOCHONDRIAL DISEASE:
GENETICS WITH A SINGLE PARENT

The mitochondrion is the cell's furnace: oxygen and food materials are burned there to produce energy. Unlike most of the cell's constituents, mitochondria have their own piece of DNA (which, quite unlike that of the nucleus, is a small closed circle of DNA bases). Sperm do not transmit mitochondria, which means that this DNA is passed down only through egg cells: both sons and daughters inherit their mitochondria from their mothers, but only daughters pass them on.

Several rare diseases arise from mistakes in mitochondrial DNA. Sometimes, only a single DNA base is changed; more often, a whole segment is missing. Some of the diseases lead to blindness because the optic nerve is damaged; some to muscle weakness. Several cause brain damage of various kinds. All are rare, but all show the characteristic pattern of inheritance through females.

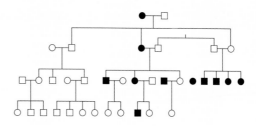

ABOVE: *The pedigree of a particular nerve and muscle disease, coded for by a mitochondrial gene. Notice how both males and females may be affected; but that every affected child has received the damaged genes from his or her mother.*

BELOW: *A section across a mitochondrion (the red ovoid object) within a cell. The membranes that run across it are the site of most of the cell's energy production.*

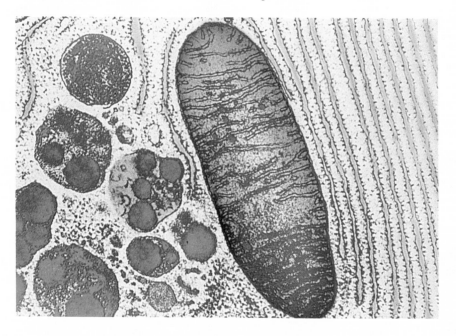

All this happened in a mere three centuries. In time, should the process go on and should Saguenay stay isolated, more and more of those asexual lineages will disappear. Sooner or later, inevitably, just one mitochondrial and one Y chromosome line will survive. Everyone in the area would then trace their own ancestry to a single woman and a single father some time in the Saguenay past.

This is the process that, on a global scale, gave rise to the ideas of the ultimate aristocrats, mitochondrial Eve and her supposed partner Y-chromosome Adam. They are the woman and the man from whom we all descend. In some statistical sense, they certainly existed. There is no reason, though, to suppose that Adam ever met Eve; that the individuals upon whom mitochondrial or Y-chromosome lineages converge lived in the same place or even at the same time. In fact, Eve almost certainly died long before Adam. Simply because so many males fail to find a mate, and as shown in the diagram on page 91, Y chromosomes go extinct more quickly than do mitochondria. What is more, whenever (and wherever) Eve and Adam lived they were, just as in seventeenth-century Saguenay, surrounded by other men and women. They are distinct merely in that – like the Bassetts with their much-proclaimed male descent from William the Conqueror – their lineages survived while those of their fellows did not.

Their descendants' genes also suggest that Adam and Eve never had the chance to fall from grace by indulging in the first, and least original, of all sins. The Y chromosomes of the world are remarkably similar, with only about one hundredth as much variation as on the other chromosomes. Mitochondria, in contrast, are quite variable. This lack of divergence among male lineages suggests that their common ancestor lived so recently that there has not been time for his descendants' Y chromosomes to accumulate differences. One estimate is of only twenty-seven thousand years before the present. The last shared mitochondrial ancestor – Eve – may have lived tens of thousands of years before Adam, the last universal forefather. Oddly enough, African Y chromosomes are particularly invariable. Perhaps only a small number of men monopolized most of the females and succeeded in passing on their genes. The genetic legacy of the others has disappeared.

Financial and social legacies that pass down the male line face the same fate. Extinct English titles revert to the Crown. There would, in time, if the rules were applied strictly, be just one aristocrat left as the titles of sonless families follow each other into extinction. Only the creation of new members of the nobility prevents this. That is the tragedy of aristocracy – it is exclusive, but it does not last. The most important aristocrats of all avoid the risk by bending the rules, which is why England is ruled by a Queen. In time, should estates follow their titles, the monarch would end up owning everything. Queen Elizabeth II has, indeed, been declared the country's richest person, with assets of more than two billion pounds. The claim is disputed by the Royal Household on the somewhat curious grounds that her wealth is held in trust for the nation; but, should the process continue, a future monarch would have a monopoly both of nobility and of wealth.

The American Revolution was directed towards breaking that monopoly. In the nation's early days democracy was narrowly saved from a House of Lords; an assembly of land-owning autocrats based on inherited authority. The victorious generals of the Revolu- tionary War petitioned George Washington to be allowed to set up an elite, the Society of Cincinnati. Membership was to be open to the generals them-selves and, as in the British peerage, to their first-born male descendants in perpetuity. Seeing the dangers of a hereditary aristocracy that would act as a means of concentrating money and authority within a few families, Washington forbade it.

The developing state was, nevertheless, built on the idea that property belongs to individuals and that inequality is inevitable. Long before, America had been grounded on common ownership. The New World was almost a repository of early socialism. Montaigne, in his essay on Cannibals, gives an account of some Tupinamba boys brought from the Americas to France in 1562. When asked by Charles IX what most impressed them about Paris, they replied that they had noticed how: 'some men gorged to the full with things of every sort, while their other halves were beggars at their doors, emaciated with hunger and poverty. They found it strange that the poverty-stricken half should suffer such injustice, and that they did not take the others by the throat or set fire to their houses.'

Even after European ideas were well established, Indians built success-ful societies on shared possession. Some negotiated with the invaders as equals. When the Cherokee were first encountered by Europeans, they were ruled by a princess, the Lady of Cofitachiqui. The tribe was divided into seven clans, in which membership was inherited asexually, down the female line. Every child had to marry outside their mother's clan. By 1730 the Cherokee nation was thirty thousand strong, controlling an area the size of Britain. One young man, Attakullakulla, the Little Carpenter,

Sequoyah, of the Cherokee tribe, and a document in his invented alphabet, using eighty-five characters, some based on arabic letters, to denote sounds distinct from those in English.

came to London (where his portrait was painted by Hogarth). He went, dressed in his robes, to Windsor, swearing that 'the great King George's enemies shall be our enemies; his people and ours shall always be one'. In return, he received a pledge of friendship 'as long as the mountains and rivers shall last, or the sun shine'.

In the nineteenth century, the Cherokee took up farming. By 1825 most could read; a proportion greater than in the white community itself. By 1850, they had spinning wheels, ploughs, girls' schools and even a newspaper – published in a unique script, in which arabic letters each stood for a sound different from that in English. Nearly all this was based on joint ownership.

This was an affront to the young United States, a country founded on individualism. Senator Henry Dawes of Massachusetts admired the Cherokee's communal society, but saw it as a dead end: 'The defect of the system was apparent. They have got as far as they can go, because they hold their land in common . . . There is no selfishness, which is at the bottom of civilization.'

He acted on his belief, pushing through the Dawes Severalty Act of 1877. This divided the tribe's land into plots of one hundred and sixty acres for each family. Conveniently enough, a great deal was left over. It was sold at bargain prices to European settlers.

Other, more radical, Americans hoped to develop the new Republic on different lines. They were impressed by the Indians' egalitarian way of life. For many, it was a model of what the United States should become – equality of ownership and of opportunity; a system based on co-operation. What wealth the Indians had was shared more or less equally on the death of those who held it. The Society of Tammany was named after the Chief of the Delawares who had greeted William Penn in 1682. Its members, working men, set up May Day as Tammany Day, wore Indian head-dresses, and proclaimed St Tammany as their patron. The Improved Order of Red Men, founded soon after the Revolution, was more socialist in tone. It promoted shared ownership of property, on the Indian model. The society abjured alcohol. It failed, as did the Tammanies (whose name later became attached to a group of corrupt New York politicians).

Money, it is said, is the one thing that distinguishes man from animals; but the rules governing its transmission from one generation to the next are the same as those that determine the inheritance of biological assets. Who gets what is owned by one era, in terms of cash or genes, when it passes to the next? The quarrel between the Indians and the United States in the nineteenth century emphasized the contrast between the two modes of inheritance. The Cherokee dispersed their wealth whenever it was bequeathed. The Society of Cincinnati and its intellectual

Senator Henry L. Dawes (1816–1903), the Republican Senator from Massachusetts whose belief in the new American way of life spelt disaster for many of the Indians who practised the old.

descendants, though, hoped to ensure that it was inherited asexually, with capital staying in the family line.

By establishing a landed gentry, the Cincinnatians hoped to follow the traditions of their ancestral home. It is no coincidence that many of those with ancient British titles are rich, as both title and estate are transmitted asexually. In the 1970s, three-quarters of the millionaires who died were members of the House of Lords. Often, wealth can buy nobility. The great brewers of the nineteenth century all became peers, leading one of Dickens' characters to say, in *Great Expectations*: 'I don't know why it should be such a crack thing to be a brewer; but it is indisputable that while you cannot possible be genteel and bake, you may be as genteel as never was and brew.' The fortunes of the Beerage, the brewers Allsopp, Bass and Guinness (now my Lords Hindlip, Burton and Iveagh), have followed their titles.

The inheritance of both title and property down a single line allows inequality to persist. The great estates of England are a record of its success in so doing. Often, they are in the hands of ancient families who have avoided any dilution of their holdings for generations. In 1883 the four largest English estates were owned by dukes; and the ten over sixty thousand acres all belonged to peers. In the 1870s, the Duke of Devonshire had nine great houses; Chatsworth House and Harwick Hall in Derbyshire, Holker Hall in North Lancashire, Bolton Abbey in Yorkshire, Compton Place in Sussex, Devonshire House and Chiswick House in London, Beaufort House in Newmarket and Lismore House in Ireland. His successor still has most of them – or the assets realized when they were sold.

Often, the insistence that wealth be inherited asexually is quite overt. Some noble estates are obliged to pass in the male line. Should no son be born, the property disappears to a distant relation who can trace the crucial male descent from long ago. In the eighteenth century, the Cumberland Lowthers succeeded in producing just one male heir between them. As a result, in 1802 their estates passed to a distant cousin connected with them only through a great-great-grandfather who had died in 1637.

A trip across the border between England and Wales shows the importance of inheritance rules. In mediaeval Wales, the custom was redistribution. All the sons of an aristocrat received part of their father's fortune and took a noble name. Soon, three-quarters of the population were *bonheddig*, nobility, with a pedigree stretching back through the mists of time, but most of this aristocracy starved on peasant smallholdings. West

Wales is still a patchwork of tiny fields. They are a relic of an inheritance system that died centuries ago. One set of rules produces something rather like socialism – the equal ownership of the means of production – while the other leads inevitably to the retention of resources by a few.

Although asexual reproduction in the biological sense is, even for the rich, impossible, many arrange matters to reduce the number of alien genes that penetrate their house through indiscriminate coupling. They do this by marrying their relatives; people who share their own genes. The Rothschilds began to accumulate a fortune at the beginning of the nineteenth century. The two eldest sons of the founding dynast Meyer Amschel Rothschild married before he became rich. They chose wives from unrelated – and undistinguished – Jewish families. His next two sons married daughters from the richest English and German Jewish houses. Soon, the Rothschild fortune began to dwarf all others. Meyer Rothschild's youngest son married his own niece, and, in the next generation, ten of twelve marriages of sons were with first cousins. Five of the six daughters, too, married other members of the family. The urge to diminish the redistribution of wealth and the recombination of genes intrinsic to sexual reproduction is a strong one.

The years since the Second World War represent what capitalism sees as its triumph. They are often thought of as 'the enterprise culture', the decades of the self-made man. Riches are justified because, however unfair it seems, they are the reward for hard work. Without wealth, the economy could not progress. Poverty in the midst of affluence may be unjust but is inevitable as it reflects the contributions made to society by the rich and the poor.

The truth about wealth is, of course, that most of the rich – and nearly all the very rich – owe their fortunes to inheritance. In the 1920s, the top one per cent of the British population owned more than sixty per cent of the total private wealth. By 1990 this had dropped to the top one per cent – half a million people – owning eighteen per cent of the total. This, though, is less of a triumph for equity than it might seem. The richest five million, ten per cent, in Britain still own more than half the nation's assets. The redistribution has been mainly between the grotesquely wealthy and the merely affluent. Lower down the scale, inequalities are still enormous; there, no doubt, the reduction in disparities between the moneyed classes are of rather little interest.

There are now fifty thousand millionaires in Britain. Only about a third of them inherited their fortunes. Of course, to the really rich a million pounds is nothing. The wealthiest of all are still rich because of the shrewdness of earlier generations. In America things are slightly fairer. Some of the richest people – Bill Gates of the Microsoft Corporation comes to mind – have made their fortunes from their own efforts (and of course from those of their employees). Even so, only a small portion of the American plutocracy have actually earned their riches.

Human weakness does lead to some fortunes being dispersed. In Britain, about half of the sons of wealthy families are 'dissipators': they leave less than they received because they have simply spent it. Particularly in the middle ranks, there is some turnover among the affluent, families rising and falling in the social scale. In 1995, Lord Caithness – twentieth heir of an earldom dating to 1455 – began work as an estate agent: as Voltaire put it, 'history is the sounds of hob-nailed boots ascending the staircase and of silk slippers coming down'.

Whatever the burden of tax, there has been a great reduction in the disparities in national wealth since the Industrial Revolution. Much of this has nothing to do with inheritance, but is because the economy has grown. Individual incomes have increased and many new fortunes have appeared. As a result, the importance of endowments in determining financial success has decreased compared to their overwhelming significance in more static societies. Before acclaiming the triumph of capitalism, though, it is worth remembering that no economy can grow indefinitely. As the days of stagnation return, inheritance will regain its power. There is a parallel in nature. Plenty of creatures – aphids for example – abandon sex when times are good, in the spring, and grow enormously in number. Even the genetically weakest prosper. As winter comes, though, and competition builds up, the population stops growing. There is sexual reproduction and a mass extinction of some lineages in favour of those few who can survive.

The best way of measuring the inheritance of wealth is to think like a geneticist; to compare the fortunes of one generation with those before and after them. The information needed is held in wills. Comparing the amount left by parents with what is left by their children estimates how much of the variation in assets within a society is due to differences in what individuals inherit. Wills are a telling statement of just how much of a nation's wealth 'cascades down the generations' (to quote John Major, the British Prime Minister). Cascade it certainly does: twenty years ago, men leaving over half a million pounds (then a substantial sum) were two hundred and fifty times more likely to have had fathers who themselves passed on a fortune than was an average Briton.

Fortunes are often made from vices. The tobacco company W. D. and H. O. Wills is based in Bristol. It takes its name from the Wills family, whose wealth began with Henry Overton Wills, a tobacco importer. The chronicles of their fortune (recorded in pounds at their 1960 value) cover six generations spanning a century and a half.

Henry Overton Wills died in 1826 worth seventy-two thousand pounds. By 1911, the fortune had grown. Sir William Henry Wills, Lord Winterstoke, left, in that year, ten million pounds; his son, William Overton Wills IV, who died within a few weeks of his father, twenty-one million pounds. Over the next half-century, many of the direct descendants of the first Henry Overton Wills (by then numbering well over a hundred) died. All were well off; but there were enormous disparities among them. Ten of those who died between 1900 and 1950 left more than two million, but among the others there were many who bequeathed a mere hundred thousand or so to their children. The Wills family have managed to protect their capital from the effects of redistribution with some success.

Its genetical equivalent, recombination, remains more or less universal. The reason is familiar to economists. It is that without sex there is less chance of innovation, of new mixtures of genes that may be more effective in dealing with a changing environment.

Sex is important in dealing with competition. If a competitor can evolve more quickly than can its rivals, sooner or later it will defeat them. Once sex gets started it is self-sustaining. A struggle against sexual creatures with their ability to evolve at speed means that few asexual lineages survive for long. Asexuality produces one set of genes that monopolizes the population but is in constant danger of obsolescence and decay.

Recombination starts a system of free trade in which new assortments of genes are steadily produced. They are the raw material upon which evolution acts to adapt the population to changing conditions. Most fail, but some are better than what went before and the population evolves to deal with new challenges. Adam Smith would have been delighted.

Enthusiasts for the free market see it as the most flexible and rapidly advancing economic system, because – like an evolving plant or animal – it can never afford to stay still. There is, though, an inbuilt contradiction common to both sex and the market; the simple expense of keeping them going. One temptation is always open – to give up and hope for the best. Many animals (and almost as many companies) have yielded to it.

THE JOY OF RECOMBINATION, OR,
SEX AMONG THE SLUGS

1. *Arion ater var. atra, p.* 175.
Barmouth, J. Hopkinson.

Helix nemoralis, the snail on the right, is overtly sexual. There are thousands of shell patterns. Only about a dozen different genes are involved, each altering the colour or striping of the shell in one way or another; but sex reshuffles them so often that in some places every snail is different. The black slug *Arion ater*, in contrast, has a more equivocal existence. It is a hermaphrodite, bearing both male and female organs in the same individual. In southern Europe (below) it is as sexual and as variable as its shelled cousin; but in the north it takes up self-fertilization, abandons sex and – in time – evolves as a single genetically identical population of tens of millions of black slugs (left).

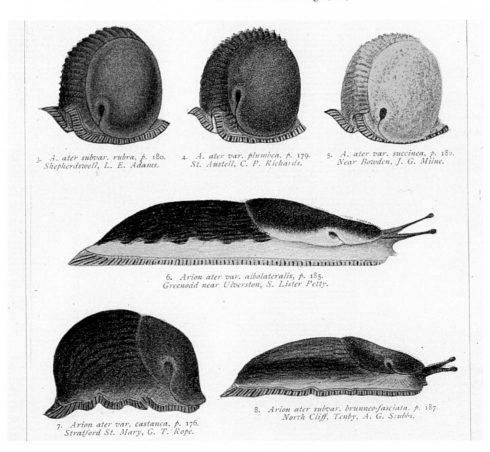

3. *A. ater subvar. rubra, p.* 180.
Shepherdswell, L. E. Adams.

4. *A. ater var. plumbea. p.* 179.
St. Austell, C. P. Richards.

5. *A. ater var. succinea, p.* 182.
Near Bowden, J. G. Milne.

6. *Arion ater var. albolateralis, p.* 185.
Greenodd near Ulverston, S. Lister Petty.

7. *Arion ater var. castanea, p.* 176.
Stratford St. Mary, G. T. Rope.

8. *Arion ater subvar. brunneo-fasciata. p.* 187.
North Cliff, Tenby, A. G. Stubbs.

HELIX NEMORALIS L.

Helix nemoralis Linné.
Truro, J. H. James.

H. *nemoralis* v. *rubella* Picard.
Valentia Island, E. Collier.

H. *nemoralis* v. *rubra* Baudon.
Lisdoonvarna Spa, E. Collier.

H. *nemoralis* v. *rosea* Baudon.
Knottingley, J. Cordukes.

H. *nemoralis* v. *libellula* Risso.
Valentia, E. Collier.

H. *nemoralis* s.v. *albescens* Pic.
Ballyvaughan, E. Collier.

H. *nemoralis* v. *flavovirescens* Pic.
Bristol, Miss Hele.

H. *nemoralis* v. *studeria* Moq.
Castleton, G. H. Taylor.

H. *nemoralis* v. *olivacea* Risso.
Limerick, E. Collier.

H. *nemoralis* v. *castanea* Picard.
Blagdon, Miss Hele.

H. *nemoralis* v. *citrinozonata* Ckll.
Carrickfin, E. Collier.

H. *nemoralis* v. *hyalozonata* Taylor.
Carrickfin, E. Collier.

H. *nemoralis* v. *lateritia* D. & M.
Blagdon, Miss Hele.

H. *nemoralis* v. *fascialba* Picard.
Barnsley, W. E. Brady.

H. *nemoralis* s.v. *mista* B. & B.
Hereford, Dr. Boycott.

H. *nemoralis* v. *olivaceozonata* Coll.
Magilligan, E. Collier.

H. *nemoralis* v. *roseolabiata* Kob.
Bath, Miss Hele.

H. *nemoralis* s.v. *tenuis* Baudon.
Ennistimon, P. H. Grierson.

H. *nemoralis* v. *rubello-libellula* Ckll.
Bordeaux, R. F. Scharff.

103

Sometimes, it works. Plenty of creatures avoid the cost of sex. One route is through hermaphroditism. Some plants and animals bear male and female sexual organs on the same individual. It needs but a small leap of the evolutionary imagination to indulge in self-fertilization; to mate with one's closest relative – oneself. After many generations, all the off-spring begin to share the same genes; they are, in effect, identical twins.

There are patterns in celibacy. It is easier to relinquish males in high mountains or cold climates than in the tropics. Slugs go in for hermaphroditism. As one walks up the few hundred feet of the Winnat Pass in Derbyshire the local slugs – the big juicy ones – give up sex. At the foot of the valley they come in a variety of colours, are sexual and each is unique. At the top, they are all black – and all, more or less, genetically identical to the black slugs who live north of the Arctic Circle a thousand miles away. Rather like the Rothschilds, they achieve this by mating with the closest available member of the family – who, for a self-fertilizer, is quite easy to find.

Asexuality works best when the opponent – bad weather, or poor soil – is predictable. A single strategy, unimaginative though it is, may well succeed. In the same way, huge fortunes accumulate mainly in places where there is political stability. Economists talk of 'natural monopolies'; situations in which one company prevails as its competitors cannot get into the market. A small village may need only one bus a day. Anyone trying to run a second will find it hard to succeed as it can never sell enough tickets to make a profit. Only if it comes up with a new idea – a smaller bus, say – can it win. The natural genetic monopolies produced by asexual reproduction are like this; safely in control of a stable set of resources.

Once sex has disappeared, though, there is the constant risk of being unable to cope with a competitor who has thought of a new strategy. Asexual creatures can become confined to doing such a small and specialized job that they are at risk of going out of business altogether. Like monopoly capitalism, abandoning sex has short-term advantages that are outweighed by long-term risks. In almost every case, asexual creatures have descended from sexual ancestors but – in spite of the apparent benefit of doubling the rate of production of copies of their own genes – have not themselves given rise to successful heirs. Giving up sex leads nowhere.

Senator Dawes said as much of the Indian way of life. It was bound to die, because it was not selfish enough. In the United States, the triumph

The Cherokee on a three-hundred-mile forced march in 1838. On the Trail of Tears, twenty thousand people moved west to Indian Territory (now Oklahoma). Four thousand died and the survivors faced further oppression.

of capitalism is more complete than anywhere else. Competition is universal and the law jumps on monopoly as soon as it appears. The battle between collective ownership and individual greed has been played out in its starkest form and, it seems, greed has prevailed.

There has, however, been an unexpected renewal of the conflict between rules based on self-interest and those of the Indians and their vision of shared wealth. For today's Indians, the contrast between the systems of inheritance of genes and of money is more pointed than for anyone else.

There has always been an ambiguous relationship between native and immigrant in North America. Sometimes the Indians have been admired, sometimes despised. Invariably, though, they have been exploited. The United States drove Indians almost to extinction. Tribes who had governed huge tracts were reduced to small reservations, often hundreds of miles from their homes. The Cherokee were driven from their farms. On the Trail of Tears, west beyond the Mississippi, thousands died.

Davy Crockett, 'King of the Wild Frontier', is painted as a hero, but in

truth he was a land speculator involved in driving the Cherokee westwards. He bragged that his finest meal had been of potatoes from the
basement of a gutted building, roasted in the fat of Indians burned alive.
Even after the days when Indians were hunted, many of their children
were forcibly removed to boarding schools and brought up for a life of
servitude. Although the details of the negotiation between the Indian
nations and the United States differed from tribe to tribe, in essence
many were the same. The Indians ceded the land itself in return for
keeping some rights over it. They included, for example, hunting, fishing
and timber and, in more recent times, the right to sell tax-free petrol or
cigarettes on the reservation. The rights belonged to the tribe, rather
than to any individual. They were part of a common wealth.

For many years, the Bureau of Indian Affairs acted as a colonial power
to its subjects, organizing their lives but denying them representation.
The treaties themselves were more and more ignored. In the 1960s,
though, Indians began to assert their rights. This soon caused trouble. In
Minnesota there were riots between hunters and Indians; in upstate New
York murders over the sale of cheap cigarettes. Grudgingly, the states
conceded that – like it or not – they had agreements with Indians and that
there was no choice but to obey them.

Many Indians began to exercise one prerogative they scarcely knew
they had: the right to gamble, whatever a state might say, on their land.

Indian children learning their position in American society at the Riverside Indian
School in Anadarko, Oklahoma in 1901.

George Washington saw gambling as 'the child of avarice, the brother of iniquity and the father of mischief' (although this did not stop him from sponsoring lotteries when funds ran low). Today, gambling in the United States has a turnover greater than the film, book and music industries combined; around six hundred billion dollars a year. In 1978, Nevada was the only state with legal gambling. By 1995, largely through the efforts of Indians, it had been joined by forty others. There are some bizarre loopholes that allow it to exist. States bordering the Mississippi once allowed gambling only on riverboats, peddling a false Mark Twain experience as people lost their money. Now there are 'boats on moats', floating casinos in ditches, that hold only to the letter of the law. Gambling provides a million jobs and raises one and a half billion dollars a year in state and local taxes – but costs the state three times as much in crime and social expenditure.

Gambling is the sale of hope to those who despair of success by other means. It is, above all, a method of transferring money from poor to rich. The largest casino in the world is not, as might be expected, in Las Vegas. Instead it is situated between New York and Boston (although Vegas plans to hit back with 'New York, New York', a casino based on a one-third scale replica of the Manhattan skyline). The State of Connecticut, in which the record-breaking casino stands, was once opposed to gambling on moral grounds and for fear of the corruption and violence that accompanies it. It has been forced into a reluctant acceptance of a massive gambling operation.

The casino is called Foxwoods; a bland name, but one summarizing the extraordinary history of its owners, a tribe called the Mashantucket Pequots. The Pequots refer to themselves as 'The Fox People'. 'Mashantucket' means 'much-wooded land' – and, around the casino, there are still forests, grown up from the abandoned farms of pioneers as they moved west. Four centuries ago there were ten thousand Pequots. They lived as hunters, fishermen and farmers around the Thames river and the coast of Connecticut.

In 1637, in a war over land, seven hundred were massacred in the seaport of Mystic by an English army under the command of Captain John Underhill. In his diary he recorded how 'Many were burnt in the fort, both men, women and children. Others were forced out and came in troops . . . twenty or thirty at a time, which our soldiers received and entertained at the point of the sword . . . those that escaped us fell into the hands of the Indians that were behind us.'

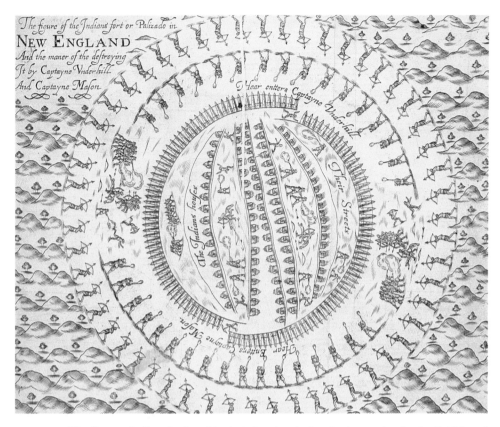

The Pequot Indians besieged in their fort, just before its destruction by the British and their Native American allies at the Battle of Mystic in 1637.

Those allies of the British, Narragansett and Mohegan tribesmen, received many of the remaining Pequot as slaves. Under the Treaty of Hartford in 1638 others were sent in slavery to Bermuda, where they faded from history. They might have been useful in Britain, but Queen Elizabeth had, a few years before, expelled from England all 'negars and blackamoors' and they were not welcome.

In 1666, there was a grudging acceptance of their existence and the remnant, two thousand or so, were given an acre apiece at Mashantucket. Over the years the Pequot reservation was whittled down to a mere two hundred and fourteen acres, and by 1970 just two elderly half-sisters, Elizabeth George Plouffe and Martha Langevin Ellal, remained, living in poverty in an old trailer. Once they died, the State could seize the land and use it as a park.

Elizabeth George's grandson, Richard Hayward, had been to the reservation as a child and was proud of his heritage. In 1974, he began a search for descendants of the Pequots and re-established the tribe on its ancestral land. By the beginning of the nineteen eighties, twenty-nine of his fellows were living there, making a living from selling firewood, lettuce and maple syrup.

Their future was transformed in 1976. James Billie, a chief of the Seminoles in Florida, took advantage of a Supreme Court decision that Indian reservations were, in certain senses, 'sovereign nations', able to defy state law and open bingo games. Hayward came to see what was going on. Noticing a loophole in the Connecticut laws he set out to start a gambling operation on his own reservation. This, needless to say, incensed the State of Connecticut. Many of the Pequots, too, were unhappy. Some were Jehovah's Witnesses, others Baptists. Both opposed gambling on moral grounds. Undaunted, Hayward approached the Arab-American Bank for money. On seeing the legal loophole the bank made just one stipulation. He should ask for a bigger loan.

Only a hundred and forty miles from New York, the Pequots could not fail. In February 1992 they opened the Casino itself, with bingo, roulette, poker, craps and blackjack, all for high stakes (to enter a game of bingo can cost $350). Within a year came another bonanza. In return for paying the State of Connecticut (which, faced with the inevitable, had abandoned its moral scruples) a quarter of the profits or a hundred million dollars a year, whichever was greater, Foxwoods was allowed to install slot machines. By 1993 (a year in which seven million people gambled there) the casino was in the middle of a quarter-billion dollar expansion which would make it the largest in the world and put the Pequots on the road to unimaginable wealth. Two years later the tribe was ready to open casinos elsewhere in the State and was bidding to control the whole of gambling in Connecticut.

The Pequots spend much of their income for the good of the tribe. They are buying houses and land around the reservation, and have opened a magnificent community centre. Every Pequot child is guaranteed an education and every adult a job. Because of early inter-marriage with black slaves, many Pequots have dark skins, and the tribe is allocating money to minorities in the local community, with grants to schools in the poorest parts of nearby cities.

Their success is bringing competition. Their old enemies the Mohegans plan to set up their own casino on the site of an abandoned

THE MASHANTUCKET PEQUOT CASINO

Foxwoods has more than gaming machines. There is a vast hotel, smelling of a poisonous air-freshener; next to it, the Pequot are building the world's first non-smoking gambling hall. There is the Beauty Parlour. Faux nails, Acrylic, Fiberglass and Gel start at $50, Change of Polish at $10 and Lip Glossing at $6. An entertainment complex, opened by Frank Sinatra, promises a virtual reality ride through the world of the Pequots. The tribe's history is celebrated by a vast statue of a muscular Pequot. Made of translucent white acrylic (often used for making bathtubs) the Rain-maker stands on a revolving plinth outside the door to the gambling hall. On the hour, an eagle screams, drums roll, and there is a clap of recorded thunder. As the blinds close over the skylight, the Indian shoots a laser-beam arrow into the heavens. To the chanting of tribesmen the rain falls onto the plastic oak leaves shading him. Soon, though, the sun reappears and the crowds move on into the casino.

Richard A. 'Skip' Hayward, Chairman of the Tribal Council of the Mashantucket Pequot Indians, and author of their casino and the tribe's new-found wealth.

RIGHT: *The Rainmaker in the Mashantucket Pequot casino, firing his laser arrow into the sky in the hope of bringing rain, every hour on the hour.*

factory that once assembled reactors for nuclear submarines. A 'faux-stone' gambling hall will take its place. Granny Squannit, leader of the Makiawisug, the little people who protect the tribe, will preside over the gambling floor. The Narragansetts, joint allies in the massacre of 1637, plan to start gambling on their reservation, too.

The Pequot are part of what is becoming a huge industry. There are now a hundred and thirty Indian casinos, scattered from coast to coast. By 1998 the Indians will control a tenth of the gambling business. For the first time, many Indians will be rich. Each of the hundred and thirty members of the Shakopee Dakota tribe has become a millionaire and each is guaranteed an annual income of half a million dollars. As a tribe spokesman puts it, 'It's the American Dream come true!' The Dakota dream pales beside that of the Cour d'Alène Indians of Idaho, who hope to open a National Indian Lottery with free phone lines – and a guaranteed jackpot of two hundred million dollars to three lucky winners a year. Indians joke that they will soon be able to buy back Manhattan, purchased by the Dutch for about twenty dollars in 1626. The renewal of Indian self-confidence meant that, in 1995, even Tonto, erstwhile sidekick of the Lone Ranger, knocked his comic-strip master to the ground saying 'I'm not your Indian . . . I'm not anyone's Indian, I'm Tonto!'

All this adds new weight to two old questions, each of which has social and genetic implications. To whom does the tribe's heritage belong; and who belongs to the tribe? Before gambling, being a member of an Indian nation was not much more than a matter of self-esteem, or of the right to live in poverty on marginal land. Now, though, Indian descent can open the door to millions. Who gets through it depends on the biological laws that are used. There is no legal definition of who is an Indian: anyone is free so to describe themselves even if this gives them no particular rights. Inevitably, real Indians resent those who make such an assertion of identity as it may be the first step to demanding a share in a tribe's privileges. A society based on joint ownership is always open to penetration.

Some people want to be Indians, even feel themselves to be Indians, although they have no genetic ties with Native Americans. On the United States Census form, it is possible to tick whatever 'ethnic group' box one identifies with. Between 1960 and the 1990 the number choosing 'American Indian' rose from half a million to two million. A quarter admitted, on questioning, to having no Indian ancestry at all. They are the Tribe Called Wannabee. Playing Indian has a history as old as the United States. Black Elk, a participant in a Wild West Show, was spoken to reprovingly by Queen Victoria: 'We danced and sang . . . right in front of Grandmother England. She was little and fat . . . she said "I am sixty-seven years old. All over the world I have seen all kinds of people, but today I have seen the best-looking people I know. If you belonged to me I would not let them take you round in a show like this."'

Longfellow's *Hiawatha* and Fenimore Cooper's *Last of the Mohicans* gave respectability to the movement. Soon, quacks, Quakers and temperance advocates became possessed by Indian spirits. The game spread, with Indians as tobacco advertisements and sports teams called the Braves, the Redskins, the Seminoles and the Apaches. Hippies wore headbands, beads and fringed jackets. A group of spiritualists even attempted to register itself as a tribe with a legal identity. There is something about being Indian (something notably absent from being Black) that Americans find irresistible.

Sometimes, a change of identity is carefully planned. Hawaiians want to be shifted from the 'Asian/Pacific Islander' box to the 'American Indian/Alaskan Native' box in the census for the year 2000. The denial of gambling rights to Hawaiians has, of course, nothing to do with it.

After the Severalty Act which deprived the Cherokee of much of their land, oil was found on what remained. A second Act demanded the re-registration of property assigned to the tribe. At once, there was a rush of white settlers who, with the help of dishonest lawyers, made bogus claims of Indian ancestry, enrolled themselves into the tribe and seized the land. In 1905 these 'White Indians' began to press for statehood. Although the real Indians asked for their own state, 'Sequoyah', which might protect their rights, this was denied and the State of Oklahoma came into being. At its foundation, Theodore Roosevelt presided over a mock wedding between 'Mr Oklahoma' and 'Miss Indian Territory'. Needless to say, the dowry in this case was paid by the bride. The state was founded on the basis of false assertions of Indian descent, made to gain a share of Indian wealth.

Such spurious claims mean that Indians must demand *some* connection among those who wish to share in the distribution of assets. To do so is to define genetic rules of membership. What they are determines what the tribe becomes. For most tribes, there must be a biological link with a defined group of Indians in the past (often those who signed the original treaties or those appearing on the Registration Rolls of the Tribe set up by Senator Dawes). Although proving Indian descent is not sufficient to claim Indian rights, it is an essential first step to affiliation with a tribal group.

PLAYING INDIAN IN
THE WILDS OF WEST GERMANY

Americans are not the most ardent devotees of Indian identity. In nineteenth-century Germany, Indians were seen as a model of freedom. As the translator of a book by Chief Buffalo Child Long Lance wrote, 'The Indian is closer to the German than to any other European. This may be due to our stronger leaning for that which is close to nature'. Franz Schubert scribbled to a friend a week before his death in 1828: 'Be so kind as to come to my help with reading matter in this desperate situation. Of Cooper I have read: The Last of the Mohicans, The Spy, The Pilot, and the Pioneers. In case you might have something else by him, I beseech you to deposit such for me with Madame von Bogner in the coffee house.'

The German author Karl May wrote a series of adventure tales featuring Old Shatterhand, an Indian scout. They still sell. In 1890, Buffalo Bill came with a group of Indians, and caused a sensation. Dresdeners learned to ride, to twirl lassos and to chant in Indian style. They were the founders of the German Hobby Indian Movement.

Each year there are summer camps, packed with tepees and with thousands of participants dressed in costume. German-manufactured Indian handicrafts are on sale (including beautifully made beadwork, measured with micrometer gauges). The campers follow, as earnestly as they can, Indian tribal customs, and invite elders from the United States to attend their Grand Pow-Wows.

The Hobby Indian movement was particularly strong in East Germany. The State encouraged it as it reminded the populace that the United States had an imperialist past, but the people joined as it gave them a sense of freedom in a stifling system. For some there is an unwelcome irony in the new demand among North American Indians to be allowed to carry a card showing their blood quantum. The parallel with the Nazi regime is just too close.

Ted Aston has been a hobby Indian for most of his life. As a boy he was forced to carry an identity card showing a link with Judaism. He is dubious about the morality of issuing a card that does the same thing to Native Americans.

THE SIBERIAN COLUMBUS
AND THE PEOPLING OF THE AMERICAS

In 989, the Norseman Eirik the Red established a colony on the west coast of Greenland. His son, Leif the Lucky, travelled onwards to Newfoundland, where the ruins of his settlement still exist. They found people – the Skraelings as they called them – and traded with them before abandoning the new colony, Vinland, as hopeless. It was five hundred years before the next European met a native American.

Americans, had, of course, been there long before. The first Columbus came from the east, from Siberia. In spite of claims of ancient settlements, perhaps a hundred and fifty thousand years old, in California, the usual view is that the first humans crossed the Behring land bridge – then a vast and icy steppe, filled with mammoths and reindeer – about twenty five thousand years ago. Although the crossing itself took several thousand years people reached the southern tip of the Americas within ten thousand years of arriving in the north.

There is evidence of the pattern of movement in the genes. There are many genetic variants that are uniquely North American (some restricted to particular tribes) and have probably arisen by mutation inthe past twenty-five thousand years. Others link the Americas firmly to today's north Asians, Siberians in particular. Although the information is so patchy that there is plenty of room for argument, there is a clue to the history of America in the mitochondrial DNA (that segment of the genetic information that is inherited down the female line).

Many Indians (and many East Asians) have a small deletion of part of the molecule. A family tree of North America has four branches, all fairly closely related. Three of them are also found in Siberia. This might be a relic of separate waves of migration into the continent at different times; and, indeed, the mitochondria of Alaskan and Yukon Indians are more similar than others to their Siberian ancestors, suggesting a later arrival. The Tlingit and Haida Indians of the coast of Alaska are on a genetic branch distinct from that found further south in the Americas. Their culture and art (totem-poles included) are also very different. Both suggest a later arrival in the New World, perhaps around the beginning of European recorded history, five thousand years ago. Some groups (such as the Nuu-Chah-Nulth Indians of Vancouver Island) have a genetic identity of their own, suggesting a separate and perhaps even more recent origin across the ocean.

Pocahontas, portrayed here in fashionable London dress under her real Indian name of Mataoka and her Christian cognomen, Rebecca. Hers was one of the first of many marriages between native Americans and European colonists.

North American Indians, like everyone else, have a genetic identity of their own. There are differences between Indians and Europeans in blood groups, proteins, and DNA sequences that are more than enough to distinguish them.

Native Americans are nearly all blood group O. Patterns of difference at the DNA level, too, are enough to cause the FBI to keep a separate Indian data-base for forensic work. Many American Indians have a characteristic deletion of a short segment of the mitochondrial DNA. In most of the world's population, this is a closed circle of about sixteen thousand bases; the deletion removes a section of these and provides a statement of shared Indian descent from the women who had crossed the Bering Straits from Siberia to Alaska more than twenty thousand years ago. It might seem easy to establish who is and is not a North American Indian; who has at least the prospect of sharing in their new-found wealth. Anyone with white skin, blood group A or B, and an uninterrupted mitochondrial genome would be excluded. Even though a few undoubted Indians might be light-skinned, or group A, or lack the mitochondrial deletion, almost no-one of native ancestry would combine all three. As more genes are brought into the equation it should be easy to distinguish a Native American from an immigrant and to develop a test of the ancestry of someone hoping to join the Indian pedigree.

There is, though, a problem in using genes to decide who can claim an Indian heritage. Sex has confused the issue. There has been much mating between Indians and non-Indians. Some tribes came into contact with Europeans early, others late, but all have mixed to some extent. In the early days, Pocahontas, the playful one, daughter of the Virginian chief Powhattan, is supposed (at least according to the other actor in the drama) to have saved the life of Captain John Smith by cradling his head in her arms as he was about to be clubbed to death. Later, in 1614, she married the Englishman John Rolfe – a predecessor of the Wills family as a tobacco magnate – and had a child by him. She died the following year in England, of smallpox; and is claimed as an ancestor by many today (including the Countess Mountbatten of Burma).

For the Cherokee, too, intermarriage began early. The French had tried to persuade Attakullakulla's rival Oconostota ('Groundhog Sausage') to turn his people against the King and a British garrison was sent to the Tennessee valley. Many of the soldiers took Cherokee wives. In the 1760s two Scots, Alexander Cameron and John McDonald, lived there as Crown Agents. They married Indian women and McDonald's grandson John Ross became Principal Chief of the tribe.

Other tribes adopted soldiers captured in battle. Often, the captives savoured their bondage. Benjamin Franklin noted that 'When white persons of either sex have been taken prisoner young by the Indians, in a short time they become disgusted with our manner of life . . . and there is no reclaiming them.' By 1802, Thomas Jefferson was, in word at least, promoting mixed marriages. At a reception for Indian leaders he foresaw the day when 'You will unite yourselves with us, join our councils and form one people with us, and we shall all be Americans; you will mix with us by marriage, your blood will mix with ours, and will spread, with ours, all over this great island.'

Such gene mixing quickly gave rise to questions of identity. Who belonged on the Indian pedigree? It was a problem that faced both the Federal Government and the tribes themselves. The argument turned on what genetic rules were used. By manipulating them it was possible to extend or contract the Indian family almost at will.

The 1887 General Allocation Act was the Government's attempt to define who belonged. It used the quasi-genetical idea of 'blood quantum'. To be an Indian, one had to be the offspring of a full-blooded Indian married to a European, or of two three-quarter blood Indians; or any combination which provided more than half 'Indian blood'. In 1918, the quantum was reduced to one-quarter. Those who passed the blood test could carry a Federal Indian Card. The idea is still being written into racial law. In 1990 the Act to Promote the Development of Indian Arts and Crafts made it a crime punishable with a million-dollar fine and a fifteen-year prison sentence for anyone to 'offer to display for sale any good . . . which suggests that it is Indian-produced' unless the artist is 'certifiably . . . one-quarter or more of Indian blood by birth'.

Used strictly, the law says that even the offspring of a marriage between two full-bloods from different tribes count only as half-bloods. There is a certain irony in seeing genes uses to establish rights in a nation claiming equality under the law.

Some tribes accepted the blood quantum, but set it at a lower level. The Pequots demand only one-sixteenth blood: one great-great-grand-parent among a list of some fifty Pequots registered at the turn of the century. For other tribes, one Indian ancestor was enough – one drop of blood, a single recombination of European with Indian genes, was an admission card. Blood quantum, of its nature, accepts that Indian ancestry is transmitted sexually: it can be dispersed, by recombination, among people whose ancestors include non-Indians.

This contains within itself the risk of defining the tribe – and its collective rights – out of existence. The blood quantum was designed to reduce the numbers of Indians. Whenever an Indian marries a European there is genetic recombination and the blood quantum of the children is reduced. As this goes on, more and more fall below the threshold. In time, there will be no quarter-bloods left. The system is hard at work. In 1900 about half of all Indians were full-bloods. By 1990, one in five were. A third of registered Indians are already at the cut-off point, and unless they marry someone with a blood quantum higher than their own, their children will no longer be Indians. As seventy per cent of American Indians marry people belonging to another ethnic group there will in less than a hundred years be no officially recognized Indians at all.

Many refuse to register with the authorities, even though they may pass the quantum test. Some artists, by taking this stand, have already lost the right to exhibit as Indians. To go along with the government is, they say, to take part in a genetical genocide. The Federal Indian Card is identical in kind to the Yellow Star worn by Jews in Germany. The government's behaviour is, to quote the definition of genocide formulated by the Pole Raphael Lemkin in 1944, an attempt at 'destruction of the national group as an entity, and the actions involved are directed at individuals, not in their individual capacity but as members of the national group'. The United Nations statement on genocide fits even better, as it includes 'the systematic moral debasement of a group, people, or nation'. Infuriated by the debasement of the Indian heritage by the sports establishment, with their 'Braves' and 'Chiefs', some Indians have proposed the renaming of football teams as the Chicago 'Niggers' (who might wear bones through their noses) and the Kansas City 'Kikes'. Other Indians, though, are all in favour of racial classification. A Canadian tribe has tried to exclude several families from their reservation to protect the group's 'genetic quality' and to reduce pressure on land. They are still in conflict with constitutional lawyers about their right to do so.

Those who base their definition simply on sex, with no statement of how much exchange there must have been, face another threat. The one-drop rule may swamp the tribe by turning everyone into an Indian. A single mating between a British soldier and an Indian woman two centuries ago may by now have produced thousands of descendants. The rule would transform them all into Indians. If so many are attached to the tribal pedigree, the idea of specifically Indian rights loses all meaning.

Because tribal membership depends on inheritance, it is in principle open to genetic test; and many aspirants are asking for one. The one-drop rule calls for only a single Indian gene. No pure-bred European has ever been found with certain uniquely Indian DNA variants. Almost all native Americans, though, carry one or more of them. Anyone, whatever their appearance, with these short DNA sequences must hence have an Indian ancestor. Many other genes differ to a greater or lesser extent between Indians and Europeans. Survey enough of them and it would be possible to construct a composite genotype for everyone, defining what proportion of their heritage is Indian. Although there is in some tribes the added complication that a link must be made to the small group that signed the treaty documents, any claimant to Indian descent could, in this way, at least have his or her blood quantum assessed.

The conflict between biological laws of inheritance and the legal rules stating who can share a tribe's wealth exemplifies the dilemma of sex. The Pequots, with their new-found fortune, are caught firmly on its horns. Their rules say that, to gain a share in the gambling fortune, an aspirant must have one-sixteenth descent from a small group of Pequots living in 1900. This may itself bring hundreds of claimants into the tribe. Intermarriage long before 1900 means that many times this number have Pequot blood. Elizabeth George Plouffe and Martha Langevin Ellal (who were almost the last of the Pequots) looked no different from most other natives of Connecticut. Richard Hayward is a prosperous businessman indistinguishable from any New York broker.

Other Pequots have dark skins because of matings between their ancestors and local black slaves. Both belonged to oppressed minorities and admixture was common. The first casualty of the War of Independence was one Crispus Attucks, who fell in the Boston Massacre of 1770. He was an African-Indian. Martin Luther King, too, had Indian (as well as white) ancestors. Three hundred years of recombination have distributed the original Pequot genes so thinly that visible clues of their heritage are concealed. No doubt there are Indian genes coursing through Pequot veins, but – as yet – no-one has tracked them down.

Deciding who gets a share is a real problem for the Pequot nation. There are three hundred undisputed members of the tribe, but thousands are keen to join. A television report about their search for lost kin – and the possibility of instant wealth – brought a deluge of claims. Many, no doubt, were fraudulent, but some had a basis in fact. There was much mockery of a West Indian who called to assert descent from 'Peacock' Indians. The claim seemed ludicrous: the man was, after all, black. But, after the battle of Mystic, many Pequots were transported to Bermuda. There were marriages with the locals, and, over the years, descendants of the exiled Indians merged into the Afro-Caribbean population.

Indians who have become rich are faced with a simple choice. It turns on the difference between sexual and asexual reproduction. If wealth is shared out among all those who can claim Indian ancestry (even when an arbitrarily defined cut-off point is established) it is lost to the tribe. If it is confined, in the western way, to single families, then the tribe loses much of its reason for existence.

The Cherokee were among the first to face the problem. They were happy to accept Europeans, usually through the marriage of white men to their own women. For the descendants of such marriages just one Indian ancestor – one drop of blood – was enough for membership. As, in the nineteenth century, the tribe grew richer the immigrants began to insist that their wealth – but not their tribal affiliation – should be inherited asexually, according to European rules. Shops and houses stayed in the family line; and, quite quickly, a class system developed.

Joe Melius, an aspirant to Pequot membership, in his house near the reservation. He has, he hopes, found a link with those on the tribal rolls at the beginning of this century.

Some Cherokee became substantial slave owners while others laboured in the fields.

Many Indians today are in the same quandary. The right to gamble (or to fish, or to sell tax-free petrol) lies with the tribe. Its consequence, unimagined wealth, does not. Some tribes have made large cash payments to their members, others have set up trust funds. Inevitably, these are retained in a single family. Two systems of inheritance have come into conflict. Its resolution is leading to the death of the Indian sense of solidarity.

In upstate New York, the Mohawk Reservation spans the US–Canadian border (which was defined after the War of 1812 without much thought of Indians). There are bingo games, and there have been failed attempts to set up casinos. Large sums of money come from smuggling cigarettes between the United States and Canada in speedboats across the St Lawrence River, which bisects the Reservation. The Mohawk claim the right to control border traffic, and surreptitiously move tax-free cigarettes into the surrounding communities, where they are sold at a large profit.

This has led to conflict, with riots, murders and barricades of the border bridge. On the United States side, Federal Agents have raided casinos and arrested cigarette smugglers. The tribe is split as many Mohawk resent the explosion of crime, violence and drug-taking that accompanies the gambling and bootlegging. Most of the profit, they say, goes to a few rather than to the tribe as a whole. Others point to the new earnings that have allowed the Mohawk, for the first time, to develop decent schools. Some members of the tribe plan to build a massive casino; but others have left to set up a new community which retains the shared values that once made Indians unique.

The Mohawk conflict contains within itself the ancient dilemma of greed as the cost of progress; of the short-term advantages of giving up sex versus its long-term costs. In economics, self-interest usually triumphs. Adam Smith, in *The Wealth of Nations* (published in the year of the Declaration of Independence) spoke frankly: 'It is not from the benevolence of the butcher, the brewer or the baker that we expect our dinner, but from their regard to their own interest. We address ourselves,

A young Mohawk stands defiantly on an upturned patrol car after a failed 1990 attempt by the police to remove road blocks on the reservation.

not to their humanity but to their self-love . . . Every individual . . . intends only his own gain, and he is in this, as in many other cases, led by an invisible hand to promote an end which was no part of his intention. By pursuing his own interest he frequently promotes that of society more effectually than when he really intends to promote it.'

Adam Smith was, had he but known it, talking about sex. In nature, each individual does indeed promote only his own gain, or at least that of his genes. Altruism always fails in the face of self-interest and the system of diversity and competition that is inevitable once sex evolves is the invisible hand that leads to biological progress. Whether the Indians have gained from embracing with such enthusiasm what Senator Henry Dawes called 'selfishness, which is at the bottom of civilization' is, no doubt, a matter for them.

CHAPTER III

The Search for the Lost Tribes

*'Thus saith the Lord GOD: Behold, I will
take the children of Israel from among the
heathen, whither they be gone, and will
gather them on every side, and bring them
into their own land: And I will make them
one nation in the land upon the mountains
of Israel . . .'*

EZEKIEL 37: 19–22

CREMATION WAS A CRIME in Britain until a century ago. How could the
faithful spring from their graves at the last trump if they had been
reduced to a handful of ashes? In spite of its demonstrating a certain lack
of faith in divine ingenuity, the argument held sway until 1884. In that
year, a Welshman, Dr William Price (then aged eighty-four) ceremoni-
ally burned the body of his infant son, Jesus Christ, on a hill overlooking
the village of Llantrisant. He was attacked by an outraged crowd, the
body snatched from the flames, and Dr Price committed for trial. He
defended himself dressed in his robes as Archdruid of Wales; a cap made
from a fox pelt, a red suede waistcoat, green trousers, plaid cape, and no
socks (which 'prevent the proper exhalation of the feet'). William Price
was found not guilty on the grounds that cremation had not been shown
to be against the law. Nine years (and two more children) later he was
himself cremated in front of a huge crowd beneath a brass crescent moon
on a sixty-foot pole. The words 'consigned to fire' were used for the first
time at a funeral in Britain and, in 1896, the first crematorium opened at
Woking. Now, seven in every ten corpses in Britain are cremated.

Dr Price claimed to be the reincarnation of a Celtic priest, a
Welshman dead for ten thousand years. With other members of the
Druidical Order, founded a century before his death, he hoped to revive
the imagined lives of the original inhabitants of these islands. Their
ways included, he thought, vegetarianism, naked sunbathing and open
marriage. The Celts had, in his view, been brutally replaced in most of

Dr William Price of Llantrisant, dressed in his druidical robes, with a torch ready to light a funeral pyre and an elegiac poem written in his own version of the original Welsh tongue.

The cremation of Dr Price in 1893; his body, encased in a perforated steel box, was burned on a fire of oil-soaked wood.

Britain by Saxon raiders. His Druids were the successors of the priests who had filled the sacred groves of Britain long before the arrival of Angles, Saxons and Jutes. According to the Venerable Bede, the Cymbri – now, approximately, the Welsh (the Cymry in their native tongue) – were themselves an ancient Eastern people who, after the Flood, migrated from the lands of the Bible to the British Isles. Gomer, the grandson of Noah, was the first Briton.

This naive vision of history as a repeated wave of invaders was once universal. Anthropology was, for many years, no more than a search for lost tribes of one flavour or another. In some ways, and with different tools, it still is. A subject nation was conquered by a superior race, who brought their culture with them. In time, the invader moved on or sank into degeneracy, leaving only ruins behind. The Benin bronzes – superb African figures in classical taste – were supposed to have been made by a lost nation of Europeans. Thor Heyerdahl's voyages set out to re-create longer journeys; those of a people who worshipped the sun. They came from the Middle East, and reached the furthest places of the Earth. Wherever they passed, they left stones: pyramids, circles, or statues. These remained for lesser breeds to marvel at long after the master masons had faded away.

All these beliefs are theories about ancestry, about the connections between the past and the present and among the peoples of the world. All can, as a consequence, be tested by looking at genes. Deny it though they might, most nations define themselves to some extent by virtue of shared blood. They retain a vestige of the common descent that gave cohesion to the tribes and clans that preceded them.

The map of the world's genes is rapidly being filled in. Soon it will be possible to make a pedigree for the human race. The Human Genome Diversity Project, as it is known, once hoped to sample genes in a rational way, with a specimen every few hundred miles. Expense put a stop to this and the project is now aiming to collect DNA from five hundred of the five thousand or so of the world's 'ethnic groups'. It has shown much interest in tribal peoples. This was a mistake. Although its expeditions include doctors who treat the locals, there was outrage (some of it synthetic) that the first world was exploiting the third. The involvement of drug companies in finding genes that might predispose towards diabetes and the patenting of lines of living cells from tribal peoples were seen as particular affronts.

The Diversity Project has been scaled down and may never be

completed. Nevertheless, science is still, as an incidental to the study of genes of medical importance, uncovering the hidden links between nations. It is making biological ties between their inhabitants and what may be a homeland far away.

No nation is more explicit in making a connection between land and people than is the State of Israel. For most of their history, the majority of Jews have been exiles. Winston Churchill, in a speech in the House of Commons in May 1939, at the grimmest moment in the Jewish ordeal, described them as 'that vast, unhappy mass of scattered, wandering Jews, whose intense, unchanging, unconquerable desire has been for a national home'. The very idea of Israel depends on the right of a people united by blood and experience to a country of their own. Nearly all Jews claim, symbolically or otherwise, the same ancient source; the patriarch Abraham, two hundred generations ago. The long list of 'begats' in the Book of Chronicles is said to have provoked nine hundred camel loads of commentary. Two and a half thousand years later, the first chapter of a 1994 history of Judaism claimed that: 'A person is Jewish if he or she has a Jewish mother . . . Biological descent rather than religious conviction is the crucial criterion.' Judaism is the most genetic of all religions.

Whether that descent is figurative or literal is at the heart of what it means to be Jewish. In spite of early episodes of exclusiveness (as when Ezra insisted that non-Jewish wives be banned) there is not much in ancient texts about the role of the blood-line and the primacy of descent over conviction. In its early days, Judaism was anxious to convert others and its boundaries were fairly porous. Since then, though, a history of persecution and separation has made Judaism a more exclusive faith than it once was. The idea of the Jews as an extended family has gained new meaning.

A family tree can, imperceptibly, evolve into the pedigree of a nation. If being a Jew depends on descent, then genes have something to say about who does, and who does not, belong. Biological science is alive and well in Israel, and there is an active interest in human inheritance. Much of it comes from a wish to understand genetic disease, but some arises from the desire to discover what affinity there might be among the Jews of the world. It involves a search for patterns of common ancestry and shared belief tracing back to the earliest history of the nation. Israel is, more and more, having to accept that genes show a conflict between the two.

The vision of dispersal, re-gathering and collective descent goes back to the beginnings of Judaism. It is attached to the story of Armageddon,

THE TOMB OF THE PATRIARCHS

The Tomb of the Patriarchs – or the Cave of Machpelah or the Abraham Mosque, depending on who is talking about it – is a symbol both for Judaism and Islam. According to tradition, it contains the tombs of Abraham, his wife Sarah, Isaac, Rebeccah, Leah and Jacob. Abraham's purchase of the land is recorded in Genesis. Hebron is now on the Israeli-occupied West Bank, and during its three thousand-year history the building has in turn been a Hebrew shrine, a synagogue, a Christian church, a mosque, a Christian church again, and once again a mosque. King David was crowned in Hebron and, in the latest of a long series of political upheavals, in 1994 an American Jewish fundamentalist, Baruch Goldstein, massacred a group of Arabs worshipping there before himself being shot down. There is still a Jewish presence in Hebron although it was almost wiped out by Arabs in the massacre of 1929. At times Jews have been denied access to the tombs: in the thirteenth century they were allowed only to climb half way up the steps to the building and to insert petitions to God through a hole drilled six feet through the stone.

In fact, the supposed tomb is probably an ancient water cistern, but this does not reduce its symbolic importance.

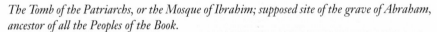

The Tomb of the Patriarchs, or the Mosque of Ibrahim; supposed site of the grave of Abraham, ancestor of all the Peoples of the Book.

A detail from the Arch of Titus, in Rome, erected to celebrate the destruction of
Jerusalem in AD70. Roman soldiers are seen taking spoils (including a menorah, the
seven-branched candelabrum) from the Temple. The Arch was erected by the brother
of the victorious general, Titus Flavius Sabinus Vespasianus, who later became Emperor
and built the Colosseum.

the scattering of the people of Israel – the Lost Tribes – by their enemies.
The tale begins with the fall of Megiddo in 722BC. As the Assyrians
gloatingly recorded on a plaque, 27,280 people were deported from the
Northern Kingdom. Most were never seen again. The Southern
Kingdom, Judah, survived. Within it lived the tribes of Judah and
Benjamin. All the tribes descended from the twelve sons of Jacob. Those
lost from sight were the dynasties of Reuben, Simon, Issachar, Zevulun,
Manasseh, Ephraim, Dan, Naphtali, Gad and Asher.

The banishment of the Tribes was just the beginning of a history of
exile. In 586BC Judah, too, was conquered, this time by the Babylonians.
Solomon's Temple was destroyed. Fifty years later, Babylon in its turn was
overpowered by Cyrus of Persia. A few of the Jews returned to Palestine,
but most set off on a journey across the world, the Diaspora. In AD70
there was a war between the Jews of Palestine and their Roman occupiers.
It led to another great scattering of the Jewish people. The conflict was a
disaster not matched until the unique horror of the Holocaust. According

Jacob and his twelve sons – the
progenitors of the Tribes of Israel
– by the seventeenth-century
Spanish painter Francisco
de Zurbarán.

THE SAMARITANS

A few inhabitants of Israel can trace both a biological and a religious heritage from the time of the Tribes. They do not need the Law of Return, as most of them never left. They demonstrate the difficulties of fitting into a society that depends on ancestry.

Not all the people of the Northern Kingdom were exiled. The City of Samaria and its surrounds were spared. Its inhabitants practised their own form of Judaism. Over the next three thousand years, their land passed to Babylonians, Romans, Christians and Muslims. Its occupants, the Samaritans, kept their faith. They still regard themselves as closer to the teachings of Moses than are other Jews. Most stayed in their native place and stuck to their piety in the face of endless attack. During the decaying years of Turkish rule, at the turn of the present century, their number dropped to a hundred and forty-six from what had been three hundred thousand.

Their descendants are concentrated around Nablus (the ancient Shechem) on the West Bank with another group in Holon, a suburb of Tel-Aviv. Their shrine overlooks the town from Mount Gerizim, upon which they had been allowed to build a temple by Alexander the Great. Although the temple was destroyed long ago, there are still pilgrimages to the mountain. Some Samaritans still live in Nablus itself, but with increasing political tension a well-guarded settlement has been built on Gerizim, safe from Palestinian attack.

The main festival is at Passover. In an elaborate ritual, prayers are said, sheep slaughtered, and the story of the Exodus recited. The Samaritans' unbroken lineage within the Holy Land gives them a less equivocal tie with the Land of Israel than anyone else. They are, they say, the direct descendants of the tribes of Ephraim and Manasseh. Until the seventeenth century, their High Priest could trace his ancestry straight back in the male line to Aaron. One patriarch then failed to have a son. The Samaritans took their laws seriously, and the priesthood passed to a family of Levites. They themselves descend, through males, from the Servants of the Temple.

The High Priest of the Samaritans, at home on Mount Gerizim, just before celebrating the Feast of Passover.

132

Mount Gerizim, overlooking Nablus; the site of the ancient temple of the Samaritans.

Genetics shows that the Samaritans retain a distinct identity. Their exclusiveness has made them the most inbred population in the world, linked by both genes and history to the People of the Book. Their adherence to strict marriage practices means that even within the Samaritans there are genetically distinct family lines who avoided intermarriage for centuries. As in the remote villages of Finland, such isolation and shared descent means, inevitably, that harmful recessive genes are likely to manifest themselves as those with common ancestry meet and have children. Among the Samaritans, an inherited form of deaf-blindness is relatively frequent. It was first recorded long ago, but only now has the gene been found.

Although Samaritans are now prominent members of the Israeli nation, much admired for retaining their ancient settlement, their acceptance is new. Ancient theological schisms between Samaritans and Jews turned on how many commandments, how many books of the Bible and how many holy days there are. They were used for two thousand years to deny them a birthright. The Good Samaritan of the New Testament belonged to a despised minority. When, in the nineteenth century, Samaritans exiled in Cairo and Damascus began to flee to Israel in the face of persecution by Islam, they were not welcomed by most Jews. Instead, many were sheltered in Christian monasteries. Having a descent from ancient Israel was not enough: a link with a precisely defined set of religious practices was demanded as well.

133

A French version of the universal European myth of the Wandering Jew; supposedly a Jew who had refused to allow Jesus to rest his Cross at his door on the way to Calvary and was condemned to wander the earth until the Second Coming. The myth became a convenient excuse for anti-Semitism and, in an irony lost to those who promoted it, the people driven from their homeland were accused of having left because of their own iniquity.

to the census of the Emperor Claudius in AD48, there were eight million Jews in the Empire, two and half million of them in Palestine. This may have been an overestimate; but a century later the number of Jews in Palestine had declined to well below a million and by AD400 there were probably no more than a million or so Jews in the whole Roman empire.

Most of the fourteen million Jews alive today claim descent from the survivors of the conflict with Rome. Their historic and genetic trail can be traced, with its many diversions, to the modern world. Only a few of the inhabitants of Israel (including many Samaritans) stayed in their native land and can claim an unequivocal link with the ancient kingdom. Some of them, though, were later rejected by the exiled Jews who returned to the Promised Land.

Biblical prophecy has it that the Diaspora must be complete – with Jews scattered to the ends of the earth – before the Messiah can appear. The hope of fulfilling the vision was one of the forces leading to the formation of modern Israel and, in surprising ways, to political change in other parts of the world. One Israeli political group is quite explicit about the biblical foundations of its policies: according to the Agudah religious party 'The world was created for the sake of Israel . . . the raison d'être for the world is the establishment of the Torah in the Land of Israel.'

This dream is reflected in some unlikely places. Each year at the Conference of the British Labour Party, after the compulsory and somewhat sheepish singing of 'The Red Flag', there is a more fervent rendition of the hymn 'Jerusalem'. William Blake's words are glorious; a Bow of Burning Gold is part of every child's memory of school. The Jerusalem seen by Blake as rising in England's green and pleasant land is, to those who sing the hymn, a symbol of the new society that may some day arise from the ashes of the old.

For Blake, though, his words were not a parable but a plain statement of fact. With many others of his time he saw Britain as the site of the Jerusalem at which the elect would gather at the Second Coming. The British (said by true believers to be the Brit-Ish, or Men of the Covenant) were a noble race, remnants of a Lost Tribe of Israel. In his long and somewhat unreadable poem *Jerusalem the Emanation of the Giant Albion* Blake had a carefully planned mental geography of Britain as the promised land. Some of it has an implausible feel – 'The fields from Islington to Marybone,/ To Primrose Hill and Saint Johns Wood/ Were builded over with pillars of gold,/ And there Jerusalem's pillars stood' – but the agenda was clear. Britain was great because it was chosen by God: its fate was ordained. By ruling much of the world it was doing nothing more than fulfilling prophecy. In the poem he addresses the Jews: 'Your ancestors derived their origin from Abraham, Heber, Shem and Noah, who were Druids: as the Druid Temples (which are the Patriarchal Pillars and Oak Groves) over the whole Earth witness to this day.'

The idea that Britain was Israel grew with the Empire. The Metropolitan Anglo-Israel Association was founded in 1878, with the Bishop of Rangoon on the council. By the 1930s it could attract twenty thousand to its annual meetings, many of them aristocrats. Its rolls contained two duchesses, a marchioness, two earls, three countesses, three barons, thirteen baronesses, nine baronets and a wide selection of knights, admirals and generals. All were convinced that the Britons were a lost tribe, ordained to rule the world.

Dr Price, William Blake and the British Israelites were in a tradition of claims that biblical figures had visited the British Isles. Joseph of Arimathea planted the sacred thorn at Glastonbury; the Stone of Scone, which sits under the throne upon which English monarchs are crowned, is the pillow upon which Joseph slept at Beth-El. It was taken to Egypt, carried by the exiled Children of Israel to Antrim, passed to Scone in Scotland, and thence to London in 1291 by Edward the First. In the 1950s it had a brief and ignoble trip back to Scotland when it was stolen by a group of Scottish Nationalists as a political stunt.

The return of the Jews to England was itself tied to the story of the Lost Tribes. Two centuries before Blake, the English Puritans saw the Second Coming as close at hand. It could, they thought, take place only when, as the Bible promised, the Jews were reinstated in their homeland. The Puritans lived in the manner of the Old Testament as far as they were able. The Chauncy family named their children Isaac, Ichabod, Sarah, Barnabas, Nathaniel and Israel. Thomas Tamy had a revelation that he was a 'Jew of the Tribe of Reuben'. He took the disclosure seriously. After circumcising himself he claimed first the throne of England then that of Rome. Denied both, he caused an affray at the House of Commons. His last recorded appearance was his departure in a home-made boat in the English Channel, crying 'Ho for the Holy Wars'.

In 1650 Menasseh ben Israel in his pamphlet *Spes Israeli* asked that the Jews, expelled from England four hundred years earlier, be allowed to return to allow the Diaspora – the dispersion of the people of Israel – to be completed before the Messiah appeared. The Bible said 'The Lord shall scatter thee among all peoples from one end of the Earth even unto

OPPOSITE: A page from William Blake's *Jerusalem the Emanation of the Giant Albion*, written between 1804 and 1820. The Giant Albion looks gloomily over the sea, contemplating Jerusalem, the Lost Tribes, and the Temples of the Druids.

The Spectres of Albions Twelve Sons revolve mightily
Over the Tomb & over the Body: raving to devour
The Sleeping Humanity. Los with his mace of iron
Walks round: loud his threats, loud his blows fall
On the rocky Spectres, as the Potter breaks the potsherds;
Dashing in pieces Self-righteousnesses: driving them from Albions
Cliffs: dividing them into Male & Female forms in his Furnaces
And on his Anvils: lest they destroy the Feminine Affections
They are broken. Loud howl the Spectres in his iron Furnace

While Los laments at his dire labours, viewing Jerusalem,
Sitting before his Furnaces clothed in sackcloth of hair;
Albions Twelve Sons surround the Forty-two Gates of Erin,
In terrible armour, raging against the Lamb & against Jerusalem,
Surrounding them with armies to destroy the Lamb of God:
They took their Mother Vala, and they crown'd her with gold:
They nam'd her Rahab, & gave her power over the Earth,
The Concave Earth round Golgonooza in Entuthon Benython.
Even to the stars exalting her Throne, to build beyond the Throne
Of God and the Lamb, to destroy the Lamb & usurp the Throne of God
Drawing their Ulro Voidness round the Four-fold Humanity

Naked Jerusalem lay before the Gates upon Mount Zion
The Hill of Giants, all her foundations levelld with the dust:

Her Twelve Gates thrown down: her children carried into captivity
Herself in chains: this from within was seen in a dismal night
Outside, unknown before in Beulah, & the twelve gates were filld
With blood: from Japan eastward to the Giants causway, west
In Erins Continent: and Jerusalem wept upon Euphrates banks
Disorganizd; an evanescent shade, scarce seen or heard among
Her childrens Druid Temples dropping with blood wanderd weeping!
And thus her voice went forth in the darkness of Philistea.

My brother & my father are no more! God hath forsaken me
The arrows of the Almighty pour upon me & my children
I have sinned and am an outcast from the Divine Presence!

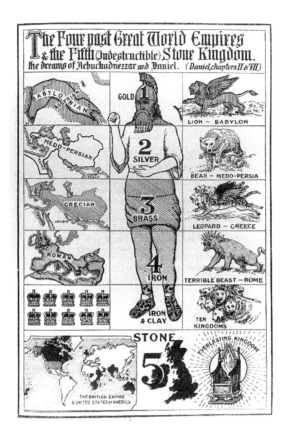

A prophecy published in 1941. The New World Order and the Everlasting Kingdom of the British Empire and the United States of America as imagined by the British Israelites.

the other.' Menasseh 'conceived that by "the end of the earth" might be understood this Island'.

This greatly excited the Millennarians of England. Explorers in South America had claimed that Indian tribes, albeit scorched by the sun, practised Jewish rituals and might well be the Lost Tribe of Reuben. Only England had no Jews: they must be restored if the Messiah was to return as ordained. Menasseh was invited by the Council of State to come to London from his home in Amsterdam, but war between England and Holland prevented his visit. Cromwell, though, pursued the idea and, gradually, the Jews began their return. A violent controversy followed. Jews, it was said, were planning to buy St Paul's Cathedral and even the Bodleian Library; perhaps Cromwell himself was a Jew. Nevertheless, they were restored. At first, the revival involved Jews already secretly living in England plucking up courage to proclaim their faith, but soon the country began to attract others from overseas.

To the true believer – William Blake included – the completion of the Diaspora was not enough. The Jews, and those Lost Tribes that might still exist, must be converted to Christianity. The effort persisted for two hundred years. Lord Shaftesbury, the nineteenth-century Prime Minister, acclaimed the appointment of a baptised Jew as Anglican Bishop of Jerusalem as 'An accomplishment of the prophecy of Isaiah' (even though his congregation consisted of just eight converts). He favoured the idea of a Jewish homeland: 'A nation must have a country. The Old Land, the Old People. This is not an artificial experiment, it is nature, it is history.' A Lieutenant Kitchener (later hero of Omdurman) made a map of Palestine showing, as might be expected, the territories of the Tribes.

The Balfour Declaration of 1917 stated that 'His Majesty's Government view with favour the establishment in Palestine of a national home for the Jewish People'. It marked the beginnings of today's Israel and had its roots, in part, in the affinity felt by many Britons for the Holy Land. Lloyd George, on meeting Chaim Weizmann in December 1914 to discuss the question of Palestine, commented that the place-names involved were more familiar than those of the Western Front. The end of the First World War gave a real chance to realize the prophecy of a return to the homeland. The disasters of the Second led, at last, to the establishment of the State of Israel.

The Law of Return was drawn up in 1950. It is the formal statement of the existence of Israel as a nation based on a shared heritage. It makes an unequivocal promise: that all Jews have the right to reside in Israel. In 1952 it was widened to allow even the spouses of those with a single Jewish grandparent to become citizens. Not until a 1970 amendment was there an attempt to define what is meant by a Jew in this context: 'A person who was born of a Jewish mother or who has become converted to Judaism and who is not a member of another religion'. Even then there remains an unresolved question. How is that Jewish mother to be defined?

Israel is the only country in the world to welcome all immigrants, whatever their age, health, wealth, or politics, as long as they can find a place on the national pedigree. More than two million have poured into the country under the tenets of the Law of Return.

It has, though, a central ambiguity. What counts when it comes to claiming citizenship? Are Jewish genes enough: are they even relevant? Perhaps religion matters; or, perhaps, a combination of the two. Israel

The founding of Tel-Aviv, the Hill of Spring, on a sand dune north of the then Arab city of Yafo in 1909; an image of the desire for a return to the Promised Land.

embodies the problems that arise when biology conflicts with belief. Some immigrants have been accepted as citizens although they have no links of blood with the Promised Land. This is true, for example, of a group of Black Americans who live as practising Jews in Tel Aviv. Others – perhaps as many as a hundred thousand of the Russians who migrated there from 1985 onwards – claim (often without evidence) some Jewish ancestry, but certainly have no ties of faith. There are many more who would like to enter Israel. Their request is based, more or less tenuously, on descent, on piety or on both.

As well as DNA, everyone inherits a culture, a common history: nowhere more than in Judaism where the identity of a scattered people was defined by their stubborn adherence to a shared way of life. Israel today – and those who hope to return to it – shows better than anywhere else the ambiguities of a society built on ancestry. Is it necessary to prove descent from the Tribes, from the Kingdom of Judah, or from a more recent Jewish ancestor? Is descent, indeed, involved at all?

Where did the Lost Tribes go after the Assyrian victory, and where might they now be? Initially, they were exiled, beyond the River Sambatyon: 'In the ninth year of Hoshea, the king of Assyria captured Samaria, and he carried the Israelites away to Assyria, and placed them in Halah, on the Habor, the river of Gozan and the city of Medes'; places now in Syria and Iraq.

The river itself should be easy to recognize. As Pliny the Elder noticed,

JEWISH GENETIC DISEASE:
CHANCE OR NECESSITY?

All populations have their own set of unique inherited diseases (although there are others, like cystic fibrosis, that encompass millions of people living in very different places). Sometimes, no doubt, these diseases arise by mutation and disappear either because they kill those who inherit them immediately (as is true for many dominant genes) or because, after many generations hidden within healthy individuals, two copies of a recessive gene come together and cause severe harm to a young child. In such cases, how common a gene is depends only on the balance between a mutation arising and it disappearing through the death of those who inherit it. This is probably true of many rare diseases.

Occasionally, though, particular genetic illnesses are so common that something may be acting to maintain them in the population. The famous examples of this are all associated with the red blood pigment, haemoglobin, and the ability of those carrying single copies of particular variants (the 'sickle-cell' gene, for example) to resist malaria, where those with two are severely ill. There is an inevitable temptation to ascribe local patches of particular diseases to such mechanisms rather than to simple accidents of nature. In many cases, this is wishful thinking by those interested in one particular illness. Sometimes, though, there are patterns of disease that suggest that something other than a balance between the appearance and the removal of genetic errors is at work.

Ashkenazi Jews have relatively high frequencies of several different inherited illnesses. As well as the Tay-Sachs disease found in the family of Rabbi Ekstein (the founder of the Dor Yeshorim movement: see inset) and many other Jews, these include Gaucher's Syndrome, Niemann-Pick Disease and others associated with the development of nervous tissue. Often, studies of the DNA suggest that the mutation happened only once or a few times and has since become relatively common among Ashkenazim.

The apparent concentration of illnesses of the brain and nervous system in this one group may, perhaps, be more than a coincidence. Some even suggest that it reflects an advantage accruing to those with a single copy of such genes. Given the historical emphasis on learning in this community and the respect for those willing to devote their lives to religious study the claim is that they have an intellectual (and reproductive) advantage of some kind over those with two copies of the unmutated gene. If this is true, the damaged gene would tend to become more common and would, in time, manifest its presence in the birth of genetically affected children.

This is, it must be said, pure speculation. However, it reflects a move in human genetics to suggest that many of the inherited illnesses that plague us may have balancing advantages. Those with a single copy of the cystic fibrosis gene may have been more able to resist cholera in ancient times, and those with genes predisposing to diabetes might be more able to deal with starvation in societies in which famine is common. So far, much of this is conjecture, but if it is confirmed it may alter the attitude at least of evolutionary biologists to inherited disease.

Rabbi Josef Ekstein, one of the many Ashkenazim who learned of their own genetic status only through the birth of a child with an inherited illness, Tay-Sachs Disease.

it rested on the Sabbath. This prevented the Tribes from fording it to make their way back to Israel, as it was too swift to cross on six days of the week, and Jews could not travel on the holy day. In some versions, the river consisted of sand and stones rather than water. A Jewish traveller to India reported hearing its roar from two days' journey away. It was seventeen miles wide and threw rocks as high as a house. Indeed, he wrote, if its sand was kept in a glass it was agitated on weekdays and calm on the Sabbath.

In spite of these clues the Sambatyon and the land beyond have never been identified. There is, today, no sign of the Lost Tribes in Syria or Iraq. They must, it seems obvious, have moved on. As biblical prophecy could not be achieved before the Tribes were reunited, believers in its literal truth have always been anxious to identify them. The sons of Joseph reappeared whenever they were needed. At the time of the false Messiah Shabbetai Zevi there was talk of the Tribes' advance to fight the Turks, then threatening Europe. The rumours grew so strong that in 1665 the Muslims of Tunis cancelled their pilgrimage to Mecca.

Many hope to enter Israel under the Law of Return. The legend of the exiled tribes has inspired them; and they claim the right to live in Israel on the basis of a supposed descent from those missing ancestors. They include groups from Africa, Europe, Asia and the New World. The idea of the chosen people is so powerful that it has been appealed to by some who have – apparently – only a flimsy link with the ancient Kingdom of Israel. A few have made their way to Israel, and practise as Jews. Although many admire their devotion, other Israelis take exception to the entry of people so obviously lacking a link to the homeland. They demand a stricter congruence between genetic and intellectual descent. The Lost Tribes have, metaphorically at least, come back to haunt the land from which they were driven.

Israel's second president, Yitzhak Ben-Zvi, was among the many who have searched for the living descendants of the biblical exiles. Some claims do seem frivolous. An immigration minister of the 1990s, faced with an assertion by Indian adherents of the legend, the Bene Israel, of the right of their fellows to migrate to Israel as they were the descendants of the tribe of Manasseh, accepted that they could; but only when the Messiah was there to greet them.

Pathans today claim the progeny of a tribe, as do Afghans and Burmese. Even Japanese are adherents to the idea, claiming membership of the Tribe of Zebulon. Some Jewish refugees from oppression during

Those hoping to return to Israel at the end of the war were, understandably, masters of propaganda. The *Exodus* (once an American riverboat) sailed, packed with Jews from camps in Germany, to Palestine – despite having been forbidden to do so. The Zionists arranged to broadcast the assault by the British sailors who attempted to stop them. Once returned to a French port, the four thousand five hundred Jews aboard refused to disembark, staying aboard in what they termed a 'floating Auschwitz'. After two British sergeants had been hanged (and their bodies booby-trapped) by Zionist terrorists, the British forced the refugees on transports back to Germany. The propaganda defeat that this represented helped to persuade Britain to abandon its role in Israel.

the Nazi period fled to Japan, where, in spite of the political alliance with their persecutors, they were welcomed. The Makuyo sect still claims a relationship with Judaism. Perhaps, they say, Shinto Temples (like the one at Miyajima) are copies of the Second Temple in Jerusalem. The Star of David, or something uncommonly like it, is on the Ise Shrine, the most famous of all. It is even said that the Japanese Royal Regalia, never seen by the outside world, includes a mirror upon which is engraved the word Jehovah.

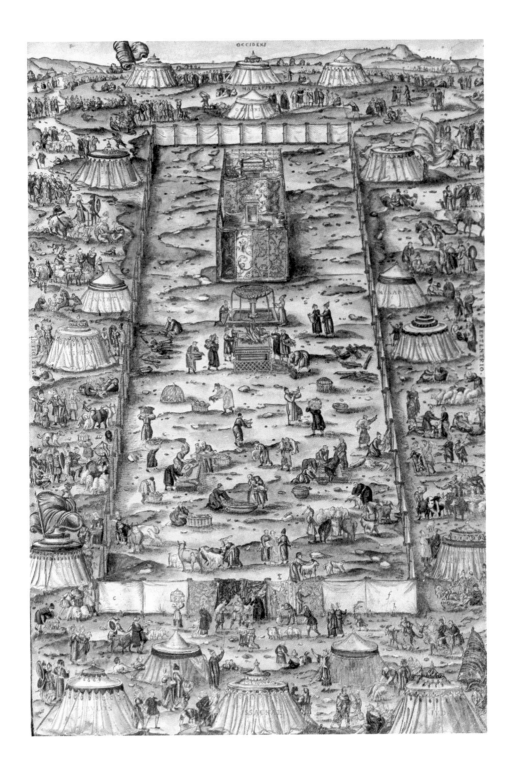

RIGHT: A sixteenth-century map
showing the Red Sea, the course of the
Nile and the Kingdom of Prester John,
supposedly the home of one of the
Lost Tribes of Israel.

OPPOSITE: The Tribes of Israel
encamped around the Tabernacle in the
desert. An etching from a Latin Bible,
Geneva 1557.

A particularly potent story ties the Lost Tribes to Prester John, the
Christian emperor who was supposed to have ruled an African kingdom,
the biblical land of Ophir, full of gold. One of the great paragraphs of
mediocre fiction reads 'I, Jose da Silvestra, who am now dying of hunger
in the little cave where no snow is, on the north side of the nipple of the
southernmost of the mountains I have named Sheba's Breasts write this in
the year 1590 with a cleft bone on the remnant of my raiment, my blood
being the ink. With my own eyes I have seen the countless diamonds
stored in Solomon's treasure chamber behind the White Death . . .' Rider
Haggard was well aware of the beliefs of his audience when, in 1885, he
wrote *King Solomon's Mines*, set in a mountain range in East Africa.

His book drew on his experiences as a colonial administrator in the
Transvaal. Its plot was suggested by an extraordinary finding, made just a
few years earlier. To the astonishment of the settlers – who had seen
nothing like it elsewhere in Africa – there had been discovered in what
later became Rhodesia the ruins of an abandoned city, Great Zimbabwe.

Cecil Rhodes at once identified its builders – and they were certainly

The Enclosure at Great Zimbabwe, on the plain below the Hill Fort. Walled town, palace, temple, or slave camp; what the building was for nobody really knows.

not Africans. He wrote that 'Zimbabye is an old Phoenician residence and everything points to [it] being the place from which Hiram fetched his gold; the word "peacocks" in the Bible may be read as "parrots" and among the stone ornaments from Zimbabye are green parrots, the common kind of that district, for the rest you have gold and ivory, also the fact that Zimbabye is built of hewn stone without mortar.'

Rhodes was quite unable to believe in the ability of Africans to build, without help, an object so magnificent. He turned to the Old Testament as the source of the talented adventurers who had built the great city. Excavation began in the nineteenth century. Much was destroyed by the removal of 'native' work in a fruitless search for their Semitic foundations. The desecration was described as 'timely preservation work . . . removing the filth and degradation of the Kaffir occupation'. Most of the gold was melted down as it was merely African. Some scraps of cedarwood excited great interest as they might have been the remains of Solomon's Temple.

Modern research, including radiocarbon dating of the 'cedar' fragments, dates Great Zimbabwe to the thirteenth century. It was abandoned, for unknown reasons, in about 1450. It was the centre of the empire of Mwene Mutapa – the Great Pillager – trading even with China.

Lost Tribes of Israel had nothing to do with it. Rhodes' successor, Ian Smith, himself assumed that the city could only have been built by an extinct white-skinned people. His government prevented the publication of a guide book that dared suggest anything else. There is a certain irony in the fact that the downfall of the Smith government and of white minority rule was accompanied by a change in the nation's name from Rhodesia to Zimbabwe.

The myth still exerts its power, but now on an African, not a European, people. The Lemba, who are dispersed across the northern part of South Africa and the south of Zimbabwe, claim to have built Great Zimbabwe. They have another and, on the face of it, less likely belief; to be themselves a tribe of Israel. Their ancestors came, they say, from the lost city of Sena, and travelled across Africa to build a new city. On the way they followed a great wooden drum – perhaps the Ark of the Covenant itself. Because they had broken God's laws by eating unclean food, they were forced to abandon their city and to live, like Jews, scattered among people who do not share their beliefs. In the early days of South Africa they were known as President Kruger's Jews. The first Jew to open a butcher's shop in the Northern Transvaal would hire only Lemba as slaughtermen – further proof, perhaps, of their origins and the purity of their faith.

That faith today has clear Jewish elements. Lemba do not eat pork (hence the name: the 'people who refuse'), are circumcised and often use biblical names such as Solomon. They lay claim to a secret language, Hiberu. The Star of David and 'elephant of Judah' are everywhere in their homes. They believe themselves to be the descendants of the Sons of Sena named in the Old Testament among the Jews who came back from Babylon. There certainly is a city in the Yemen, Sana'a, to which many Jews were exiled and which, the Lemba say, sounds remarkably like their supposed ancestral home.

Perhaps the most fantastical of all claimants to be Lost Tribes are in the Americas. The Indians' supposed history as a lost tribe had saved them: in the early days of South American exploration there was debate as to whether they were human at all, or whether they could be killed like beasts. Only the belief in Indians as a remnant of the tribe of Reuben prevented an even more complete destruction. But how could a band of migrants from the Middle East have got there, two thousand years before Columbus? How could anyone believe anything quite so implausible? In fact, the story of the Lost Tribes is very much alive in the United States. Many Americans have pursued the belief to – or even beyond – its logical limits.

A Rhodesian tourist poster of the 1930s showing the ghost of the Queen of Sheba, with Solomon in the background, stepping down from the mysterious stone Tower in Great Zimbabwe. An African pays homage to the white-skinned builders of the great monument.

The idea goes back to the early days of their nation. In 1837 Mordechai Manuel Noah published *The Evidences of the American Indians being Descendants of the Lost Tribes of Israel*. He planned to establish a Jewish State, Ararat, near Buffalo, New York. His state came to nothing, but the vision of America as the destiny of the exiles from Armageddon has gained a power that affects the lives of millions. The story is tied to the visions of Joseph Smith and the history revealed to him by the Angel Moroni.

According to the Book of Nephi, after a century of captivity the ten tribes escaped to the North. They passed through the unknown region of Arsareth and were then lost to mankind. Some of the theories as to where they now live are frankly speculative. They may be on another planet (as is the City of Enoch, which 'was translated or taken away from the earth . . . is now held in reserve, in some part or portion of space . . . not yet revealed'). In 1842 Philo Dibble preserved a drawing made by the Prophet Joseph Smith himself showing the earth joined by a narrow neck to another sphere, home of the Tribes. A more plausible idea had it that the earth was hollow, with the tribes within. This theory was popular in the early nineteenth century, when a Captain Symmes had applied, without success, to Congress and to the Government of Russia for funds to find the entrance.

Other Mormons believe the Tribes to be scattered among the peoples of the earth, lost only in identity, not in location. Brigham Young himself felt that 'The sons of Ephraim are wild and uncultivated, unruly, ungovernable. The spirit in them is turbulent and resolute; they are the Anglo-Saxon race'. Saxon does sound suspiciously like Isaacson and many Mormons believe themselves, because of Brigham Young's words, to belong to the Tribe of Ephraim. Wherever they are, at the Second Coming, the tribes will return to the New Jerusalem to be built in Jackson County, Missouri.

The Mormon Church studies the monuments of the Aztecs and the Maya in the hope of establishing a link with the Hebrew peoples they

Great Zimbabwe today: the myth revised. Two Lemba elders, Professor M Mathiva and the Reverend William Masala Mani, dressed in his Hebrew prayer-shawl, in front of the Tower – claimed by them to be a sacrificial altar of the Jewish faith of their Lemba ancestors – inside the enclosure at Great Zimbabwe.

suppose to have built them. They have a centre for Near Eastern Studies in Jerusalem, where attempts are made to search for a connection of the peoples of the ancient world with today's Mormons. This led to demonstrations by the Orthodox, infuriated by what might become a base to convert Jews. Only by promising to avoid all discussion of religion have the Mormons been allowed to stay.

A belief in ancestry can be pursued in many ways. Occasionally, as the Mormons have realized, the records can attach an aspirant to his desired past. Genes, though, can do more: they can uncover hidden links between the peoples of today – those who strive for Jewish status included – and tribes and homelands of long ago. The Jews, with their claim of common ancestry, have a particular interest in pursuing their family tree.

For some, the task is relatively easy. Rabbinical families can trace their history as one rabbi succeeds the next; an event always carefully recorded. Many of their family lines converge on one individual, Rabbi Shelomoh ben Yishaq (Rashi, as he is known), who was born in Troyes in the eleventh century. As Rashi's descent from ancient Israel is itself chronicled, they can claim a direct link through him with the sons of Jacob. Some other inhabitants of Israel, such as the Samaritans, are also proud of their long family trees and can recite a dozen or so generations with no difficulty. For most Jews, though, searching for a tie with the Tribes by probing the records is a hopeless task. Fortunately, genes have come to the rescue.

The Ashkenazim (from whom the majority of European and American Jews descend) moved from the east into the Rhineland in the ninth century, and from there into much of Germany, Eastern Europe, the Ukraine and Russia. The family histories of their eleven million descendants are almost impossible to find as most had the good sense to avoid registration by a state likely to use the information against them.

In mediaeval Europe, Ashkenazim named themselves, as in biblical times, after their father. Surnames (those attached to a family line rather than an individual) were not used until the eighteenth century. In Poland, they did not come into use until 1844. The millions of Jews with Polish ancestors can hence use documents to take them back for only a century and a half. The name supplied depended on what the family could afford to pay. The rich bought flowers or precious metals (Rosenthal or Goldstein), those less so steel (Stahl) or iron (Eisen). For the very poor there were nonsensical names such as Ochsenswanz (Oxtail) or Wanzenknicker (Bug-Squasher). Some names had associations with the

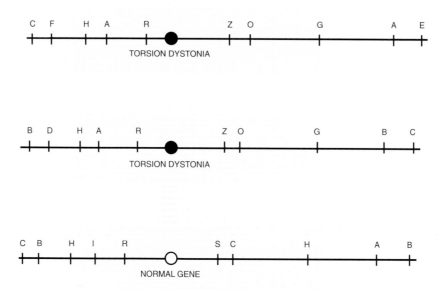

The DNA surname (or 'haplotype') of two torsion dystonia patients, and of the unaffected spouse of one of them. The gene itself, (mutated or normal), is shown as a circle; a series of ten variable sites near it on the DNA chain shown as vertical bars. The DNA variant present at each one is given a letter (chosen to represent a real surname here). All torsion dystonia patients share the same set of DNA variants near their damaged gene; distinct from that found in unaffected people. This suggests that there has not been enough time for this 'genetic surname' to be broken up as the generations succeed each other, so that the mutation must be quite recent.

Lost Tribes. Naphtali was, in legend, associated with a stag; hence Hirsch, Herzl, Hertz, Harzog and Harz (which, later, often became Harris).

Ashkenazim though, possess another record; one which is, more and more, being used to unite Jews with their kin. They have genes almost unknown in other peoples that can be used to trace their movements across the world. About one Ashkenazi in four thousand has a genetic disease called torsion dystonia. This illness causes uncontrollable twisting movements. Occasionally these do not show themselves at all; and sometimes they are so mild as to be scarcely noticeable. For a few patients, though, they are crippling.

All those with the condition share exactly the same genetic damage in just the same place in the DNA. This suggests – as in the Finnish diseases discussed in a previous chapter – a single origin for the mutation. It arose only once, so that there is shared descent for all today's sufferers. The DNA around the gene also points to a common origin as it has not been disrupted by recombination. Imagine the gene to be a single letter in a family name – the letter 'a', for example. The mutation changes this from, say, an 'a' to an 'e'. The whole genetic 'surname' represents the set of DNA letters on either side of the gene itself. The surname, written in DNA, of every torsion dystonia patient is the same. This, too, suggests an ancestry stemming from a single individual. The mutated gene and the stretch of DNA surrounding it have both been preserved unchanged in all the descendants.

The shared 'surname' can also be used to estimate when the mutation actually happened. To do so depends on the process of genetic recombination that takes place when sperm and egg are formed. Unlike those in real names, letters in the genetic message are reshuffled each generation. The further apart they are, the more likely they are to drift apart. Two DNA letters a long way from each other will often be inherited in a different arrangement in children compared to their parents. As each generation – each reshuffling of the cards – succeeds the last there is an increased chance that the original array is disrupted.

Because there has been no change in the alliance of the torsion dystonia mutation with a lengthy set of DNA variants on either side there have been too few generations for the original order of letters to be broken up. The distance between the gene and its surrounding variants – the length of the surname – and the rate of reshuffling are both known. A simple sum dates the origin of the torsion dystonia mutation to only about a dozen generations ago. Any older, and the association would have been broken up by recombination.

This dates it to about 1650. There were then about a hundred thousand Ashkenazim in Europe. Their numbers were reduced by pogroms: in Poland, for example, the Chmielnicki massacres killed a quarter of the population. In the eighteenth century, however, there was a massive growth among the Jews of Central and Eastern Europe, largely because of their relatively good living conditions. In Frankfurt, Jewish life expectancy was forty-eight years, compared to thirty-seven among non-Jews.

By 1800 the Jews numbered two million and by 1900 seven and a half million. The increase was concentrated among wealthy families, many of whom had ten surviving children. The poor left fewer progeny. Most present-day Ashkenazim hence derive from a small proportion of the Jewish population of those days. Torsion dystonia probably became common because, by chance, the mutation arose in a family who left a large number of descendants. The mutation is now found all over the world. Wherever it is, its carriers can use their gene to retrace a journey from a single well-off household in a village somewhere in Poland or Lithuania three centuries ago.

Disease genes can also help to track the history of other Jews. Cystic fibrosis is the commonest single cause of inherited illness among Europeans and is equally frequent among Ashkenazim. Both groups have cystic fibrosis mutations that reveal patterns of historic affinity. The disease is much rarer in Jews whose families originate around the Mediterranean or in the Middle East. Iraqi Jews have an incidence ten times lower than in Europe. In European non-Jews one particular mutation causes seven in ten cases of the disease. Among Jews, though, this mutation is found in only about a third of patients. Each Jewish group has its own characteristic set of cystic fibrosis mutations: among those from Tunisia one mutation – found only there and in Libya – causes half the cases. The differences point at the long history of separation of the groups. Ashkenazim are quite distinct from their Mediterranean and Middle-Eastern co-religionists in the incidence of the disease and in the mutations responsible.

Any system of genetic variation – blood groups, enzymes, or diversity in the structure of DNA – can be used to trace the path of Jews, or any other group, across the globe. The most obvious feature of the emerging map of the world's genes is that, in general, people are similar to their neighbours and less so to those living further away. Genetic distance and geography tell the same story. That sounds trite. It would, though, have been a shock to anthropologists of an earlier era, who saw the world as a palimpsest of ancient migrations. Hitler, no doubt, would be disappointed to learn that his blond Aryans (supposedly invaders from a distant land) were not very different from the Jews he despised so heartily. There are, nevertheless, some subtle patterns in the genes that uncover the hidden history of those who carry them.

The genetic family tree of Jews from different parts of Europe shows that they are not a unique group, biologically distinct from other peoples around them. There is, though, evidence of common ancestry that gives Jews at least a partial identity of their own. In most places, there is overlap between the genes of the Jewish population and those of local non-Jews. There has been interchange; sometimes through recent marriage, but more often as a result of mating long ago. This is super-imposed upon the genetic affinity of Ashkenazim themselves. The effect is subtle, but the separation of European Jews from their non-Jewish neighbours – incomplete though it may be – is clear. Genes link most of them together into a diffuse family.

Sometimes genes confirm the details of history. Jews from Turkey have genetic ties with non-Jewish Spaniards, rather than with the local Turks. After a century of persecution, including the typical blood-libels and claims that Jewish sorcerers were brewing up poisons from spiders (earnestly proclaimed by the Catholic monarchs, Ferdinand and Isabella) many Jews were expelled from Spain in 1492. Some twenty-five thousand found their way to Constantinople and the surrounding country. Their descendants in Turkey today retain the genetic links with non-Jews made before they were forced to move.

Genes also hint at the nature of the interaction between Jews and others. The Y chromosomes of Jews are – unsurprisingly – not all the same; the idea of the sons of Abraham is a symbolic one. They do show that many males, some only distantly related to each other, have contributed to the genes of European Jewry. On the average, most Jewish populations contain more diversity for male lineages than for female (whose history is recorded in mitochondrial DNA). This means that there has been more invasion of the Jewish gene pool by the genes of non-Jewish men than of women. The Y chromosomes of Jewish men from the Balkans are rather unlike those of other European Jews, perhaps because there was more admixture in this unstable part of the world.

Judaism itself is inherited down the female line – to be Jewish one's mother must be a Jew. The practice arose because in biblical times (and in Mesopotamia into the middle ages) some Jewish men had a Gentile wife (or concubine) in a polygamous family. Descent of faith hence had to be through the Jewish mother. Later, in times of turmoil, whoever the father might have been (and it might be difficult to tell) the mother knew her children and could pass her heritage on to them. The extensive penetration of foreign Y chromosomes into the Jewish gene pool shows the value of this tradition.

A history of conversion has also blurred the biological boundaries of Judaism. People change identities more quickly than they do genes, a fact noticed long ago. The Roman historian Tacitus lamented the

Yemenite Jews, none of whom had ever flown before, en route from exile on a return to Israel in 1950; as prophesied, 'on eagles' wings'.

disappearance of many of the Germanic peoples described by Caesar only a hundred years earlier. In the same way, nearly half the Indian tribes named by Lewis and Clark during their explorations of North America at the beginning of the nineteenth century had vanished by its end. The Germans and the Indians did not evaporate; they simply changed their allegiance. Just the same can happen with religion. A whole people can switch its spiritual identity within a single generation.

In general, Christianity is keener on accepting converts than is Judaism. In earlier times, though, Judaism too was a proselytizing religion. In AD740, no doubt to general astonishment, the king of the Khazars (who had conquered the Crimea as his new Empire) embraced the Jewish faith. His kingdom and Israel are the only nations to have adopted it as a state religion. The Khazars stayed Jewish for several centuries. Some claim that as Khazars moved to the Ukraine, Poland, Hungary and Lithuania they – rather than the people of Judaea – may be the ancestors of modern Ashkenazim. There were also waves of conversion in the other direction. Before the Jews were finally driven from Iberia, many had been forced to profess Christianity. Those remaining were expelled because of concern by the Inquisition that they might contaminate the new Catholics. There are still some Catholic families in Spain and Portugal who retain vestiges of Jewish practice; and one-third of the modern Spanish nobility is descended from Jewish converts.

Movement of people between faiths confuses the biological frontiers as, whatever their religion, their descendants will preserve the genes of their unconverted ancestors. Sometimes, a conversion long ago has genetic and political resonances today.

Between 1948 and 1951 a whole community of devout Jews was air-lifted from the Yemen to Israel in Operation Magic Carpet. It was one of the first and most dramatic statements of the Law of Return. The Yemenites saw themselves as a prototype of the Diaspora, driven from their native land and keeping separate from the Islamic people around them. Their dialect and religious customs are subtly different from those of other Jews. They are, in some ways, a living fossil of ancient Judaic practice. While other Jews have changed, those in the Yemen have stayed the same, holding steadfastly to their beliefs.

They trace their origin to the days of King Solomon, a thousand years before Christ, to a small group of Jews who arrived at the southern end of the Arabian Peninsula – in fact to the city of Sana'a much later claimed as a homeland by the Lemba. Jews certainly did migrate there more than two thousand years ago. Soon, though, there were some remarkable developments. From the fourth century onwards, the paganism of the locals began to give way to a religion in which one God was elevated above others. By AD500 most of the state was Jewish. However, this brief flowering of Judaism in a foreign land did not last. In one of the forgotten religious conflicts of history, the Yemen was, in AD525, defeated by Christian invaders from Ethiopia.

Some Jews remained. Who they were, history does not say. Perhaps they were – as modern Yemenite Jews believe – the original group who had moved to the Yemen centuries before. Perhaps, though, they retained no direct connection with those migrants from Israel. There was, no doubt, plenty of mixing with the locals when the state had taken up Judaism. What is more, some of those who retained a Jewish identity when the Yemen fell to militant Christianity may themselves have been converts, with no biological descent from Israel at all.

The Christian Kingdom was defeated by Muslims in AD628. In a Writ of Protection, Mohammed gave instructions not to convert the remaining Jews. By so doing, he set the agenda of tolerance for other religions which characterized Islam for much of its history. From the eighth century onwards, the Jews of the Yemen began to live separate lives. More and more, they were confined to humble trades; smiths, weavers, and collectors of human waste. Perhaps in rejection of their Islamic neighbours (who avoid alcohol) Yemenite Jews are almost unique among their co-religionists in their acceptance of it. Their community persisted through the dismal years of the Ottoman empire. By 1948, the Yemen was in uproar. To save them, the Jewish Agency flew the whole community – as predicted in Exodus 'on eagles' wings' – to Israel.

Many of the Yemenites are still in their original settlement of Rosh Ha'ayin, near Tel-Aviv, once a British air-base. Scholars see them as practising a pure and undiluted form of Judaism that has persisted since the Diaspora. Their own vision of history is one of separation and a refusal to mix with members of other faiths, giving them a unique and unbroken link with the earliest days of Israel.

The genes tell a more equivocal story. The Yemenites are, in fact, biologically distinct from other Jews. None of the cystic fibrosis mutations found among Yemenites is present in other members of their faith; and none of the screening tests for the disease effective in nine-tenths of world Jewry can be used in those of Yemenite origin. What is more, some genes for blood groups and enzymes common in Yemenites are not found in other Jewish groups, but are frequent in Arabs. Some genes link them to Ethiopians; and some are found only among the Yemenites themselves. Their biological heritage reflects, not unbroken descent from the people of Israel at the time of Solomon, but intermixture, due partly to intermarriage and partly to conversion at the moment when their state briefly took up the Jewish faith. Many of those returning on eagles' wings to what they saw as their ancient home were in fact being exiled from the land of their ancestors. This discovery caused a certain embarrassment to those who made it and has still not been widely advertised in the Yemenite community.

Judaism has gained much of its resilience in the face of two thousand years of persecution through its vision of being an extended family. The new insights into genetic exchange between Jews and others contain a dilemma. How is the family to be defined? By strict laws of descent, or by accepting that there is more to Judaism than genes? There are inevitable differences between a heritage based on faith and on Mendel.

Many people have an ambiguous relationship to Judaism but lay claim to a place in the Holy Land. For most, their declaration of Jewish ancestry is just illusion. The Lemba doctrine that they came from the

North and were the builders of Zimbabwe seems to be little more than this. The Star of David, their favoured symbol, did not come into widespread use as a symbol of Judaism until the middle ages and could not have been brought to Africa two thousand years earlier. Hiberu is, in spite of its name, closer to the African language Shona than to any middle eastern tongue. There is indeed a city called Sana'a in the Yemen, but there are also candidates for the mythic Sena much closer to home. The Lemba have been accused of merely incorporating the nineteenth-century European obsession with Judaic builders of Great Zimbabwe into their own myths and defining themselves as the Lost Tribe who built it; a noble past based on wishful thinking.

All this might appear to dispose of any claims of descent from Semitic ancestors; but in the pedigree of the Lemba there is a surprise. Most of their genes – blood groups, enzymes and the like – unite them with the African peoples around them. However, those on the Lemba Y chromosome (passed, of course, down the male line) have a different origin. On a family tree of the world's male lineages the Lemba are linked, not with Africans, but with the Middle East. The Lemba legend of their origin contains a hidden truth. Some of their heritage is indeed shared with the people of the Bible.

The tale of how those genes reached Africa is more prosaic than that of a band of exiles fighting their way across the continent to build a great temple. The town of Sayuna in Mozambique was a centre for Arab traders (many setting out from Sana'a) for hundreds of years. Africans – including the ancestors of today's Lemba – traded there and learned Moorish customs, circumcision and ritual slaughter included. The Arabs took wives from the coastal tribes. Their children were brought up in Islam. In the sixteenth century, Sayuna was destroyed by the Portuguese, and its Arabic culture disappeared.

The Lemba, though, retained memories of Solomon and Moses, both of whom are as important in Islamic as in Judaic belief. Rather like the Falasha of Ethiopia (whose Judaism may derive from an attenuated form of early Christianity stripped of its New Testament elements) Lemba Jewishness stems in part from a diluted and almost forgotten Islam. Compared to the Falasha, indeed, they have a closer tie to Israel. The genes (Y chromosomes included) of the Falasha unite them, not with the Middle East, but with other Africans.

Both the beliefs and the genes of the Lemba contain an important message for those who depend on ancestry to define nationhood.

Cultures and genes can both be transmitted without the need for one people to supplant another. The Lemba have no direct intellectual connection with Judaism, but picked up its elements from a related source. No member of the tribe has had uninterrupted genetic contact with the Middle East: they are not a Lost Tribe, but, manifestly, black Africans. However, some of their genes came from middle-easterners who once took mates on the coast of Africa. Since then, those alien Y chromosomes have diffused for a thousand miles inland from the point of contact. The Arabs did not replace the Lemba and the coastal peoples did not dislodge those living in the interior. Instead, genes were passed down the generations and across the landscape by mating. One population absorbed part of the genetic heritage of another, but had no sense of being supplanted by it: genes moved far further than any individual did.

This disengagement of the fate of genes from that of their carriers is central to population genetics. Anthropology could, in its early days, see only one way for genes or cultures to travel: with a marauding band of invaders. It had an oddly Puritan view of the past that disregarded the simple truth that conquest is a less powerful force than sex. In the same way as religions spread more by conversion than by the sword, genes travel across the globe with the more or less willing participation of those who transmit them. History is a story of love as much as war. Mass movement – of Lost Tribes or anyone else – is not needed.

Dr William Price, Thor Heyerdahl, and their successors saw the spread of genes as a journey with no breaks. They are brought by their carriers, like an express train, from source to destination, without a stop, replacing the genes of its original inhabitants. The truth is more mundane. The voyage of a piece of DNA from its origin is a slow and tortuous process involving many delays and changes. The vehicle – the individual – within which a gene starts its journey never reaches the final stop; but the gene itself, accompanied by others whose voyage started long after those boarding on the first leg of the journey, does. Genes move through people, not just with them. Most maps of the geography of genes do not reconstruct mass migrations, or lost tribes, but just the exchange of DNA between men and women over many years.

This leakage of genes between peoples and over vast distances can be seen in Jews today. There has already been exchange between them and their neighbours. Now, it is speeding up. In many places, Jews are merging with local non-Jewish populations by intermarriage. In 1950, more than eight marriages in ten of Jews was to a person of their own faith. Forty years later, the United States census estimated that fifty-two per cent of Jews who married did so to a non-Jew. In Germany, the proportion of mixed marriages was nine in ten. As a result, the numbers identifying themselves as Jewish has, outside Israel, dropped by around three million from the eleven million or so who claimed this status in 1948. In Europe in 1939 there were ten million Jews. After the war there were four million. In 1996, there are fewer than half that number. In Britain, the Chief Rabbi has written a book entitled *Will We Have Jewish Grandchildren?* With nearly half of all British Jews marrying outside the faith he has reason to be concerned.

What were once specifically Jewish genes (such as torsion dystonia) are, as a result, seeping into other groups. The same is true, of course, of genes coming the other way. Jews have a low incidence of phenyl-ketonuria (an inborn inability to break down a food substance which can lead to mental impairment); but, in time, as intermarriage goes on, the descendants of today's Jews will begin to show its effects.

The centre of gravity of Judaism in terms of population density moved out of Israel long ago. Ever since the Diaspora, there have been more Jews living outside the Promised Land than within it. By 1880, around three-quarters of world Jewry lived in Europe and Russia. By 1939 a third had migrated onwards to the United States, shifting the hub even further west. The Holocaust reduced the number of European Jews by almost two-thirds. This, the greatest of all Jewish catastrophes, continued the move of the Jewish pivot westwards, further from the ancestral home.

Migration was accompanied by increased assimilation of Jewish genes by others. In the nineteenth century, absorption was much further advanced in western Europe than in Poland. Many French Jews were shocked by the Dreyfus case of 1894 (in which the false conviction of a Jewish soldier on a charge of treason unleashed a storm of anti-Semitism) as they thought themselves well integrated. Already, there had been extensive intermarriage between Jew and non-Jew in France. In Britain, the process had gone even further. Many Jews had become fully absorbed: Benjamin Disraeli (who himself wrote a novel based on the theme of the Return of the Lost Tribes) was baptised a Christian by virtue of his father's quarrel with the elders of his own synagogue.

In the United States intermixture is well advanced. The process is self-generating: three-quarters of the children of couples from the two different faiths are themselves brought up as non-Jews and are hence likely to marry someone from outside Judaism.

The history of European Jews over the past two centuries is one of the migration and dilution of genes away from an ancient centre. Population growth led to movement, those who moved exchanged genes with their neighbours, and as the process went on, generation after generation, integration became more and more complete.

The process is known as 'demic diffusion', the genetic absorption of one population by another. Who assimilates whom depends on numbers. Inevitably, in Europe and America, Jews are being absorbed into the more numerous peoples who surround them. The genetic identity of European Jews was stronger fifty years ago than it is today. It will be weaker yet fifty years from now; but even if cultural homogenization goes so far as to remove any clues as to which populations were once Jewish, the record of their genes will remain.

Genes can trace a nation's history further into the past than can any record, even one as venerable as the Old Testament. The new map of the world's genes hints at a surprising truth: there may indeed have been a lost tribe, millions strong, emerging from the Middle East to lose its cultural, if not its biological, identity as it moved across the globe. The peoples bound together by this common genetic history range from the Atlantic to the Bay of Bengal and from the North Cape to Ceylon.

The first clue came from language. Shared words can make a family tree of the languages of the world. Some are close relatives – English and German, say; others less so. English and Sanskrit – an extinct tongue once spoken in the East – seem quite distinct but, 'father' in English is 'pitah' in Sanskrit, showing their shared ancestry. Both are members of a larger family known as Indo-European, which includes tongues as different as Bengali, Albanian and Welsh.

Other languages, too, can be grouped into families. Altaic, for example, includes Turkish and Mongolian, while the Uralic group includes Finnish, Hungarian and the Samoyedic languages of Siberia. This shows that languages, like genes, evolve. Although the mechanisms of change are different, both retain vestiges of a history that can be used to trace relationships among them.

Humans are obviously kin to chimps, less so to lizards, and scarcely at all to yeasts. A few yeast genes, though, are identical to our own. They show how, long ago, men and yeast shared an ancestor. In the same way, certain words evolve slowly and their ancient origins can be traced. One vast group of languages – the Nostratic group – unites Welsh with Samoyed, Mongolian with French, Tibetan and Berber. How did people

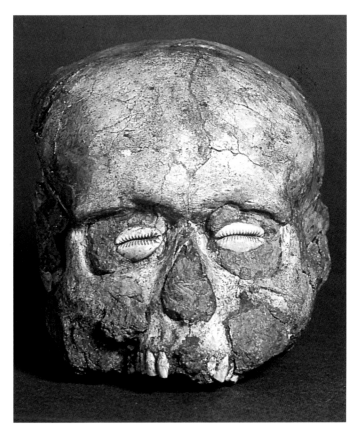

At the beginnings of farming: a skull covered with plaster, with cowrie shells as eyes. From Jericho, before the appearance of pottery, nine thousand years ago.

now living thousands of miles apart come to speak languages descending from the same source?

The answer lies in the family tree written in the genes. It suggests an intriguing truth in the legend of the Lost Tribes of Israel and puts the idea of an ancestral homeland around the Jordan into a new light.

Peoples separated by great distances naturally diverge. Isolation itself promotes change: in genes – just as in languages – there are chance fluctuations that cause populations to drift apart. In many places the geography of words and of genes lacks any common pattern. In Africa there is not much consistency in the word for 'dog' or 'fire' between Morocco, Nigeria and Kenya, and an equivalent lack of shared geography for, say, different blood groups. Each population has evolved without contact and changes in language or in genes have taken place independently.

Superimposed on the speakers of Nostratic tongues, though, are genetic trends that accompany those of language. Both radiate from the

Middle East to the north, west and east. They are consistent for fifty or more genes and for hundreds of words, suggesting that a common force produced them all. The effect is strongest among speakers of Indo-European languages, but exists in the Altaic group as well. Only the peoples of the African shore of the Mediterranean seem not to fit: although they once spoke Nostratic, they do not share in the trend.

Why do lines of shared biological and cultural descent point towards a common centre for such distinct peoples? One theory turns on an exodus, seven thousand years before the Lost Tribes. Farming began in the Middle East, around the valleys of the Jordan and the Euphrates, about ten thousand years ago. From there it spread, reaching the western edge of Europe around five thousand years later and the Far East at about the same time.

Just as in the Jewish population of Central Europe, the economic success of the first farmers led to a population explosion. Soon, they began to move away from their crowded homeland into the lands of their hunting neighbours. Some of the hunters, no doubt, mated with the incomers; others moved from hunting to farming. The newly mixed population, and their offspring, moved step by step across the globe. Slowly, one population became integrated into the other, the farmers soaking up the genes of the hunters into whose lands they moved. The process is at work today. African fertility is four times that of Europe. In Rwanda, the average couple has 8.5 children; while in Italy the figure is 1.3. Migration has already begun. Whatever politicians might wish, there will be mass movement from South to North and, sooner or later, an absorption of European genes into a population of partly African ancestry.

As the genes of the farmers travelled further from their source, they were diluted by those of the hunters already there. Perhaps, thousands of miles away from where the farmers began their journey – on the shores of the Indian Ocean or the Atlantic – their distant descendants possessed (as do the Lemba) just a few lineages linking them to their distant homeland.

The radiation of bloodlines from a centre is due to an ancient emigration from the Middle East and its peoples' assimilation of their neighbours' genes. It contains the solution to the mystery of the Lost Tribes. In fact, they never were lost: instead they live on in the inheritance of a thousand million people alive today. The Tribes can never return as their heritage has been diffused among their innumerable descendants, who know nothing about a historic link with the Middle East.

Genetic trends in Europe, built up from dozens of separate genes to reveal the trends across the continent. Many radiate from south-east to north-west. Some geneticists believe that this reflects a penetration of the genes of farmers who spread from the Middle East into those of the original hunting population. There are, though, some puzzling exceptions to the general trend and for certain genes (such as those on the mitochondria) it appears not to hold at all.

A COMMON MARKET OF GENES:
GENETIC PATTERNS IN EUROPE

Genes reconstruct history (although, as in most images of the past, a certain amount of guesswork is involved). There may be large-scale patterns of relatedness, descending from long ago. A map of the distribution of the many mutations in the cystic fibrosis gene shows that one is relatively common in north-western Europe, but declines in abundance towards the south and east. The trend is quite similar to that of the pattern of spread of early farmers across Europe from the Middle East. This suggests that this form of the disease was common among the pre-farming population of Europe, but was displaced by other mutations in the same gene as farmers spread westward ten thousand years ago.

The geographic patterns of many genes at once make a map based not on a single gene, but on the average of many: rather like a school atlas that uses colours to show the heights of mountains and the position of landmarks it does the same thing with genes. An atlas, though, maps points only in terms of longitude, latitude and and height – just three measures for each location. When a hundred or so different genes are involved, things are more complicated. One way to plot the information is to show shared patterns as red, blue and green. The trends for each colour then hint at ancient migrations and population mixing.

In Europe, this is not easy because – in spite of its long history of political separatism – the most obvious feature of the Common Market and its neighbours is that most people are much the same. There is much less genetic differentiation than there is in, for example, Africa. However, some trends are apparent. There is a wave, shaded red, of shared similarity tracking across north-west Europe; and a similar pattern of common ancestry, coloured green, pointing west along the north shores of the Mediterranean. These might represent two branches of a surge of farmers from the Middle East, penetrating the original hunting population. The orange wave in central Europe may be the relics of a separate immigration of nomads from the steppes. None of these trends is very striking, and because of the genetic homogeneity of Europe other interpretations are possible. Sardinia – not shown on this map – is, for unknown reasons, very different from the rest of Europe.

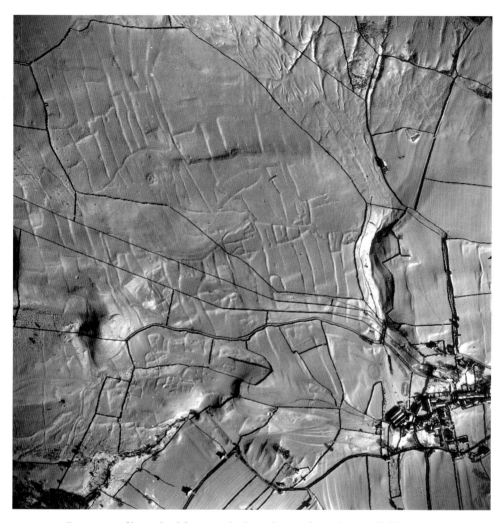

Remnants of long-dead farmers: the boundaries of a prehistoric field system seen in the slanting light of early morning, beneath the modern fields of Grassington, Yorkshire. The absorption of the ancient fields into those of today has a parallel in genes, as some of the DNA circulating in the veins of modern Britons may be that of ancient farmers who spread from the Middle East.

In Israel itself, though, there is a new genetic return that is the mirror of the ancient diffusion from the farmers' homeland. The social changes – intermarriage and small families – affecting Jews outside Israel apply to a smaller extent in the Holy Land itself. The numbers identifying themselves as Jewish are increasing there as they decline everywhere else.

Israel is beginning to contain proportionately more of world Jewry than it has for many years. This is due in part to the disaster of the Holocaust which destroyed the Jewish population of Europe; but it arises mainly from changes in demography, the persistence of an older pattern of life in Israel while for Jews elsewhere the modern world has taken over. The reinstatement of Jews to their ancient home is by population growth rather than immigration. Jewish genes are returning in just the same way as they left ten thousand years ago: not contained in a wandering band of exiles, but on a journey throught time and space directed by changes in the societies (most notably the rate of population growth) of those who bear them.

What, then, of the ashes of Dr Price, the visionary of the Welsh as a people banished from that Promised Land? To him, Wales was a special place: the site of the New Jerusalem. Now there is evidence that, in quite a different way, it is indeed unique. Patterns of mitochondrial genes across Europe do not follow the trends found in those passing through both sexes. This suggests that – as in the Lemba or in European Jewry – most of the transfer of genes from the East was from invading males to local females. Women moved less, and their own genes stayed where they were. The family tree of European mitochondria contains a surprise. The lineages from a small patch of mid-Wales are distinct from all others. They are less related to the mitochondria of England or elsewhere in Europe than to those from – of all places – Papua New Guinea. Perhaps, unknown to anyone, there is a lost tribe of women (or at least a lost clan of female lineages) living in these remote Welsh valleys. They may be the remnant of an ancient people who have been overwhelmed elsewhere in Europe; possibly an early migration from Africa, obliterated in other places by later waves of emigrants from the same continent.

Dr Price's druids were a notably masculine group: their consorts' role simply to produce the next generation of high priests. The same was true of the Tribes themselves, named, quite emphatically, after the sons of Jacob. How would Dr Price, or William Blake, have coped with the discovery that their mythic remnants of a defeated Celtic race were women?

CHAPTER IV

The Soul Beneath the Skin

My mother bore me in the southern wild,
And I am black, but O! my soul is white;
White as an angel is the English child:
But I am black as if bereav'd of light.

WILLIAM BLAKE,
Songs of Innocence, 1789

A DISSECTED CORPSE is a reminder that beauty is only skin deep and that, beneath that façade, we all look much the same. As William Hogarth put it in his *Analysis of Beauty*, written in 1750: 'The fair young girl, the brown old man and the negro; nay, all mankind, have the same appearance and are alike disagreeable to the eye, when the upper skin is taken away.' Any anatomy museum shows how right he was.

That in the School of Medicine in Paris has one of the oldest and finest collections in the world, with many specimens that are works of art in their own right. In one display, a wax cranium explodes into its constituent parts. Nearby, a liver injected to show the blood vessels resembles nothing recognizably human. Only the skin of a flayed face, its arteries an unlikely green, retains a vestige of humanity.

The museum also has on display a series of skulls from the races of the world classified as black, white, australian and oriental. These are, in turn, overlooked by a shelf of wax impressions taken from the heads of those guillotined as they fell into the basket. Each is labelled with its crime: parricide, murder or rape. Most have an irritated expression (marred, in some cases, by a missing chin as the victim tried to withdraw his head from the falling blade).

The skulls and brains they survey are, in the main, anonymous, mere racial types. A few, though, are labelled with the names of their former owners. They include those of the greatest French anatomists of the nineteenth century. Among them are the brains of Paul Broca and Joseph Arthur, Comte de Gobineau. Broca was a serious scientist; the founder of neurology and the first to find that damage to a particular part of the

The Little Black Boy

My mother bore me in the southern wild,
And I am black, but O! my soul is white
White as an angel is the English child:
But I am black as if bereav'd of light.

My mother taught me underneath a tree
And sitting down before the heat of day
She took me on her lap and kissed me.
And pointing to the east began to say.

Look on the rising sun: there God does live
And gives his light, and gives his heat away.
And flowers and trees and beasts and men recieve
Comfort in morning joy in the noon day.

And we are put on earth a little space,
That we may learn to bear the beams of love.
And these black bodies and this sun-burnt face
Is but a cloud and like a shady grove.

For

brain led to a specific loss of function (in this case the ability to speak). Gobineau has a more equivocal place in history and is better known (in France at least) as the author of flamboyant novels set in exotic places. Both are notorious as the founders of 'scientific racism', the idea that the races of mankind can be classified, and their value judged, on the basis of biology.

The last government to use that notion was that of South Africa, where *apartheid*, separation by race, died only in the 1990s. It began with the very foundation of the state. In 1652 Jan van Riebeeck settled at the Cape of Good Hope. Nearby lived some twenty thousand San people, the last of the hunter-gatherers, and five times as many KhoiKhoi, herders of sheep and cattle. The Dutch thought their language mere stuttering and referred to them, mockingly, as 'Hottentots'. John Barrow's 1801 *Account of Travels into the Interior of Southern Africa* described the Boers as 'an inhuman and unfeeling peasantry, who, having discovered themselves to be removed to too great a distance from the seat of their former government to be awed by its authority, have exercised, in the most wanton and barbarous manner, an absolute power over these poor wretches'. The natives were seen as the lowest of the low, a missing link between humans and apes. One anatomist saw them as 'the nearest approximation to the lower animals – the women are represented as even more repulsive in

Paul Broca, the great French anatomist. As well as being one of the founders of brain science and of anthropology, he was elected a Life Member of the French Senate and served until his death in 1880.

Hottentots herding cattle, from a seventeenth-century drawing rediscovered in 1986.

appearance than the men'. Their speech was 'a farrago of bestial sounds resembling the chattering of apes'. The Dutch settlers treated Hottentots with particular brutality; a curious Dutchman, it is said, killing and eating one to compare the taste with that of a monkey.

They were quickly exploited. From 1809, the Hottentot Code obliged them to have a fixed abode, and to move only with permission from their masters. It was – almost – slavery and, as such, already an anomaly. The trade in human beings had been abolished and reformers were pressing that slavery itself be done away with. As a result, the Hottentots were among the first in the Empire formally to be emancipated. In 1828 an ordinance stated that 'no Hottentot or other free person of colour shall be subject to any forced service which does not apply to others of His Majesty's subjects, nor to any hindrance, interference, fine, or punishment of any kind whatever under the pretence that such person has been guilty of vagrancy or any other offence unless after trial.' This was the precursor of the law that, in 1833, abolished slavery throughout the Empire. In principle at least it gave every British subject, regardless of race, equal rights.

However progressive their views on emancipation, though, it was assumed by nearly all Europeans that the other peoples of the world had mental abilities lower than their own. The Paris anatomists were not the first to turn to the taxonomy of intellect and the progress from low to high – from African to Frenchman, from parricide to Academician. Linnaeus, the founder of the classification of animals and plants, himself believed that there were divergences in talent between races. Whites – *Homo Europaeus* – were, he said, lively, inventive and ruled by custom; *Homo Americanus* tenacious, contented, choleric and governed by habit; *Homo Asiaticus* stern, haughty, avaricious, led by opinion; and *Homo Afer* (the African) cunning, slow, phlegmatic, careless and ruled by caprice.

Race today means colour. To the Victorians, though, it had a wider significance. Remote peoples, such as Hottentots, were distinct – and inferior – but so were the lower classes. The display of skulls of the executed and of the African in the same gallery was no accident. Gobineau, in his *Essays on the Inequality of Races*, had written that 'The social order is founded upon three original classes, each of which repre-sents a racial variety; the nobility, a more or less accurate reflection of the conquering race; the bourgeoisie, composed of mixed stock coming close to the chief race; and the common people who live in servitude or at least in a very depressed position. These last belong to a lower race which came about in the south through miscegenation with the negroes and in the north with the finns.' Nobody knows why Gobineau thought so ill of Finns.

In South Africa there was a close tie between the ideas of race and class. Talk of racial conflict referred, in the state's early days, not to Europeans and Africans but to the quarrel between the affluent whites of British origin and the poorer Afrikaners. It took economic problems to bring colour into the equation. In 1922 there was a strike by white mine-workers concerned that blacks were being allowed to take their jobs. Marchers in Johannesburg carried banners saying 'Workers of the World Unite for a White South Africa'. They asked for a political leader who would promote the interests of the white race over those of the despised blacks. Although the strike failed, they got their way. Prime Minister Hertzog began to dismiss blacks from government service (the first step towards the policy of complete separation). As he said 'The native cannot blame us if in the first place we try to find work for our own class.'

The Victorians, too, were great believers in the undeserving poor; in a class whose weakness was inborn. Henry Mayhew in his *London Labour and the London Poor* claimed that:

> There are – socially, morally, and perhaps even physically considered –
> but two distinct and broadly marked races, viz., the wanderers and the
> settlers – the vagabond and the citizen – the nomadic and the civilized
> tribes. The nomad is distinguished from the civilized man by his
> repugnance to regular and continuous labour – by his inability to
> perceive consequences ever so slightly removed from immediate
> apprehension – by his passion for stupefying herbs and roots and, when
> possible, for intoxicating liquors – by his immoderate love of gaming,
> frequently risking his own personal liberty upon a single cast – by his
> love of libidinous dances – by his delight in warfare and in all perilous
> sports – by the looseness of his notions as to property – by the absence
> of chastity among his women and his disregard of female honour – and,
> lastly, by his vague sense of religion.

The language is more elegant than that of today, and colour did not
come into it, but the agenda is familiar. Social status was innate, and
people of differing biological ability found their own economic level.
'Vagabonds', the lowest of the Cockney working class, were distinguished
by 'a greater relative development of the jaws and cheekbones' and 'broad
lozenge-shaped faces', producing 'distinctive moral and intellectual
features'. Social differences were formulated as Ammon's Law; that
people from cities – those enterprising enough to move from the land –
had longer heads than those from the country. The upper classes had the
longest skulls of all. Although vagabond and citizen might look much the
same, under the skin they were distinct. Mayhew blamed the social
disparities between them on biology.

The idea of a class inferior by nature – whatever colour it may be – and
beyond redemption by charity, exhortation or good luck has a long
history. For much of the present century, though, society's role as a
defence against the mob seemed to be at an end. In the 1950s the idea of
a rabble, determined to defy the law, was a nightmare from a distant past.
Now, there is renewed alarm at crime, drugs, and alienation. Some
people, it seems, are programmed to fail. Nothing can be done but to
contain them; society must return to its ancient task of subduing those
who do not wish to be assimilated.

In the late nineteenth century, the reformer Charles Booth made a
map of the quality of London streets. Each was coloured according to
its merits. Some were the homes of professionals, others of the decent
working class. Many, though, were the abode of the lowest segments of
society. 'The men who live in this quarter', it was reported of one street

PREVIOUS PAGE: A section of Charles Booth's map showing the quality of London streets. The map itself, in several sheets, covered most of inner London. The section illustrated here shows the area around Euston Station: the poverty-stricken streets of Somers Town to the east, the opulent terraces of Regent's Park (part of the Crown Estate, owned by the Royal Family) and Bloomsbury; then a less-than-fashionable resort of the middle classes but, a few decades later, the centre of the city's intellectual life. Not much has changed since the map was made.

in the East End, 'are not human, they are wild beasts.' Such places were hotbeds of poverty, crime and disease, all of which were in constant danger of reaching out and infecting the rest of the city.

To walk through modern London is to retrace Booth's journeys in almost all their detail. Although the buildings have changed, the people are the same. Just north of Bloomsbury (home of Virginia Woolf, the British Museum and University College London) is a council estate, Somers Town. In Booth's time, parts of it were described as 'Lowest class, vicious and semi-criminal'. Nowadays it is a series of dingy 1930s blocks with pretensions to Bauhaus style and its quota of drugs, crime and the despairing poor. Somers Town is the scene of one of London's most bitter racial divides, between the Bangladeshi community and some of the local whites; both trapped in unemployment and each turning on the other.

A century ago, the inhabitants of the Nash terraces that overlook Regent's Park, half a mile away, dealt with their neighbours by building gates around Somers Town. Each night they were closed and anyone passing through was searched. If the underclass could not be controlled, at least it might be contained. The last of the British class walls – a seven-foot barrier with revolving spikes – was demolished a mere thirty years ago. It was built in the 1930s across a road in Oxford to segregate houses built for slum-dwellers from others designed for those rich enough to buy. Today only an unexplained change in name, from Aldrich Road to Wentworth Road, is a reminder of its existence.

In America, such barriers are returning and the agenda of those who build them is a familiar one. *The Bell Curve* by Richard Herrnstein and Charles Murray spent several months on the 1994 *New York Times* best-seller list. Its central claim is that of Henry Mayhew: that status is ruled by biology. Herrnstein is clear about the problem: 'By removing artificial barriers between classes, society has encouraged the creation of bio-logical barriers. When people can take their natural level in society, the upper classes will, by definition, have greater capacity than the lower.' The *Bell Curve*'s argument can be summarized, briefly but accurately, as

'Those who have been to Harvard do better on IQ tests; Harvard gradu-ates are paid well and send their children to Harvard.' So compelling is this logic that America's ills can only be explained in biological terms.

Herrnstein and Murray's claim that the poor are to blame for their own predicament goes straight back to the earliest days of racial thought. Its vision for an America that has allowed low-quality genes to sink to the bottom is that of the walls of Victorian London: 'We have in mind a high-tech and more lavish version of the Indian reservation for some substantial minority of the nation's population, while the rest of America tries to go about its business.'

The Bell Curve promotes a nineteenth-century agenda but skirts, with the delicacy of a Victorian vicar, the central question of race. Class and colour, though, soon become entangled. In mediaeval Spain, the aristoc-racy had lighter skins through which the veins could be seen. They were, quite literally, blue-blooded. In India, higher castes are lighter than are lower. In America, links between social class and skin colour are so close that 'poor' has become a coded term for 'black' in the way that 'interna-tional banker' was once used by anti-Semites as a convenient label for 'Jew'. This means that statements about race which would be outrageous if made without qualification can be hidden under a veneer of social concern. The racist agenda in modern ideas of a genetic underclass is less obvious than in the days of Broca, but it certainly exists. The only difference between the new Right and their predecessors is that today's proponents of biology as fate are too cowardly to admit it.

The most obvious role of skin pigment is as a social label. Colour itself is inherited but those with the wrong genes are placed in an environment from which it is impossible to escape. People with dark skins are, in most places, less successful, less healthy and – perhaps – less contented than those with light. In 1993, the median black household in the United States (that half-way through the whole list, from richest to poorest) was worth \$4,418. For whites, the equivalent figure was \$45,470. The financial differences transcend class, with black lawyers earning, on the average, three-quarters of the income of their white colleagues. American blacks have become another nation in social terms, too. Most black babies are born out of wedlock, a majority of single black women have had children, and the typical household for a black child lacks a father.

Whites are well aware of the advantages of their colour. When American students were asked how much compensation they would expect if they were, all of a sudden, to become black, the average was a million dollars a year. The stigma persists beyond the grave. In the United States, the records of infants who die within a year of birth often show a shift in the racial status of the child. In nine out of ten cases in which the race description has changed, a black child is reclassified as white. There is a Brazilian proverb that 'Money bleaches'. Wealth is enough to overcome the effects of colour; and, however dark the skin, someone with a large enough bank balance is accepted into whatever class they choose. In the United States, death, not money, does the job.

As happened in South Africa and in Victorian London, such disparities in wealth have led to strife. The nineteenth-century French political commentator Alexis de Tocqueville wrote of the young United States that 'The most formidable of all the ills that threaten the future of the Union arises from the presence of a black population on its territory – The danger of a conflict between the white and the black inhabitants perpetually haunts the imagination of the Americans, like a painful dream.'

Although the proportion of blacks in the USA was higher then than today, that dream has, according to some, come true. The figures tell the story. More black males are in prison than in college. In 1995, for the first time, blacks made up more than half of all prisoners. By the turn of the century, if the trend continues, most black men will have been behind bars. One group is most culpable; young black men – just one in a hundred Americans – commit a third of the country's violent crimes. Blacks are victims, too, as a black man has a chance of being murdered seven times greater than has a white. Black lives are, on the average, six years shorter than those of whites, and a teenage boy living in Harlem has a smaller chance of reaching retirement age than does a citizen of Bangladesh.

The temptation to ascribe all this to inborn failings – to blame the victims – is as irresistible in the United States as it once was in Europe. Of course, even the most rabid partisans of genes as destiny no longer maintain that lower races, be they black or poor, are altogether distinct from their superiors. They concede, grudgingly, their common humanity. Instead, there is a more subtle agenda. Racial differences involve not the genes studied by anatomists or by molecular biologists but those, yet undiscovered, that control talent and ability; those that make us human.

Paul Broca's biology, unlike his views on society, evolved into a science: anthropology, the study of what it means to be human. It is a field so conscious of its history that some of its followers are as blinded by liberal

IN AFRICAN BLOOD: THE DUFFY BLOOD GROUP AND RESISTANCE TO MALARIA

What blood groups are actually for, nobody really knows. One system, though, hints about how they may have evolved. The Duffy system has two variant forms. One, Duffy-negative, is common in west Africa, the other in the rest of the world. In Africa and elsewhere, malaria is common (and is becoming commoner as control measures fail). The disease is due to a single-celled parasite that is transmitted by a mosquito. Within the mosquito it has sex; and the female mosquito transmits the parasites to a human when she sucks blood. Their life-cycle involves first an invasion of the liver and a huge multiplication in number; then an attack on the red blood cells, whose contents are devoured.

The Duffy-positive blood group is the site on the red cell surface where malaria parasites attach themselves before boring in and destroying its contents. The protein involved is built up from more than three hundred amino-acid building blocks, and snakes back and forth across the red cell membrane. In west Africa, there is a genetic change in the mechanism of its production. It allows the protein to be produced on most of the body's tissues but specifically shuts it off on red blood cells. The invading parasites find no docking site on the red cell and cannot break into it, protecting those who carry this gene against malaria. Perhaps an ancient history of differential response to other diseases explains the existence of other blood groups too – but perhaps not.

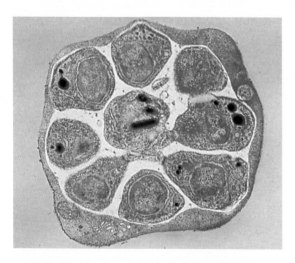

A slice through a misshapen red blood cell packed with malaria parasites.

prejudice as were their (notably illiberal) predecessors. Genetics has, at last, rescued anthropology from its past. For the first time it can test what lies beneath the skin and whether races, however defined, differ in fundamental ways, intellect included.

Distinct the races undeniably are. It is easy to tell from a blood sample whether its donor is black or white. Africans have blood groups absent from Europeans and are more diverse than are people from outside that continent. Looking at a dozen or so selected genes distinguishes individuals from different parts of the world with certainty. The blood-group system known as Duffy, for example, has a uniquely west African variant. Anyone – whatever the colour of their skin – who has the African form must have some African ancestry.

To measure how different races really are demands a larger sample of genes. They can be chosen in various ways – by looking at gene products such as blood proteins, at the DNA of the genes that make them, or at the vast amount of genetic material that appears to have no function. One of the most telling statements about race comes from medicine, when to measure racial difference is a matter not of politics but of survival. An organ transplant needs a match between many of the genes that control antigens, the cues of identity on cells that are recognized by the immune systems of donor and recipient. The less similar they are, the higher the chance of the organ being rejected. In the United States, a national system of tissue testing pairs organs with patients using a computer to compare the genes of donor and recipient in the hope of finding a match. The prospects of success are best when six or more cell surface antigens are shared. Any genetic divergence between groups – blacks and whites, for example – will manifest itself in a reduced ability of a member of one group to accept transplants from the other. As a result, the tissue-matching computer contains, almost incidentally, a vast body of information on the genetic divergence between races.

In America, most donated tissues come from whites. The computer shows that one white kidney patient in ten matches this waiting pool of organs for six separate genes. Just one black patient in fifty, though, makes such a good match. This is itself a convincing statement of the existence of genetic divergence between races. It shows that blacks and whites have inborn differences in the ability to accept an organ from someone whose skin differs in colour from their own. However, tissue-matching makes another essential point. Only a minority of patients ever corresponds with a member even of their own race at six of

THE BIOLOGY OF REJECTION:
TISSUE TRANSPLANTATION AND ORGAN MATCHING

The Second World War gave a great boost to surgery. The wounded poured in to hospitals, set up in the knowledge that getting the injured back on to the battlefield was as important as providing ammunition. Some surgeons were daring enough to attempt skin grafts on those with burns. Their many failures led to a new field of biology and of medicine.

When skin from – say – a soldier's leg was grafted on to his face the operation usually succeeded. However, any transfer of skin from someone else to a patient so badly burned as to have insufficient skin of his own was always rejected. Experiments with mice showed that this was due to genetic differences between donor and recipient. The genes involved – the *histocompatibility* genes – have been much studied.

A foreign transplant is attacked by specialized white blood cells called T-cells. They detect it because its cues of identity – antigens – coded for by histocompatibility genes differ from their own. These genes are very variable: some exist in more than a hundred forms, differing from person to person. With the exception of identical twins, everyone is unique and distinguishable from everyone else.

Why is there so much variation? After all, the genes evolved long before transplantation was ever thought of. Now it seems that it is because the antigens usually act to concentrate the immune system's protective machinery onto cells under attack from bacteria or viruses. They bind the assailants and, by so doing, give the infected cell a distinct identity so that it stands out from the crowd. Rather like the elaborate uniform of a mediaeval army, the histocompatibility genes give everyone a unique genetic identity that cannot easily be copied by invaders. Any cell subverted by an outsider changes its coat and is killed. A transplant between people is equivalent to introducing – say – a kilted Scotsman into an army of Italians wearing feather plumes and is bound to fail.

The immune battalions include circulating antibodies and specialized cells that shower the infected cell with sharp molecular lances that kill it (or persuade it to commit suicide). They are in constant action. When they are damaged by diseases (such as AIDS) that target the immune system, sooner or later the patient succumbs to infection. Making a transplant involves matching donor and recipient as closely as possible and suppressing the immune system with drugs. In the embryo there is a 'learning' process in which T-cells that recognize the body's own antigens proliferate and others fail. If this could be imitated it might be possible to persuade the body to accept a foreign transplant. This approach has not yet succeeded but, with the increase in understanding of the immune system, gives hope for the future.

A corneal graft in the process of being rejected. Usually, the outer surface of the eye is relatively willing to accept transplants as little blood reaches it. This individual, though, was unfortunate; and a second attempt to save his sight must be made.

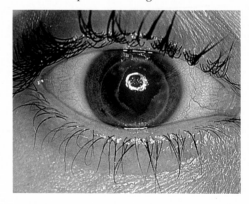

Studying human evolution is like writing history without books. There are few fossils and most are just fragments. Darwin thought that humankind originated in Africa, but plenty of others disputed this. There was even talk of an origin on a lost continent, Lemuria, now submerged beneath the Indian ocean.

After the discovery of Neanderthal Man in Germany and the evidence of that species' replacement by humans of modern form about forty thousand years ago, it seemed obvious that the birth of our species took place in Europe. After all, Europe saw the highest refinement of culture; why not that of humans themselves? French scientists took the argument to its logical end: a skeleton found in the Dordogne looked like those of today's Asians, another in the hills above Menton on the Riviera resembled those of Africans. Cro-Magnon Man (another inhabitant of the Dordogne) was similar to today's Europeans. The result was clear: France was the birthplace of the peoples of the world.

Now, most palaeontologists agree that the oldest human fossils are from Africa. Some, though, believe that skulls of our earliest ancestors appear at about the same time in other parts of the world as well. A little over a hundred thousand years ago, humans of modern appearance left remains at two places in South Africa (Klasies River and Border Cave, to the north of the country), in Ethiopia, and near Mount Carmel and Nazareth in Israel. The earliest fossil from China is around sixty thousand years old and from Australia about fifty thousand. Modern humans appeared in Europe almost last of all, at around thirty thousand years before the present. Only the Americas and the Pacific were colonized more recently.

Genes, too, suggest an African root for humankind. A family tree can be made using variation in the DNA to unite peoples of differing degrees of affinity. It shows that Africans have more genetic diversity than others and that most of the ancient lineages in the human gene pool originate in that continent.

BELOW LEFT: *A skull of an early non-African, from the excavation at Qafzeh (now in Israel). Only a few tens of thousands of years after early modern humans appeared they left their native continent and began their spread across the globe. The Qafzeh skull is similar to those of the earliest humans – and not very different from our own.*
BELOW RIGHT: *Fanciful and factual ideas about how modern humans spread across the world. The map was drawn by Haeckel. Many of its details are now known to be correct. Some are frankly speculative: like Lemuria.*

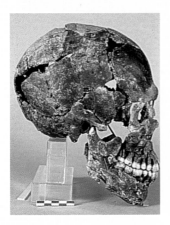

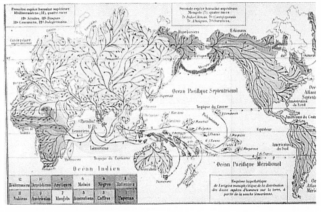

the decisive genes. This is because of inherited variation within each racial group. Its extent is much greater than the genetic divergence between them and means that most attempts at a transplant, because of genetic differences between individual whites or individual blacks, involve fewer than six matches between donor and recipient. Drugs are then used to ensure that the body's ability to recognize a foreign tissue is overcome. The matchmaking computer (together with tests of many other genes) shows that the average genetic difference between blacks and whites is smaller than that between individuals, whatever race they come from. As variation between people is so much greater than that between races, almost all patients have to undergo the same drug treatment, whether or not their new organ comes from someone of their own colour. When faced with the challenge of life and death, claims of racial distinction fade away.

Transplantation shows – as Hogarth was the first to point out – that the essence of race lies on the surface. The genes involved, and many others, show that *Homo sapiens* is, compared to other mammals, very uniform from place to place. This is, no doubt, because humans evolved not long ago and spread over the globe even more recently. What makes us human involves the evolution of ideas rather than DNA.

Superficial though race may be, it is foolish to say that it does not exist. If people from different places can be seen to be distinct they can, on any rational classification, be placed in separate categories. Even though the term imposes a false unity on diverse groups it is worth preserving.

In spite of the lack of evidence of substantial divergence between races, the idea that black skin is an evolutionary indicator of deeper dissimilarity persists. One well-known view is that black skin, like the lozenge-shaped faces of Mayhew's 'vagabonds', is a token of low intellect. Without doubt, black Americans do less well on the average on conventional intelligence tests than do whites. Many argue that this is due to prejudice, low expectations, and poor education. Others say that it is inborn and impossible to change. They believe that colour marks a fundamental divergence between the races that is manifest not in tissue transplants but in the mind.

Champions of white genetic superiority claim that the supposed difference reflects evolutionary history. It is, they say, a relic of a time when blacks lived in places where life was brutish, nasty and short and where it paid to have as many children as possible since nearly all were doomed to die. In such circumstances intellect had no value as most problems were unpredictable and unavoidable. In those days, like dogs it was best to reproduce and run; to invest little in each child, but to have lots of them. In Africa there was no point in having a large – and expensive – brain. As humans moved to the icy North, things changed. Life was tough, but predictably so. To stay alive, the first Europeans had to plan ahead. Children could survive only if they were cared for. As each needed so much investment it was impossible to have many of them. Those with genes for high intelligence did better at keeping their offspring alive, even if their sex-lives suffered. Whites, it is said (with a surprising lack of evidence for either statement), have larger intellects but smaller penises; neatly linking the traditional obsessions about black sex and black stupidity.

The theory of evolution is infinitely flexible. It has produced quite a different version of racial history that is supported by many blacks. Whites, they say, first appeared in Africa and left their native continent because they were rejected by their black parents and forced to wander. With their pallid skins, they could not stand the heat of the sun and found

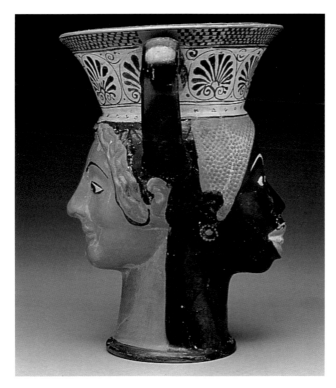

A water-jug, certainly made earlier than 510 BC, in the Attic style; an image of black and white used by the melanin movement to suggest that whites learned culture from blacks rather than that civilization passed in the opposite direction.

their way to Europe, where they lived a miserable and inbred life in a harsh environment. Whites are 'ice people', frigid, selfish and egotistical. Blacks, the sun people, in contrast, retain the open, co-operative and cordial nature that evolved in the plenty of their African home.

Far from being stupid, blacks are more talented than whites. Civilization began with the black Egyptians, not with the Greeks (who spread the myth that only whites could produce culture). The peoples of the Nile had gliders and electric batteries; they understood quantum mechanics and anticipated Darwin. Blacks discovered America before Columbus and, deny it thought they might, Freud, Jung and perhaps even Beethoven had African ancestry.

All this is the agenda of the melanin movement, a campaign by black Americans to reinterpret evolution and to reclaim their rightful place in society. They agree with white supremacists on only one thing: that the crucial genes for understanding why some succeed and some fail are those for the black skin pigment, melanin. Their new science is taught in schools in an attempt to emphasize the African roots of America (a venture which includes the replacement of Thanksgiving with the African harvest festival of Kwanza). It began in Portland, Oregon, where in 1987 an 'African-American Baseline Essay' was circulated to give children an insight into the society in which they live. Now there are broadcasts about melanin directed towards Detroit children and, in New York, some members of the school board support the theory. There have been several 'melanin conferences' at which the wonders of the chemical are proclaimed. The idea has British adherents. A disc jockey on a Manchester pirate radio station (who has taken the name 'DNA') often broadcasts about melanin science and it is much discussed in the black community.

Melanin has been much disregarded by biologists because it is hard to study and because, at first sight, its function is obvious. It is found in all kinds of creatures and comes in several varieties. Stag beetles and over-ripe bananas are full of it. Most dark-haired mammals – the black panther, say – have melanin in the hair and pale skin. The polar bear, though, has black skin and white hair. The chemical is very stable, and a picture of a hundred and fifty-million year-old squid was once drawn with the ink – pure melanin – taken from its remains.

Chemically inert though it may be, melanin is socially and politically explosive. The argument of those blacks who have taken it up as a symbol not of weakness but of strength is summarized in a recent book. *Melanin,*

Much of the controversy about melanin is centred around the City College of New York. This was founded as a university for the people of the city. For many years it taught the children of the Jews who flooded into America. Now, situated as it is on the edge of Harlem, many of its students are black. It is short of funds and plagued with bickering about an alleged decline in standards.

Leonard Jeffries is chairman of the Black Studies Department. He supports the view that white civilization began in a black Egypt and that melanin endows blacks with unique qualities. Much of the controversy that surrounds him emerges from his claim – a painful one, given the history of CCNY – that the conspiracy against black Americans comes from Jewish sources, and that Jews were much involved in the slave trade. The swastika is, he says, an African symbol, hijacked by the Nazis. There should be no objection to its coming back into use. His claims caused outrage. City College was split by a dispute as to whether he should be allowed to proclaim them. Now he surrounds himself with bodyguards. The melanin movement has British adherents. A disc jockey who has christened himself DNA (a change from Soweto, an earlier version of his name) helps run a pirate radio station in Manchester. An enthusiast for melanin science, he preaches its power to whoever is able to listen.

His dedication to the movement for black self-esteem is not altered by the fact that both his parents are white.

The Manchester disc jockey who has taken the name DNA and is a devotee of melanin science.

the Chemical Key to Black Greatness, by Carol Barnes, although not a bestseller, is a remarkable work. It grants the substance almost miraculous properties. Blacks have, it is said, mental and spiritual gifts conferred on them by their pigment. Melanin can absorb light and convert it into knowledge. It responds to sound and led to jazz music. When rhythm meets melanin, the body produces hormones called endorphins, well known to induce contentment. Melanin is a superconductor and micro-computer that improves intellect and memory. As the nervous system is full of the chemical it follows that those with lots of it are more intelligent. Because it can bind with narcotics, though, blacks are more at risk of drug addiction. This places them at a disadvantage in a greedy white society.

The genetics of skin pigment is simple. Blacks and whites differ by just one gene, present in two forms. One makes pigment, the other does not. Whites are the result of a genetic accident in the African genome, engineered six thousand years ago by a black scientist called Yakub. Because a cross between the races produces a black child, whites fear black sexuality: 'Black males have the greatest genetic potential to cause white annihilation. Thus Black males must be attacked and destroyed in a power system designed to assure white genetic survival. Today, the white genetic survival imperative, instead of using chemicals in gas chambers, is using chemicals on the streets – crack, cocaine, ecstasy, PCP, and heroin. AIDS – is a weapon developed in laboratories by people who classify themselves as white.'

Frances Cress Welsing, the author of these words and one of the originators of the melanin theory, goes further. She suggests that melanin allows blacks to pick up energy emissions from plants. What is more, it enabled the Dogon of West Africa to detect the double star of Sirius, invisible to the eye, five thousand years ago. The only real humans are 'hue-mans', people of colour. Everyone else is an incomplete version of what mankind should be. Skin pigment is, she says, under the control of the pineal gland at the base of the brain. This has long been thought by mystics to be the 'third eye' – the 'Eye of Horus' – that opens conscious-ness to vibrations from elsewhere. Whites have their pineal filled with lime; it has been petrified, cutting them off from the world of the spirit.

A lot of this is nonsense or, at best, pseudo-science (albeit no more so than the strange ideas about black and white evolution put forward by those who see blacks as inferior). There is now, though, a real science of skin pigment. Some of its findings are surprisingly close to those put

A relief plaque of the god Amun
from the Temple of Isis at
Saqquara, Egypt (7th century BC);
a divinity with African features,
much referred to by the modern
Melanin Movement with their
emphasis on the importance of
Black culture and the mystical
influence of melanin on ancient
Egyptian thinking.

forward by the melanin movement itself (although, needless to say,
scientists are more cautious in interpreting their findings than are
polemicists, whatever the colour of their skin).

Attempts to extract melanin end up with a sticky mess whose chemistry
is hard to study. Its role as a sun-screen seems so clear that it scarcely calls
for investigation. Until a few years ago most research on the chemical was
in the tradition of the Paris Anatomy Museum; a statement of where it is
found accompanied by a certain lack of curiosity about what it does.

Now, though, it seems that the molecule, intransigent though it
may be, has remarkable and unexpected properties. It may not be the
chemical key to black greatness but its influence is far greater than once
appeared possible. Melanin is at the end of a long biochemical pathway
that, on the way, produces chemicals involved in nerve transmission. It is
made in special cells called melanocytes. These arise in a small patch of
the embryo known as the neural crest, whose main job is to produce
nervous tissue.

A SUPERFICIAL VIEW OF RACE:
MELANIN IN THE SKIN

The skin is an organ in its own right. The cells in the outer layer, a protective barrier called the epidermis, are dead and are filled by the protein keratin (which also makes up the hair). Its folds, the fingerprints (and those, similarly unique, on the lips and elsewhere), are a statement of personal identity. The inner, living, layer of the skin – the dermis – does a multitude of things. It is an organ of temperature reception, of pain and of touch (as the French saying has it, *l'amour . . . n'est que . . . le contact des deux épidermes*) and the site of the body's main thermostat. It controls temperature both by producing sweat (which causes the body to lose heat as it evaporates) and by directing blood through deeper or more superficial blood vessels depending on the temperature of the outside world. During cold weather, warm arterial blood is led in vessels that run in parallel to those containing cold venous blood returning from the surface, retaining heat within the body core. On hot days, the warm blood is shunted away from them to pass directly to the surface, where heat is lost.

In addition, the skin is the source of vitamin synthesis, has sebaceous glands that keep it moist and fight infection, and forms an important part of the immune system. The sections of black skin (below right) and white skin (below left) show the great difference in the amount of melanin that they contain. The substance is concentrated in a layer at the boundaries of epidermis and dermis. The number of melanocytes is the same in blacks and whites, but in black skin they are far more active and the melanin granules cluster around the nuclei of the cells in which they are found, suggesting that they play a part in protecting DNA from damage by ultraviolet light.

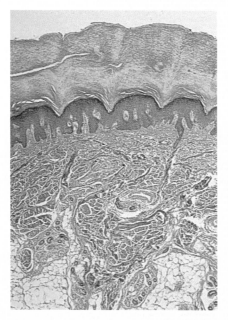
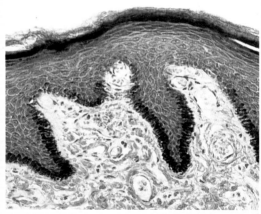

Skin sections, showing differences in the distribution of pigment between those of different racial groups.

Melanocytes do not enter the skin until the embryo is about twelve weeks old. They migrate to the iris, the retina, the inner ear, the membranes that line the mouth and those that protect the brain and spine. Parts of the brain, the ear and the eye are an intense black because they contain so much of the substance. An average male has two billion or so melanocytes, many clustered on the face, the nipples and the genitals. Together, they weigh no more than a gram, the weight of a feather: not much for a tissue with such profound social consequences. Each melanocyte produces small granules – melanosomes – that pass into the other cells of the skin. Black people have no more melanocytes than do whites, but they are far more active.

What does melanin do? At first sight, evolution has got it wrong. If humans followed the rules that apply to other animals, Europeans ought to be black and Africans white. Most creatures from hot sunny places are not dark but light, for the simple reason that black objects absorb more of the sun's heat. A black person in sunlight absorbs a third more solar energy than does someone with white skin.

Humans are tropical animals, which explains why most people wear clothes most of the time. Give people from the Equator or the Poles the choice and they set the central heating at the same level. Cold is dangerous. The blood gets sticky, veins contract and blood pressure goes up. All this makes the heart work harder. Deaths due to heart disease and stroke show a dramatic increase – by one-tenth for every three-degree drop in temperature – in chilly weather. In the British midwinter, the number of strokes is twice that during the summer. Even a cool rather than a comfortable living-room increases the risk of death. This alone explains why the increase in winter death rate is twice as great among poor people than among rich. Anything that helps people from cold places to warm up (black skin included) should, it seems, be favoured.

Cold has certainly affected the evolution of other characters. Australian aborigines can sleep naked outside on frosty nights while the effete sheep-shearers who surround them shiver in their sleeping bags. Body shape has also changed to deal with low temperatures and people from the Arctic are (with some exceptions) shorter and squatter than those from the tropics and have a smaller surface through which to lose heat.

Being cold is unpleasant, but it is usually possible to do something about it and, even if this fails, to survive a drop in body temperature. Being too hot, though, is lethal. Many animals live on a thermal tight-

Single cells from a malignant melanoma, a cancer of the skin which can be fatal if not treated soon enough. The disease is far more common among whites than blacks and is associated with damage to the DNA by ultraviolet light (which penetrates much more through white skin).

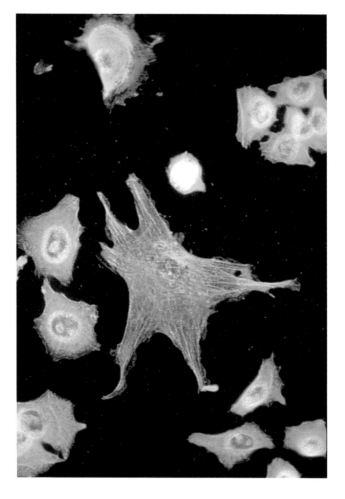

rope, shuffling in and out of the sun to stay at the right temperature. In a Spanish bull-ring, seats in the sun are half the price of those in the shade, showing the value of the right relationship with sunshine. If it goes wrong, and things get too hot, the body has a biochemical fire-brigade. It arrives bearing emergency blankets, heat shock proteins. These proteins (sometimes, rather fetchingly, called chaperonases) cluster around fragile parts of the cell and protect them. People from Siberia summon their chaperones at much lower temperatures than do those from warmer climes, so that it takes less to inflame the inhabitants of Novosibirsk than those of Naples.

All this makes it doubly odd that tropical peoples are dark and must pay a penalty by soaking up solar energy. However, there is more to staying cool than avoiding the heat. In the moist tropics blacks given an exhausting task to perform in the sun can continue working for longer than can whites. This is because blacks are, for reasons not well understood, able to sweat more than can whites. Sweating – the body's most effective cooling mechanism – more than compensates for the effects of skin colour. A black skin might, indeed, reduce overheating because it protects so well against sunburn (which reduces the ability to sweat). In a society based on hunting, in which the hunter is out all day and needs to keep cool, sunburn would slow him down and might cause him – or his children – to starve.

Ultraviolet light is powerful stuff, as anyone who has watched their carpets fade knows. Melanin is good at keeping it out. People without much melanin are at high risk of skin cancer. Because so many of its citizens have pale skins, Ireland has the third highest incidence of the disease in the world (after Australia and South Africa) in spite of the lack of chances for sunbathing. Whites with light skins are at eight times greater risk than are those with dark. Thirty times more sun is needed to cause sunburn (the prime cause of skin cancer) in blacks than in whites.

The uncontrolled cell division that is cancer is sparked off because sunlight produces reactive substances – free radicals – when it interacts with oxygen and water. These can break the DNA chain. Much of melanin's protective action depends on its ability to mop them up. By so doing it reduces DNA damage by three-quarters. This is, though, not the whole story. Under intense ultraviolet, melanin is overwhelmed and begins to produce free radicals of its own that damage – rather than protect – the DNA. This is particularly true of the form of melanin found in red hair and in freckles, which is why red-heads are particularly liable both to sunburn and to skin cancer. The genes for red hair are also responsible for producing a melanocyte-stimulating hormone, which encourages the skin to produce melanin when damaged by sunlight. Eight out of ten pale-skinned redheads have a damaged version of this gene, compared to only one in twenty-five of those who have dark hair and tan easily.

Africa contains a natural experiment on the power of the sun to damage those not well protected against it. The term 'albino' was coined by the Portuguese explorer Balthazar Tellez who, to his surprise, saw many west Africans with light skin and blonde hair. In Europe, about one person in twenty thousand is an albino, while in parts of Africa the figure

FASCINATING RHYTHMS: MELANIN SECRETION
AND THE BODY'S CLOCK

Melanin is the source of some remarkable claims by the melanin movement, all based on a more or less tenuous link with its real function. Melatonin, the hormone that, in many animals, influences its secretion is the subject of even more exaggeration. A recent bestseller in the United States claimed not only that it is a cure for jet-lag, but that it may cure cancer and even reverse the symptoms of ageing. Only one of these claims – the first – is true.

Melatonin is a hormone made by the pineal gland in the base of the brain. In some creatures, such as frogs and toads, it prompts rapid changes in colour that ensure the animal matches its background. In humans, however, melatonin has little effect on the colour of the skin (except when pineal disease may cause too much melanin to be laid down). But the hormone *is* strongly associated with the internal clock that controls sleeping and waking, body temperature, and a host of other things. Its mainspring is in a small part of the brain called the suprachiasmatic nucleus, which receives nerve signals directly from the eye. This means that the clock can be adjusted by the change from light to dark (which is why the best way of recovering from jetlag and resetting the clock is, on arrival, to spend as much time as possible in bright sunshine). Melatonin reaches a peak at night, and this is the cue for sleep.

In mammals that breed only in the spring there is an annual rhythm of melatonin secretion. It controls not only the reproductive system, but other annual changes (such as coat colour). There is a hint that the hormone may have some effect on reproduction in humans, too; and, in consort with the reproductive hormone progestin, it has been used in a contraceptive pill. Because of its affects on daily rhythms it is also used in treating sleep disorders. Some suggest that failures of melatonin secretion are associated with the severe depression – seasonal affective depression, as it is

known – that some people feel during gloomy winters; and even that those with dark skin and eyes are more likely to suffer from this condition as less light reaches the internal clock. The hormone also affects the manufacture of some of the eye pigments, and may help in vision.

The claim that melatonin reverses ageing (which has led to millions of Americans taking it on a regular basis) is made in a book diffidently titled *The Melatonin Miracle*. It claims that the hormone does just that in mice. Unfortunately, the mice used come from stocks that lack melatonin, so that all the experiments do is to restore its natural levels. The assertion that it cures cancer is even more tenuous: melatonin soaks up free radicals, but so does (more efficiently and much more cheaply) vitamin C. The hormone's natural properties are remarkable enough not to need embellishment by those who see it mainly as a source of cash.

A Snowshoe Hare: in winter, the fur is white; in summer much darker. The change in the amount of melanin is under the control of a slow-running clock: the circannual. Like that running on a twenty-four hour basis it depends on melatonin and – at least in lower animals – body clocks measuring intervals from seconds to years use exactly the same genes.

An African with no melanin in his skin because he carries two copies of a gene for albinism. The condition is commoner in Africa than Europe. Almost everyone who has it has some form of skin cancer as they grow older. Why it is so common is not known, but all its carriers seem to have identical damage to their DNA, suggesting that they descend from the same ancestor. The gene may have spread with the 'Bantu expansion', as people from the tropics began to spread, in historical times, to the south.

is ten times as high. African albinos have a rate of skin cancer a thousand times greater than their pigmented brethren. No albino more than twenty years old is free of the disease and in the sunniest parts of the continent (such as Nigeria) only about one in ten lives past thirty.

Ultraviolet light, though, is not all bad. When it penetrates the skin, it makes vitamin D; far more than comes from even a well balanced diet. Without it, children suffer from rickets, an illness producing soft bones and deformed skeletons. The amount made depends on sunlight. People in the mile-high city of Denver with its bright sunshine have half as much again as do their fellows in Boston. The old are particularly at risk of vitamin deficiency, in part because they tend to stay inside. In Europe as a whole, one old person in three sports a measure of blood vitamin D below the safe level. In Greece, Spain and Italy, in spite of their sunny climates, the figure is twice as high because the elderly do their best to avoid the sun. A smoky atmosphere, too, reduces the amount made by the body. In 1900, nine out of ten children in industrial cities had rickets. Smoke, and the window tax which led people to brick up the sole source of light to their homes, all contributed. Even today, in Africa, children wrapped in swaddling clothes are in danger. In the 1920s,

American blacks were three times more liable to suffer from the disease than were whites.

Although the idea of rickets as the driving force behind the evolution of skin colour is attractive, melanin was probably not lost because of changes in vitamin balance. Before cities and smoke most people spent most of their time in sunlight. Rickets is a disease of civilization. Even blacks need a mere two hours a week of sunlight to stay healthy. Skeletons show that the disorder became common only in the middle ages, as cities grew. With the exception of one population living in a deep and sunless Danube gorge, prehistoric burials, whether of blacks or of whites, show no sign of the disease.

Although a change in skin colour is the most striking event in human evolution, nobody really knows why melanin was lost as people emerged from Africa. There are plenty of other ideas more subtle than sunburn, cancer and rickets. Sunlight destroys the antibodies that circulate through the skin. For a white, just half an hour's exposure is enough to do real damage. Black skin may help to protect the body's defences (which are, of course, particularly important in the disease-ridden tropics). Another notion is that black skin is more liable to frostbite than white. In 1917, during the last bitter winter in the trenches, a French doctor recorded more than a thousand cases of 'frozen foot' in Senegalese troops but none in whites. Perhaps cells containing melanin are less resistant to

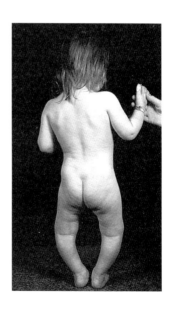

A child with rickets – note the bowed legs, due to a failure to lay down enough calcium in the bones, which remain soft as a result. Rickets is now a rare disease in the West. Many of the cases are due to inherited defects in the ability to metabolize vitamin D, and a few to the use of foodstuffs that prevent vitamin D being absorbed.

freezing. As humans filled Europe, the climate was even colder than today. Frozen foot, and its equivalents, must have been a real problem.

Albinos, whatever their race, pay some surprising penalties for their lack of melanin. Depending on the form of the disease that they inherit, an albino may have poor sight and hearing. This is because melanin does some quite unexpected things in parts of the body – ear, brain and nervous system – that never see daylight. Its powers may be over-emphasized by those who see it as the key to black greatness, but the chemical affects so many of the body's workings that its importance lies as much within the body as on the surface.

Melanin helps to organize the architecture of the brain. Dark-coloured cells direct nerves into their correct places as the embryo develops. One of the most important jobs of such cells is to organize the fibres that take the image from each eye to the opposite side of the brain and help it to sense the depth of a scene. In albinos, these guide cells are missing. The visual system is incorrectly wired up, and some of those with the condition have very poor eyesight. As those working on the inheritance of deafness were the first to notice, melanin has a role in the ear, too. The amount present is related to that in the skin or the eyes. Individuals with dark skins are, it seems, more resistant to being deafened by sudden loud noises. This explains why black people who work in noisy industries retain more of their hearing than do whites. It is even said that blue-eyed whites are more liable to go deaf than are those whose eyes are dark. Perhaps melanin protects the ear through its ability to soak up the energy transmitted (in the form of sound waves) from outside. Exactly as happens when sunlight strikes the skin, excess noise produces free radicals within the ear which are mopped up by melanin. Without this protective shield these harmful chemicals are able to damage cells.

People who suffer from ringing in the ears are sometimes helped by small doses of anaesthetic. This, it turns out, attaches itself to the melanin of the inner ear and restores normal hearing. This gave the first clue to another of the chemical's unexpected properties, the ability to bind drugs. The anti-malaria drug chloroquine can cause deafness because it concentrates in the ear, and those taking it are more susceptible to the damaging effects of noise. Because of the ability of melanin to soak up drugs, when racehorses are tested for narcotics a sample of dark-coloured tissue is taken. Any illegal substance shows traces of its presence longer there than in other parts of the body. The claim by the melanin movement that blacks might be more susceptible to the harmful effects of narcotics may have some truth.

Melanin and the senses do, then, seem to be related (although its role in jazz music remains to be proved). The fact that the brain pigment, neuromelanin, is laid down in particular parts of the brain also implies that the chemical has hidden properties. Neuromelanin is puzzling stuff. Humans have more than do monkeys; monkeys more than mice, suggesting that it plays a part in the development of intelligence. Parkinson's disease – which is quite common among the old – leads to the loss of control of body movements and, in its last stages, to coma and death. It seems to be connected with neuromelanin. In a macabre case in California, two young drug users showed up in hospital with severe Parkinsonism that had come upon them with devastating speed. A contaminant in some drugs they had made in their home laboratory had bound to the dark-pigmented part of the brain, destroying it (and giving one of the first clues about where brain damage in Parkinsonism actually takes place).

Any, or none, of these unexpected properties of melanin may help to explain why it was retained in the skins of Africans and lost from other peoples of the world. Inevitably, some claim that melanin has an effect – in one direction or the other – on intellectual ability. The amount of melanin in the brain shows no association with that in the skin. Black talent and spirituality – although it may well exist – cannot be directly credited to a more pigmented brain and there is no evidence at all that melanin itself has an effect on intellectual ability.

However, the conflict about race and intelligence shows no sign of disappearing. For most of its participants, science long ago gave way to sociology. In spite – or perhaps because – of a mass of statistics it has become almost impossible to resolve the issues surrounding the supposed divergence in the ability of racial groups, or even to discuss them in an impartial manner. Every statistic quoted by one camp is countered by the other. The study of the supposed difference in intellect between blacks and whites has largely been abandoned to polemic, with far too much consistency between the political and the biological views of the supporters of each theory. Science can, nevertheless, still say what is, and what is not, known about inherited differences in intellect among the peoples of the world.

The figures are straightforward, at least on first sight. In the United States, using standard IQ tests, blacks score, on the average, between ten and fifteen points lower than do whites. The figures for Britain are less complete (as children are not often classified on the basis of race) but the gap between blacks and whites is smaller than on the other side of the Atlantic. In the United States, certain groups (such as Koreans and those of Japanese descent) do better on the tests than do whites. Large disparities in test score also exist between people of different social class, whatever their colour.

How to interpret this causes intense rancour. The test or the testers may be biased; or like may not be compared with like. However, most now accept that IQ tests provide a measure of intellect, whatever the race or background of those involved. The tests themselves do not, of course, say anything about whether such differences are inherited, no more than bathroom scales tell whether differences in weight are due to gluttony, to genes or to both. The issue of the inheritance of IQ score has also attracted much attention. In spite of early fraudulent work, it is clear that the ability to do well or badly on tests runs quite strongly in families.

The argument about the relative importance of nature and nurture in producing racial divergence in IQ score is unresolved and probably unresolvable. Black children adopted into white homes increase their ability to do well, but may not reach the level of white children in the same household. However, black IQ does not go up with increasing admixture of white genes, as might be expected if the effect is genetic. Intensive education of black children can sometimes (but not always) increase their score to, or beyond, that of whites. What is more, the difference between blacks and whites has decreased by around five IQ points since the 1960s. At that rate, equality will be reached in the middle of the next century. Blacks will, if the trend continues, then overtake their white competitors (which may put arguments about race and intelligence into a subtly different light). What is more, average IQ score, irrespective of race, has increased by ten points over a generation – not what would be expected for a character firmly wired into the genes.

In Japan, fifty years ago, the mean IQ was around 100. It is now about 112. This must be due to an improved environment as there has not been enough time for genetic change. Japanese children in American schools start with about the same IQ as their fellows, but soon overtake them. This is not innate but, research by educationists shows, is due to harder work and to more demanding parents. American Indians, although they are closer in genetic terms to Japanese than to Europeans, have average IQ scores below those of whites, again suggesting that genes do not have an unalterable effect on test score. The case for an immutable genetic divergence in intelligence between races or social classes is, at best, unproved. This has not stopped politicians (whatever their agenda) from making capital from the results of IQ tests; a classic case of science being hijacked for non-scientific purposes.

One of the forgotten controversies about intelligence arose when IQ tests were first used in South Africa. Afrikaners did considerably less well that did whites of English origin. For many years, those of Dutch descent went to schools of their own and were relegated to the lower ranks of society. Poverty was widespread. As, with the onset of *apartheid*, their relative position improved, so did their IQ scores. Finally, it approached that of South Africans of British origin and claims of an inborn difference between the two groups faded away. South Africa contains a forgotten lesson for today's proponents of educational apartheid elsewhere in the world.

In fact, South Africa, is, with pleasing symmetry, the country that provides the evidence that the most fundamental assumptions of scientific racism are wrong. At the southern tip of Africa, at Klasies River Mouth, is a cave set high in a crumbling cliff-face overlooking the sea. It is reached by an unsteady ladder. In the steep slopes are millions of flakes chipped from lumps of flint, the remains of a stone tool factory. A hundred thousand years ago this was the home of the first of all modern humans. In those days, the sea was much higher than today and lapped against the mouth of the cave. It was then, as now, full of food. The icy surf supports millions of mussels and other shellfish. It is the work of a few minutes to strike off a substantial meal from the rocks. The cave-dwellers gathered huge numbers and cooked them by throwing the shells into open fires. The floor of the cave is made of packed ashes, the remnants of a million prehistoric feasts. Excavation reveals the homes of those who shared the cavern. Instead of a single roaring blaze used by all, the cave floor is covered by carefully spaced hearths, suggesting that its inhabitants lived in groups rather than as an undisciplined rabble. Klasies River is the first evidence of the family: of a society rather than a hunting band.

The remains of about a dozen of its inhabitants have been unearthed. Their skulls are quite unlike those of the heavy-browed creatures with receding chins found in other deposits of that age elsewhere in Africa (and even more distinct from the Neanderthals who were then the sole inhabitants of Europe). The oldest dates from about a hundred and ten

The excavation at Klasies River Mouth, on the southern tip of South Africa. The two caves, one above the other, were at different times more or less at sea level as the oceans rose and fell through the ice ages. There are only a few fragments of the early modern humans, 100,000 or so years old, but the jaw pictured here is enough to show that they looked much like ourselves. They were quite distinct from the heavy-browed people with receding chins who preceded them. Their stone tools, also, have a noticeably modern air. The cave has other, much more recent, skeletons (most of whom died within the past few thousand years). That shown here is decorated with shell necklaces; presents at birth which were dispersed through a network of mutual giving as the child grew older.

thousand years ago. It is the earliest human fossil that belongs, quite unequivocally, to the same species as ourselves.

The tools – arrowheads, spear-points and the like – invented by the people of Klasies River spread from that remote place and prevailed over much of the world for the next hundred thousand years. The southern tip of Africa was the centre of civilization long before the history of Europe began. Its culture persisted until a few centuries ago. The most recent bones in the cave are a mere thousand years old, the remains of the immediate ancestors of the Hottentots. They are evidence of a society more egalitarian than that of Europe. Europe in the Dark Ages was a feudal society based on serfdom. The people of Klasies River, though, then had a community grounded on sharing. The skeletons of their children are festooned with shell necklaces and ornaments. The adults are buried unadorned. This is because children were given gifts. As they grew older they entered a network of mutual exchange and co-operation which meant that their inherited wealth was given away.

The European conquerors of the Klasies country saw none of the richness of the natives' lives. The Hottentots were, at best, an incomplete form of humanity: a missing link between man and ape. In 1810 a specimen of these savage creatures was displayed in London as an examplar of scientific racism. Her name (or at least the one given by her masters) was Saartje Baartmann. In South Africa she had become the servant of a family who applied to the Governor, Lord Caledon, for permission to send her to England. The Governor agreed (although, as a good civil servant, he later disclaimed responsibility for the controversy that was to surround her).

On arrival, Saartje Baartmann was exhibited in Piccadilly. She caused a sensation because of the size of her buttocks. Steatopygia, as the condition is known, is common in southern Africa. It evolved as a means of storing reserves when food is plentiful. It was, though, new to London. As usual, there was a close tie between perceptions of beauty and those of quality: a lower form of human life was, in satisfying accord with the Divine plan, very ugly. Saartje went on show as the government was thought to be about to fall (although it survived and its leader, Spencer Perceval, endured to be the only British prime minister to be assassinated). Its predecessor was known as the 'Broad Bottom Ministry', and a cruel cartoon of the time entitled 'A Pair of Broad Bottoms' shows Saartje's buttocks being examined by an obese Lord Grenville, the Leader of the Opposition.

A nineteenth-century illustration of
Saartje Baartmann, displayed in her finery
for the delectation of the curious crowds
of London and Paris.

Many were outraged by the display. The Africa Association, 'a society
of benevolent and highly respectable Gentlemen', applied 'on behalf of
this unfortunate female, who was exhibited to the public under circumstances of peculiar disgrace to a civilized country, to impress the Court
with an idea of the offensive and indecorous nature of the exhibition',
which involved Saartje Baartmann being kept, almost naked, in chains
in a cage. On being questioned by the judge (in Dutch, her second
language) she seemed happy to share the profits with her keeper, and
the show went on. It toured the provinces, and in Manchester the exhibit
was baptised under the name of Sarah Baartmann.

Three years later, the now-Christian Saartje was moved to Paris, first
to an animal show and then to the Théâtre de Vaudeville as 'La Vénus
Hottentote, ou haine aux Françaises'. There was much speculation about
her genitals (which she kept hidden from public view). Those of
Hottentots had long been known to be covered by the 'curtain of shame',
the *sinus pudoris*. Some claimed that African female circumcision existed
as their men 'could not reconcile themselves to such a disgusting deformity'. The great French anatomist Cuvier, who penned those words in

his monograph on Saartje after her death in 1815, found that her buttocks – far from concealing an unknown bone as some had supposed – were 'une masse de consistance élastique et tremblante, placée immediatement sous la peau'. The curtain of shame was in fact an enlargement of the labia minora. In the interests of science her dissected genitals, her skeleton and a plaster-cast of her corpse were presented by Cuvier to the French nation.

After many years, the relics found their way to the Musée de l'Homme in Paris. The bottle containing her pudenda was hidden from view, but the replica of her body went on display. At the time, Saartje Baartmann's new home had much in common with the Museum of Anatomy on the other side of the city. Its science descended from that of the scientific racists whose brains were preserved there. Both institutions concentrated on classifying human races and arranging them on a scale of merit. Not until the 1960s did the Musée de l'Homme remove Saartje's remains from display.

Now she sits in the basement in a stout wooden box, well padded to prevent damage. Its contents are an inglorious testament to the old days of racial typology. Her cast is coloured light brown, as she herself was

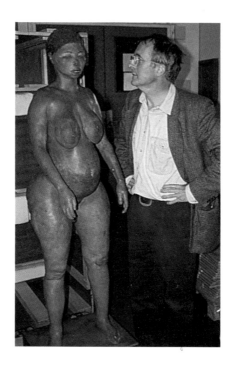

The author meets Saartje Baartmann (or at least a plaster cast of her body). It was on display in the Musée de l'Homme in Paris for many years as an ignoble commemoration of the days of scientific racism. It is now kept well hidden in a wooden box in the basement.

when alive. Saartje's hands are covered by the marks of the smallpox that killed her. Her buttocks are indeed large, but not much more so than those of millions of overweight Europeans and Americans whose ability to store food against a famine that never arrives is as much a killer as is famine itself. Her face has a melancholy expression. To the modern eye, there seems no reason to call her 'repulsive in appearance'. The South African Ambassador to France, who visited the museum in 1995, commented that Saartje Baartmann would be thought attractive by many of her countrymen and that there was no longer any reason why she should not be on display. Now there is a move by the South Africans to have her relics returned to their native land: a statement of the continuing power of the body – and even of its plaster image – in bearing a political message.

Today's face of the Musée de l'Homme could not be more different from that of a century ago. As far as is possible, it has divorced itself from its past. The museum is an affirmation of human diversity and equality. The exhibition on race – 'Tous parents, tous différents' – is politically correct to an almost painful degree. The idea of racial 'type' is, as it should be, rejected. A display of old texts (with a suitably disapproving label) shows a supposed progress from primitive to advanced varieties of mankind based on skulls and skeletons, but most of the gallery is devoted to the similarities among the peoples of the world.

Although race is seen to be useless as a statement of human worth it has, in the museum, been supplanted by a new typology. The urge to classify, and by so doing to judge, survives. Dominating the exhibition is a tableau of naked men and women. Different though they are – black or white, tall or short, old and young – they are united in one thing: each is smiling, has an intelligent expression, and is very good-looking. Hard though it is to assess social class without clothes, every one is, it seems clear, of impeccably bourgeois origin.

Nowadays, the passing crowd is much more interested in the fact of naked elegance than in the colour of the skin exposed. Hogarth (who was liberal in his views about race) would have approved: as he noted in *The Analysis of Beauty*, in spite of a 'Variety of contradictory opinions' that had led some to 'discard beauty as a reality', our perceptions of who is attractive depend only on 'custom, fashion, perswasion and delusion'. He quoted 'the most remarkable instance, that the Negro who finds great beauty in the black Females of his own country, may find as much deformity in the european Beauty as we see in theirs'. Although, as the

This tableau of racial differences in today's Musée de l'Homme shows how small the differences between the races of the world really are, but retains a subtly different assessment of human quality – based on beauty rather than colour.

Museum shows, it is still hard to divorce physical appearance from assessments of worth, at least today's judgments do not depend on the few genes that affect skin colour.

Genetics means that now, at last, perceptions of human quality need not depend on what is on the surface. For the first time it is possible to form an impartial view of just how different races might be. The answer is clear. The biological differences among them are small and the evidence for the mental superiority of one or the other so flimsy, confused and full of intellectual dishonesty as to be scarcely worth considering.

However, the dispute about whether race and class are a reflection of biological merit shows no signs of going away. Although anthropology itself is no longer a field based on opinion, some of those who use it are more than willing to allow their own convictions to rule. The Musée de l'Homme contains a reminder of how mistaken this is. Its collection of skulls includes that of René Descartes, who died in 1650. He was the first to see what science could and could not do. Man, he said, is a machine like any other, not a creature so wonderful as to be beyond understanding. Certainly, there exist attributes – justice, philosophy, religion – unique to ourselves, but these are not open to scientific analysis. As he said: 'In our search for the direct road to truth, we should busy ourselves with no object about which we cannot attain a certitude equal to that of the demonstration of arithmetic and geometry.' The soul, if it existed, was outside arithmetic. The body, though, could be studied like any other mechanism.

Descartes' philosophy led to the French Enlightenment and to the age of rationalism that followed it. The work of Broca and Gobineau was itself a product of Cartesian logic; an attempt at an objective study of human differences. Biology has moved on since their day and has succeeded where they failed. It has, quite emphatically, rejected their view that races represent fundamental divisions within humankind. Outside the dispassionate world of the genes, though, most of the modern speculation on race and class is anchored in the past. Measurements of difference are confused with judgements about quality. Which group is more intelligent, more spiritual, more deserving, more human? Which is better and which worse? Is it right to accept the reality of race, or should, because of the disasters of the past, every attempt be made to deny its existence?

Scientific racism, whatever its flavour, in a Paris museum or on an American political platform, and whether it is concerned with colour or class, has abandoned science and returned to a spiritual quest for human worth. Descartes made one thing abundantly clear: if the search is for the soul, no scientist can help to find it.

CHAPTER V

Original Sin

*'Right . . . is the child of law: from real laws
come real rights; but from imaginary laws,
from laws of nature, fancied and invented by
poets, rhetoricians, and dealers in moral and
intellectual poisons, come imaginary rights,
a bastard brood of monsters.'*

JEREMY BENTHAM,
Anarchical Fallacies

AGAMEMNON, IN THE *ILIAD*, has stolen the wife of Achilles. Apologizing
to his rival, he has a perfect excuse: 'I was not to blame: it was Zeus . . .
and the Fury that walks in darkness that blinded my judgment that day.
What could I do? At such moments there is a power that takes command.'
Achilles gracefully accepts his argument and forgives him: 'How utterly
can a man be blinded by father Zeus!'

The Agamemnon Defence, as it might be called, has a curiously
modern air. It is a strategy used every day in court. The offender is not to
blame for his behaviour; a force more powerful than he has overwhelmed
his judgment and rendered him free from guilt. He must be spared from
the full force of the law. No longer, though, are people possessed by gods.
Instead, their genes have taken control.

There is, on Death Row in Georgia, a young murderer named Stephen
Mobley. In 1991 he killed John Collins, who worked for the Domino
Pizza Company in Oakwood, near Atlanta. Collins, a large and likeable
man, had hoped, in time, to set up his own pizza delivery business. He
was behind the counter when the store was held up. Mobley had robbed
many other places but, in this case, when Collins fell to his knees, he shot
him in the back of the head. After his arrest Mobley boasted of his crimes,
and went so far as to have a domino tattooed on his arm and to decorate
his cell with pizza boxes.

Mobley's big mistake was to kill outside the boundaries of the City
of Atlanta, where John Collins' death would have been a 'dime-a-dozen

Stephen Mobley, in his cell on Georgia's Death Row, awaiting the results of his appeal for clemency on genetic grounds.

murder'. In Atlanta, a killing during a robbery is not regarded as anything extraordinary and the death penalty is seldom applied. In suburban Oakwood, however, the District Attorney (who described Mobley as an evil, heartless killer) demanded, and got, a sentence of death by electrocution.

Mobley is now held in the Georgia Diagnosis and Classification Center just outside Atlanta. The name is something of a euphemism. Not only does the state diagnose and classify people there, it kills them; for the Center is the site of Georgia's electric chair.

Nobody denies that Stephen Mobley is guilty and that he is too dangerous to be released. So foul was his crime that it is hard to find any mitigating circumstances. His lawyers, Charles Taylor and Daniel Summer, with no other grounds for appeal against the death sentence, turned to a last hope. Their case turned on Mobley's family history. His father is a successful businessman who owns a chain of shoe stores, the Sports Shoe. He had found his son hard to deal with as a child. Stephen had been out of control and had been taken to a series of psychiatrists. At one time he had been given the quasi-scientific diagnosis of 'antisocial personality disorder' based on 'a failure to internalize any kind of value system'. In the end, he was disowned.

A cousin of Stephen Mobley's father, Joyce Ann Mobley Childers, told the lawyers about four generations of anti-social behaviour, crime and violence. 'Don't marry a Mobley!' was, she said, standard advice in the small town from which they came. Stephen's great-grandfather had frozen to death while drunk. A second cousin, Dean Mobley, became violent at the age of three, and when sent away to military school ran a profitable fraud by charging other students' laundry to his father's account. He spent most of his life in prison, where, ordained as a minister, he was caught selling drugs during a Bible class. Many other Mobleys had been in trouble with the law, some for serious offences. Stephen, it seemed, was just the latest in a long line. To Taylor and Summer, a genetic case for clemency began to emerge. Mobley, they said, was not acting under his own free will. Instead he had inherited a gene that removed his ability to decide between good and evil and led him, inexorably, to crime. The lawyers went so far as to use the accused's father, successful as he was in a cut-throat business, as evidence for an inherited predisposition towards brutality in his son. As they say, 'there's a fine line between aggressive success and violent outrage'. His lawyers argued that if Stephen Mobley suffered from an inborn defect, then this might be rectified, given diagnosis and suitable treatment. The death penalty is, they say, appropriate only for those beyond correction: it is not called for here. The appeal went ahead.

The case made headlines all over the world. Almost all referred, unthinkingly, to Mobley's 'Criminal Gene'. With just as much unanimity the press dismissed the idea as a liberal sham; yet another attempt to excuse the inexcusable. Even if such a gene existed, it could never be admitted into court. If crime (or even a predisposition towards it) was genetic, what was the point of deterrence or of punishment? The idea presented problems even for those who do not think in headlines. A crime committed by someone with an inborn predilection might call, as Mobley's lawyers hoped, for a lesser penalty. It could, though, mean more severe treatment. In Texas, a jury must, when deciding on the death penalty, consider 'whether there is a probability that the defendant would commit criminal acts of violence that would constitute a continuing threat to society'. Any failed defence based on a gene disposing to violence could be a highway to the electric chair.

Such incredulity about a 'gene for crime' – the label that has, inevitably, attached itself to an inborn tendency to offend – is surprising, as nobody denies that crime is inherited. Starting in the 1960s, a group of four hundred children from Camberwell, a deprived area of south London, was followed by criminologists for thirty years, from the age of eight onwards. During that time, many committed offences ranging from

KILLING WITH SCIENCE:
THE HISTORY OF THE ELECTRIC CHAIR

Whatever the morals of official murder, electrocution has a strange history. It involves some of the great names of science. In 1745, just after the invention of the Leyden Jar, the Dutchman Pieter van Musschenbroek tried passing a current through himself: 'I thought I was done for . . . I would not take another for the entire Kingdom of France'. The first official electrocution (or 'electrothanasia' or 'dynamort', as it was almost called) had to wait until 1890. William Kemmler was executed in Albany, New York. His fate was decided by a State Commission who had been asked to apply science to death. They disliked the blood shed by the guillotine, which 'did not accord with the temperament of the American people.'

Instead, they were persuaded to recommend electricity as the most humane method.

The story puts two of the greatest engineers of the nineteenth century into an unattractive light. Thomas Edison had introduced electricity in 1882, using direct current (DC) to illuminate Wall Street. However, the voltage was too low to travel more than a mile from the power-station. Soon, George Westinghouse inaugurated alternating current, AC, which was transmitted at higher voltages and went further. At once, the 'battle of the currents' began, a battle won, of course, by AC.

BELOW: *The experimental electric chair used to kill Kemmler.*

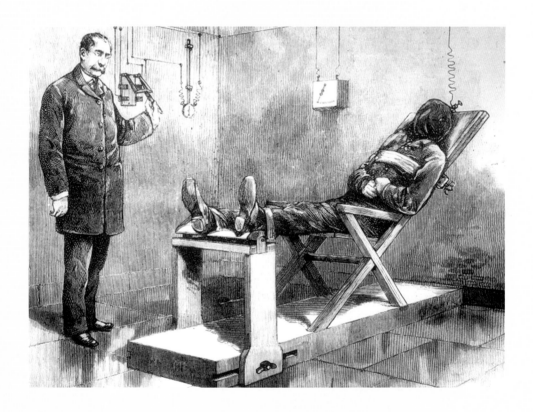

The modern equivalent to Kemmler's chair in Georgia's execution chamber.

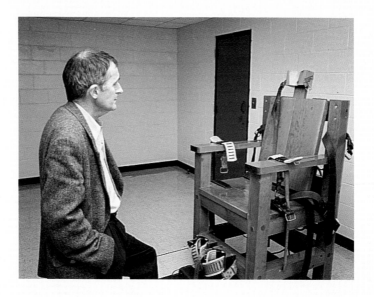

Edison's main card was that AC was more dangerous than DC. But how was he to persuade the public? Although he himself opposed capital punishment, the search for a scientific method of execution gave him an unmissable opportunity. If AC was used to kill, who would allow it into their homes? He wrote to the Death Commission, pointing out the lethal potential of the Westinghouse system. Public demonstrations on dogs, funded by Edison, showed how true this was, and his men lobbied for the electric chair, to be powered by AC, the 'executioner's current'.

Westinghouse was furious. He funded Kemmler's appeal and fought his execution all the way to the Supreme Court. The Court, though, felt that electrocution was 'a step forward . . . based on grounds of mercy and humanity'. In spite of Westinghouse's last-minute attempt to obtain an injunction to stop his dynamos from being used, the execution went ahead. Edison himself showed how to wire up a pair of generators to ensure that a lethal voltage was available.

The experiment was a disaster. The current was passed for seventeen seconds – but Kemmler started breathing again. Horrified, the executioners used a second jolt, and he died,

literally roasted to death. There were dark claims that Westinghouse engineers had sabotaged the equipment to ensure that the job was botched. So revolting was the sight that the press demanded that electrocution be banned.

Edison, though, was not discouraged. He used his knowledge of physics to recommend that the current be passed into jars of salty water in which the condemned man's hands dangled. This, too, failed. In one case a young man stood up after electrocution, only to be reprieved for a week until the equipment was improved.

All this is of more than historical interest. As more and more people are legally killed the battle against electrocution has been rejoined, on the grounds that it represents cruel and unusual punishment and is hence unconstitutional. A Florida case in which the condemned man's hair caught fire strengthened the argument. The Georgia chair, though, is often used. One of its clients, killed just a couple of weeks after this picture was taken, was a British-born youth. He asked the British government to intervene in his case, without success.

shoplifting to assault. The project set out to find what was behind their behaviour.

One dependable way of prophesying who among the eight year olds would descend into crime was, it emerged, to identify those with a parent found guilty of an offence. Of course, children who became criminals shared other things. Often, they came from broken homes. They tended to disrupt classes and to fail in school, to drink, smoke, and take drugs. As they grew up, they were more promiscuous and more liable to divorce. Three-quarters of the children identified as 'vulnerable' at the age of eight went on to offend. All this can be – and often is – interpreted as a consequence of social background. Perhaps it is, but whatever the cause of their behaviour, the study shows, quite unequivocally, that having a criminal parent predisposes a child to getting into trouble with the law; that a tendency towards crime is passed from one generation to the next.

The tale is familiar, even banal. Everyone knows that many criminals come from deprived – or even criminal – homes. Although crime runs in families it need not, of course, be coded into DNA. There is a strong association of tattoos with violence, and tattooed youngsters tend to have tattooed parents, but there is no gene for tattoos. Poverty, too, is inherited. Those born poor do not wish to be so and often try to escape. Nevertheless, poverty, like crime, is familial. The fact that one comes from an impoverished home is not seen by the courts as an excuse for wrongdoing.

In the Camberwell study, as in many others, the best predictor of whether an eight year old will commit a violent crime is a biological one. Violence is, overwhelmingly, an affliction of men rather than women. In London – and everywhere else – the rate of murder (excluding that of relatives and spouses) by males is thirty times higher than in females. No doubt, society and schooling have something to do with it, but that does not alter the fact that men, particularly young men, are dangerous. They are both victims and perpetrators. More probably than not, their be- haviour has evolved. In animals (at least in those, like humans, in which variation in sexual success among males is greater than that among females) males are at their most ferocious when they are young and searching for a mate. Even those most determined to deny that biology affects human behaviour find it hard to deny this simple fact.

It is also undeniably true that genes are involved. Like those affect- ing sex differences in height or shape, they influence the parts of the brain controlling the production of hormones. The male sex hormone,

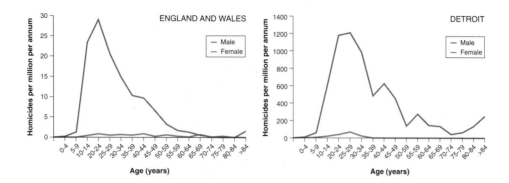

The murder rates for killings of non-relatives in England and Wales and in Detroit. The change in the pattern of murder with age is similar for men and women in each city; but the actual rates are dramatically different – from less than thirty murders per million in England to more than a thousand per million in Detroit. Genes and cultures are not mutually exclusive explanations of violent crime.

testosterone, makes both men and mice aggressive. Individual differences in its level help predict whether a man will act violently, and body-builders who take it are liable to attacks of 'steroid rage'. The amount of testosterone says nothing, though, about why some societies are more violent than others. In London, males are at their most dangerous at the age of twenty-five; in Detroit at twenty-seven. The two societies, different though they are, produce murderers at about the same age.

The numbers of murders in each place, though, are quite different. The city of Detroit is forty times more violent than its English equivalent; indeed, a twenty-five year-old Detroit woman is considerably more dangerous than a London man of the same age. Even an enthusiast for biological explanations of crime could scarcely argue that this lies in the genes, rather than the societies, of the two cities.

This points at the limits to what biology can say. Violent crime in the United States has doubled since 1985 (a trend that has recently reversed) but this is not due to a burst of evolutionary change. The best way of predicting the murder rate is not to look at the genes but to count the weapons. In the Middle Ages, it plummeted when short swords were banned and, no doubt, the same would happen in the United States if there was more effective gun control. Most murder is a matter of technology rather than biology – and, of course, most violent deaths happen within the law, when one state declares war on another.

The law is not an amorphous mass. It changes as time goes on and as cultures evolve their own practices. In Bombay, it was once a capital offence to paint a moustache on a sleeping woman (on the grounds that her wandering soul might not find its way back), in Dahomey to see the King eating. In Britain, too, beliefs have altered: at a time when those fighting for votes for women were imprisoned those now arrested for badger-baiting would have been praised.

The law's fundamental duty to protect the public transcends debate about good and evil. Nevertheless, from its beginnings, there have been arguments about its moral foundations that reflect themselves, sooner or later, in legal practices. Particularly when sentencing is involved, these turn on the extent to which a defendant acted under his own free will; on whether he was responsible for his actions. The Stoics, who flourished in Athens from 300BC, had an austere view of accountability. They saw the world as built on reason, and everyone as equally filled with virtue. The law, as arbiter of public morals, had no reason to be merciful as those who break it have strayed from their duties. This philosophy, stark though it is, had much influence on early legal thinking and on Christian theology.

So fine is the balance between free will and determinism raised by the Stoics and their descendants that the legal system remains uncertain about nature and nurture as a cause of crime. Often, it treats them as separate entities, balancing one against the other. This reflects a common – and to geneticists baffling – delusion that if a trait is influenced by genes it is somehow insulated from the environment. In fact, nature and nurture are not exclusive. Every attribute, criminality included, is influenced by both.

The law's basic assumption is that of autonomy: that everyone is liable for their deeds and is obliged to pay the price if they misbehave. The argument is simple and compelling. It has long been clear, though, that this stark view of human misconduct must have exceptions for those whose freedom to decide between good and evil has been compromised.

That notion is an ancient one: all cultures have had to wrestle with it and have used tests ranging from the theological to the scientific (one sometimes masquerading under the guise of the other). In Laos, it is said, the accused was given a choice between a bowl of rice and a bowl of human faeces. If he supped from the wrong dish his judgement was proved to be impaired and he was treated more leniently. The idea (albeit with a subtly different test) is in Roman Law and in the mediaeval law of England. Much of today's English law on diminished responsibility descends from 1843, when the assassin of a senior civil servant was deemed to be so disturbed as not to be responsible for his actions.

Daniel M'Naghten was the illegitimate son of a Glasgow wood-turner who slowly became obsessed with the feeling that he was being persecuted. Sometimes it was by the police, sometimes the Church of Rome. His tormentors pursued him, laughing and throwing straws in his face. He fled to France, but the furies followed. On his return to Glasgow he became convinced (as well he might) that he was being victimized for not voting Tory; and, in defence, decided to kill his chief oppressor, the Home Secretary, Sir Robert Peel, a Tory and founder of the police force. Unfortunately he mistook the private secretary, Drummond, for Peel himself and shot him in the back in Whitehall. Coming to trial, M'Naghten's defence was that: 'The Tories in my native city have compelled me to do this. They follow and persecute me wherever I go, and have entirely destroyed my peace of mind . . . It can be proved by evidence. That is all I have to say.'

Before his day, there had been acquittals on the grounds of insanity, but only of those who were clearly mad and quite incapable of making any rational decisions. The M'Naghten Trial changed all that. His lawyer claimed that M'Naghten was *partially* insane and had a single delusion alone. This made him unaccountable for what he had done. The Judge agreed: if M'Naghten had been 'sensible that it was a violation of the law of God or of man' to kill his enemy or if he was 'capable of distinguishing between right and wrong' then he was 'a responsible agent and liable to all the penalties the law imposes'. If not, he should be found insane. The jury agreed that he had indeed not been responsible for his actions and M'Naghten was sent to the asylum at Broadmoor, where, quite soon, he died of tuberculosis.

The M'Naghten case is still referred to when it comes to issues of sentencing and guilt. Queen Victoria saw the importance of distinguishing between them. She was outraged when a failed regicide was found 'Not Guilty by Reason of Insanity', and prevailed on the authorities that instead he be judged 'Guilty but Insane'. By doing so she identified an issue crucial to legal theory (although its niceties may have been less obvious to the accused himself).

Equivalent rules exist when setencing decisions are made in other countries, although their extent varies from place to place. In the United

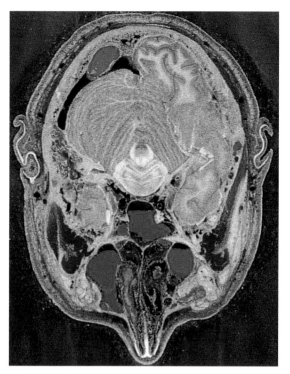

A 1mm section through the head of a male cadaver (an executed American murderer who offered his body for the purpose) loaded onto the Internet as 'The Visible Human'. This section is just below the eyes, and passes through the nose and cheek, and the air-filled maxillary sinuses. As the head was tilted when the section was made, the cortex (the 'grey matter', highest part of the brain) is visible on the left. The sinuses and blood-vessels are artificially coloured in blue.

States, certain states have accepted premenstrual tension in mitigation for offences carried out by women, but Montana, Idaho and Utah have abolished the insanity defence altogether. In most places, though, courts pronounce sentence only after – as in M'Naghten's own case – deciding whether the accused understood that what he was doing was wrong. If not, then the law accepts that he is, because of his nature, less open to its power.

In legal theory there is a tension between what is free and what is circumscribed. The mentally ill are seen as less culpable than those in control of their senses. Often, hearing voices, a sense of being followed, or unprovoked acts of rage make it clear that the accused is not fully responsible for what he does. He may be better treated in hospital than condemned to jail. The M'Naghten case established that mitigation does not rest on a proof that the individual facing the court is overtly mad: sometimes a single delusion, unrecognized for many years, is enough. The issue arises frequently. In Britain there are about five hundred convictions for homicide each year, in eighty of which the culprit is found to be suffering from a mental disorder.

ALZHEIMER'S DISEASE

Many people lose their memory to some extent as they age; a mental affliction that is almost universal, so much so that it is accepted as normal. For most, this reflects the general process of accumulated damage that affects all organs. In its extreme form such memory loss is called Alzheimer's disease. Twenty million people may suffer from it. It can be devastating, leading those who suffer from it to detach themselves utterly from the outside world except that in the instantaneous present. Worst of all, in some families the loss of memory begins early: perhaps one case in ten of Alzheimer's shows its symptoms in middle age.

Genes – more than one – are involved. In fact, the inherited form of Alzheimer's disease is probably the commonest severe mental illness with an unequivocally genetic basis. As in breast cancer, only some cases are familial, and those families differ in the gene that has gone wrong. Most, though, inherit a damaged version of a particular gene on chromosome 14. Many of the rest share genetic damage on chromosome 1. Some of the others have inherited a gene on chromosome 21 – which is the chromosome present in excess in Down's syndrome, one of the commonest of all inborn genetic errors. It may be more than a coincidence that one of the symptoms of Down's is premature ageing and memory loss. Again as in breast cancer (and in an increasing number of other inherited diseases) different families may carry different forms of each gene. The alleles are dominant and sometimes show their effects in those as young as thirty.

The discovery could be used to diagnose early-onset Alzheimer's (although there is as yet no successful treatment) and to identify foetuses who carry the gene. Discovering the genes gives a better understanding of the disease. Although the order of the amino acids in each are not particularly similar, the two genes, on different chromosomes though they are, have remarkably similar structures. Each is braided back and forth through the cell membrane, crossing it seven times. Perhaps they help transport other proteins through the membrane. If they fail, these build up in inappropriate places. This may explain a common symptom of familial Alzheimer's: the deposition of large amounts of a protein fragment called beta-amyloid within brain cells. The discovery, though, is only the first step in the search for a cure.

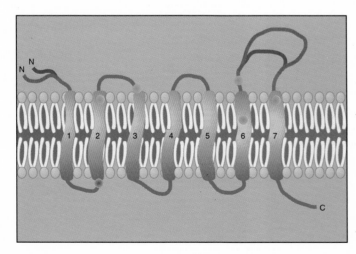

The proteins made by two of the genes responsible for Alzheimer's look remarkably similar: they snake back and forth across the cell membrane, only diverging in a couple of places outside the membrane. The mutations in each also cluster around the regions that span the membrane, suggesting that something has gone wrong in the protein's job of pumping material into and out of cells.

LOMBROSO AND THE CRIMINAL FACE

The idea that crime is in the face is an ancient one. Socrates was charged by a nomist as having a face that betrayed brutality. In the same tradition, a mediaeval law had it that, if two persons fell under suspicion of a crime, the uglier and more deformed was to be regarded as more likely to be guilty.

Cesare Lombroso, a nineteenth-century Italian physician, took the idea seriously – and by so doing began the scientific study of crime and the search for what drives some towards it. Lombroso was much influenced by Darwin and, in particular, by his theories about inheritance. He began to examine the faces – and dissect the corpses – of criminals and the insane in the prisons and asylums of Pavia in the hope of finding some difference between them. At first he did not succeed but 'at last I found in the skull of a brigand a very long series of atavistic anomalies . . . analogous to those found in inferior vertebrates. At the sight of these strange anomalies, the problem of the nature and of the origin of the criminal seemed to me resolved; the characteristics of primitive men and of inferior animals must be reproduced in our time . . . in an atavistic being who reproduces in his person the ferocious instincts of primitive humanity and the inferior animals.' In other words, just like Julius Caesar's war-horse, criminals were a throwback to earlier forms of life. One could identify sexual offenders by their full lips and murderers by their sloping foreheads. Lombroso's views were not as simplistic as they seem. He accepted that society was to blame, too, and that some people, 'criminaloids', were more susceptible to its stresses than were others. Most important, though, Lombroso championed the idea that crime was *caused*; it was not just an expression of malicious intent, automatically open to punishment. Lombroso was important in the history of penal reform as his work helped to introduce the idea of rehabilitation rather than retribution for those who offend.

Now, the idea of a criminal face is regarded with scorn. If murderers have brutal features it is because they have been brutalized. However, the idea of a criminal nature – even one not manifest in the face – is gaining respectability. Inborn defects – genetic errors – *can* dispose certain people to act in a way unacceptable to society. How the law should deal with that remains as uncertain as in Lombroso's day.

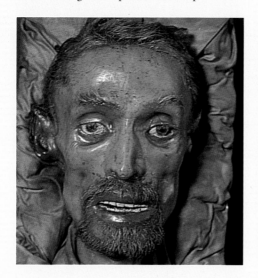 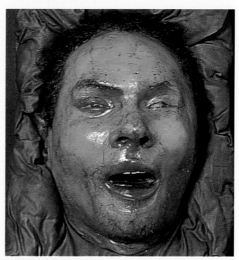

Wax casts from the Lombroso Museum in Turin, showing faces supposedly typical of (right) a thief and (left) a man found guilty of 'corruption'.

A court's decision is a legal test of responsibility and not a diagnosis of disease. In many cases, the judiciary seeks medical advice. In mental illness as much as in the rest of medicine, the argument turns towards genetics. As a result the law is facing what might seem to be a new dilemma. If someone is born with a biology that condemns him to offend – a criminal nature which seems to its possessor natural – then, surely, he is not to blame for yielding to it. If offenders have a 'criminal gene', even if its first symptom is the crime itself, then this might, on the M'Naghten precedent, be ground for mitigation.

The law has often used genetics as a tool; DNA fingerprinting is now the norm and some states of the USA require mandatory testing of infants for inherited disease. There seems to be no reason why it should utilize it to help in the diagnosis of mental state. By so doing, though, genetics is entering a province which the law sees as its own: the relationship between individuals and society.

Humans are, in the end, animals: for any pattern of behaviour, the question is not whether biology is involved, but how. The brain, with its ten thousand million cells, is the most energetic organ in the body. A quarter of the heart's output of blood circulates through it. All cells receive a complete set of DNA molecules from their progenitor, the fertilized egg, but in most cells the majority of the instructions remain unread and only a few genes are switched on. As each working gene makes a message that is passed to the cellular machinery it is easy to identify which are in use. The numbers utilized in various tissues are very different. Sixty-six are doing something in red blood cells (whose task is simple and undemanding) compared to twenty-two thousand in the more sophisticated world of the white blood cell. The heart has six thousand operating genes, the testis the same – but the brain, the master of the body's economy, has thirty thousand genes at work; almost half of all those in the body. Such genes are just as liable to go wrong as any other.

Most inherited diseases have some effect on the brain and most people in mental institutions are there because of a change in their DNA. Mutations affecting nerve cells differ from those causing – say – cystic fibrosis only in that they affect mind rather than body. They follow Mendel's rules and show their effects at birth. Cause and effect are clearly related. There is usually no difficulty in deciding who carries a damaged gene and not much in making an unequivocal decision as to which one has gone wrong. To find it may be the first step in understanding a mental illness.

The new genetics of the mind shows how much mental disease comes from inside and is not, as once assumed, the result of malign external forces. Finding the genes for such conditions marks the final demise of the ancient idea that madness is due to possession by devils, who must be driven out by torture or, if metaphorical demons are involved, by psychoanalysis.

Crime, too, was once seen (by the Church at least) to result from demonic possession. Evil was a separate force; those possessed by it at fault for allowing it in. As with madness, the dispute about crime, nature and nurture has roots deeper than those of science. Aristotle saw the problem. He thought that there were two quite different kinds of criminal. Some are of weak will. They do wrong against their real wishes and intentions. Othersthough, are vicious individuals, who offend contentedly and with conviction. They are, Aristotle said, much more of a danger and should be treated with harshness – he spoke, of course, about those he saw as morally flawed and hence deserving of punishment; but his views are, at least in their effect, not far from those of the State of Texas, which would happily execute those they see as born to offend, with a law carefully designed to include both those whose morals and those whose genes are at fault.

Now that genes are accepted as influencing so many human attributes, the question for the law is not whether to accept the idea of an inborn propensity to such crimes, but how far it will go. Is it a matter only of admitting the side-effects of some inherited disorders, most of whose carriers never transgress, or will the law allow as evidence genes that condemn all their carriers to offend? Will it – could it – ever accept that most crimes are committed by people who are born to break the rules? For the first time, science is entering a province which the law sees as its own; the relationship between individuals and society.

The side-effects of severe inherited disease have already been used to reduce blame for carrying out a serious crime. Ten years ago, in Georgia, a young woman was imprisoned for killing her mother. In mitigation she claimed that she was at risk of having inherited Huntington's disease, a progressive degeneration of the nervous system whose first signs include mental instability, often delayed until adulthood. Her father had died of the condition. As but a single copy of the gene is needed to manifest its effects she herself had a one-in-two risk of having inherited the illness. She claimed, in mitigation, that the rage which led to the attack was the first symptom of her disease. At the time, the gene itself had not been found. The judge was unimpressed by the defence, and she was sentenced to life imprisonment. A few years later, though, unmistakable signs of Huntington's disease began to appear. The judge recalled the case, and, recognizing that the unfortunate young woman had not been responsible for her acts, he ordered that she should be released.

By so doing, the judge accepted that a specific gene had reduced free will. Since that case, the gene for Huntington's disease has been located and a test is available that can tell those who wish to know the truth whether or not they have been unlucky enough to have inherited it. A genetic plea against a punitive sentence will be easier to sustain than was the case when a diagnosis depended only on the first appearance of its symptoms. No doubt, this example is exceptional, but it showed that the legal system need have no difficulty in using an inborn tendency towards unacceptable behaviour to reduce the blame attached.

By so doing it approached a question central not only to law, but to religion and philosophy. Why should there be evil? If man is born sinful, how should he be forgiven? The issue strikes at the core of belief and of society. The idea of a 'gene for crime' in fact poses a theological question. If certain people are born with a nature that makes it inevitable that they will offend, how can they be blamed, or judged? How can there be equality before God or the law if one group – how large, nobody knows – can claim lifelong immunity from its full rigours, with the evidence written into DNA?

Such questions of guilt and forgiveness obsessed early Christianity. They caused many to challenge the very reason for existence of the Church as an institution able to pronounce on human weakness. A failure to resolve them led to a split from which it has never recovered. There is a danger that science will force the law to face the same moral dilemmas and perhaps the same threat to its integrity. The question turns on human accountability and on who should pronounce on it.

The fourth-century British theologian Pelagius argued that man was liable for all his deeds, whether good or evil. He had free will. If he had not, nothing would restrain him from indulging in any sin he chose. Inborn disability was no excuse. Aristotle had been quite wrong to argue that certain people could scarcely help their actions; everyone could, and should, choose to behave well. Pelagius' doctrine was immediately seen by the establishment as dangerous. To allow man freedom to decide minimized the role of God and the power of the Church, His representative on earth. It thus went straight to the heart of the main institution of social cohesion of the time. His work *De Libero Arbitrio – On Free Will –* was denounced by the religious authorities and its author excommunicated. He sank from sight.

St Augustine had become a Christian after rejecting the doctrines of the Manicheans, a sect who felt that the world was, of its nature, wicked and that nothing could change it. Many of his views descended from those of the Stoics themselves. As Bishop of Hippo, in north Africa, Augustine disputed with Pelagius and claimed that humanity had no choice, no free will, but was programmed to transgress because of the plague of original sin. Sin – estrangement from God – was congenital and universal. It had arisen from the failings of Adam and Eve and would pursue man as long as he existed. Sin meant that nobody had the ability to decide, on their own, between good and evil and that only God could forgive, should man allow him to do so by accepting His word. Augustine's doctrine was an austere one. As children were born full of sin they were damned if they died before baptism. Hell, he said, was paved with infants.

St Augustine could not understand why God had chosen the sexual option, and the opportunity it gave for sin, for the Garden of Eden: 'If it was good company and conversation that Adam needed, it would have been much better arranged to have two men together as friends, not a man and a woman.' He knew full well, though, where wickedness came from. The taint was passed, like a gene, from one generation to the next by the sin of Adam itself, the act of sex. Lust – concupiscence, as he called it – was needed for mankind to survive, but within it there was evil. Pope Innocent III put it neatly in the thirteenth century: 'Everyone knows that intercourse, even between married persons, is never performed without the itch of the flesh, the heat of passion and the stench of lust. Whence the seed conceived is fouled, smirched, corrupted; and the soul infused into it inherits the guilt of sin.' Evil, thought Augustine, was inherited and it was not in human power alone to do anything about it.

As was to happen, much later, with the law, the issue of human autonomy – the genetics of sin – divided the Church. The rift centred on its power to judge. Since its foundation, the Church had used its authority to condemn or to forgive. Confessions, indulgences (certificates of forgiveness) and masses for the souls of the dead all attested to its right to control spiritual fate. Man might be born sinful, but with appropriate treatment he could be cured. If he refused to bow to priestly power suitable punishment (what Augustine called 'benignant asperity' – the burning of heretics to save their souls) was available.

The ruins of the castle of Montségur in the Pyrenees. After two hundred Cathar believers were burned alive following the siege of 1244, the castle fell into disrepair. It still exerts its magic. The Nazis were interested in it as a possible site of the Holy Grail (a legend not at all associated with the Cathars) and there are periodic and equally fanciful claims that it was a centre for sun worship. Now it is one of the most visited sites in France; there are many who call themselves (with more or less sincerity) Cathars, and several rival 'Bishops of the Cathars' have set up shop in different parts of Europe. The desire to commune directly with God and not through man is still a powerful one.

Many Christians disagreed. All over Europe, groups sprang up that denied the Church's right to intervene. If sin was inborn, it was not within mere human authority to judge it.

The heresies came in various flavours but all turned on the conviction that priests were claiming rights that were not theirs to exercise. In the eleventh century, dissent spread from the Bogomils, a Balkan sect who believed, like the Manicheans, that the material world was evil. Only the world of the spirit was without sin and the only hope of attaining it was to commune face-to-face with God. The idea took firm hold around Albi, in southern France. Soon, its adherents the Cathars – the *katharoi*, or pure ones – controlled much of the Languedoc. They rejected the authority of the Church and had lives of simplicity and penance in which salvation lay only in the Lord. The Pope became alarmed at the threat to his power and proclaimed a crusade against them. Thousands of Cathars were killed and many more tortured into accepting the true faith. Laws were passed to suppress the Albigensian heresy, and the first Inquisition established to ensure that they were applied. It set about its task with zeal.

By 1244, with the fall of the fortress of Montségur in the Pyrenees, the Cathars had been crushed. To celebrate their defeat the victors built a gigantic cathedral at Albi. It contains a vast mural – the largest painting in France – by an unknown genius of the fourteenth century. This depicts, in exquisite detail, the tortures of those found guilty of sin – pride, greed, anger, lust and the rest. Nobody seeing them could doubt that to reject the chance for salvation offered by the Church that commissioned it meant torment for eternity.

Triumphal statements, such as Albi Cathedral, though, were only a temporary defence. Within a hundred years the question of inborn sin tore the Catholic Church apart. The Reformation took the doctrine of Augustine to its logical conclusion; that everyone, however grand or virtuous, was equally sinful, and that God alone had the right to decide who would be saved. Nothing that human institutions (the Church included) could do could alter an inborn fate. Salvation was by the grace of God, and not by mortal efforts at reform or punishment.

Martin Luther was born in 1483. He had trained as a monk but was shocked by the laxity of his colleagues. In south-east France, for example, the peasants were invoking a folk-saint, Guinéfort, who they assimilated into the pagan image of a child-protecting dog. Luther saw the epidemic of syphilis raging through Europe at that time as a statement of the decline of the church and a presage of the Last Judgement. He proclaimed a Christianity that returned to its biblical roots and condemned many of the religious customs that had grown up since the earliest days, including 'the wicked and impure practice of celibacy'. In his Ninety-five Articles (which may or may not have been nailed to the church door at Wittenberg) he attacked the Church for its corruption. Luther's theology was austere. God alone can decide who will receive His grace. It cannot be earned – or forfeited – by any act of man.

The Reformation ignited the wars of religion that plagued the continent for the next century. In the north, at least, the revised faith won, and Protestantism still prevails. Its attraction was that it made everyone equal in the eyes of the Lord: no longer was it possible for the rich to purchase salvation. The Sacrament did not have to be earned by making a confession to a mere mortal. Many of the rites of the Church were dropped as an unwarranted barrier between God and man. The ideas of the Reformation are reflected in the modern legal system: of equality before the law, of justice blind to privilege, inborn or otherwise.

The consequences of being able to recognise those programmed to sin were first appreciated not by biologists or lawyers but by the followers of John Calvin, the ultimate genetic determinist. A destiny fixed at birth was, he argued, everything. God alone determines fate. Everyone is born a sinner and all deserve punishment, but God, in his mercy, has admitted some, the elect, to eternal life through predestination: 'by which God admits some to hope of life and sentences others to eternal death. We cannot know with the certainty of faith who is chosen.' Although Calvin himself thought initially that it was not within mortal power to identify the saved or the damned, his attention was soon drawn to the beguiling possibility that – perhaps – some of the elect could be recognized while still on earth.

Calvinism today is at its purest in Scotland and in Ulster (where religious wars continued in a desultory way long after their resolution

A less than flattering portrait of John Calvin, painted in 1566 by Italian artist Giuseppe Arcimboldo: a native of Milan unimpressed by the Protestant doctrines rampant to the north.

elsewhere). The Scottish reformer John Knox produced his *First Blast of the Trumpet against the Monstrous Regiment of Women* as a polemic against the Catholic queen of the day. Soon, he instituted Protestantism as the official creed. It denied any possibility of salvation – of reform – by good works. Free will, Knox said, had ceased at the Fall of Adam. The Damned would be damned for eternity, quite gratuitously and for no fault of their own. The Saved would enter Heaven, whatever their behaviour on earth. His sect soon became obsessed with the objective measurement of sin. Quinlan's Evangelical Barometer recognized fifteen grades; drunkenness and theatre-going, for example, scoring four, while adultery and parties on Sunday had a mark of six. Although predestination was no excuse for not behaving well, those not admitted to the elect were certain to burn, however virtuous their conduct.

The idea of a chosen few and a condemned many is still embedded in parts of Scottish and Ulster society. A Catholic priest visiting Northern Ireland was once greeted with: 'Priest Murphy, speak for your own bloodthirsty, persecuting, intolerant, blaspheming, political-religious papacy, but do not pretend to be the spokesman of free Ulster men. You are not in the South of Ireland. Go back to your priestly intolerance, your blasphemous masses, back to your beads, holy water, holy smoke and stinks; and remember we are the sons of the martyrs whom your church butchered, and we know your church to be *the mother of harlots* and the abomination of the earth'. Thus the Reverend Ian Paisley in anti-ecumenical mood in 1958.

Paisley's view of society descends from that of the new government set up by Calvin in Geneva. It adopted a grave moral tone. Laws were made regulating the style of women's hats and barbers punished for shaving men in a Catholic way. In a short-lived experiment, the city's taverns were closed and replaced with *Abbayes* in which the entertainment consisted only of copies of the Bible. So impressed was Calvin by the righteous lives of the *genevois* that he felt that they must be of their nature different from others. Surely, people so blameless could not be condemned to burn. They must, he was forced to conclude, be members of the Elect, born to eternal life. As Calvin put it, like the Israelites of old the inhabitants of Geneva were simultaneously both 'perverse and wicked' and a people to whom 'God will give his blessing . . . as a commonwealth humiliated before Him'. Geneva was an island of righteousness in a sea of iniquity.

By identifying – as he thought – those with a prospect of salvation and separating them from those liable to be damned, Calvin pointed straight towards an ancient and damaging heresy and to the ethical problem that genetics set, much later, to the law. Implicit in the notion that some, the Elect, are born to be saved is an intriguing idea. It is that certain people are guaranteed eternal life, whatever crime they commit. They are beyond censure by the Church or by the law. This, the Antinomian Heresy frees the Christian from any obligation to the moral law as set out in the Old Testament. The righteous might prefer to behave well from pure devotion, but there was also the option of simply disregarding the law and surrendering to man's basest instincts. There is no need for judgement or even for good behaviour as some are sure of salvation while others are already condemned. As this heresy trespasses on what the Church (or for that matter the law) sees as its rightful domain, the state has always suppressed the idea with whatever brutality is required.

In 1534, John Bockelson took over the city of Münster, whose clergy were among the most corrupt in Germany. They had been exempted from taxes and the city's artisans forced to pay vast sums to Rome. Bockelson, a Dutchman, drove out the priests and founded a new Zion based on a perverted (or, as he argued, a logical) interpretation of Reformed doctrine. He denied that the law had any right to rule its citizens, whose fate had been decided at birth. The rest of the world would be destroyed, and only the Elect of Münster saved. Anyone who defied him could not be among the chosen; and they were executed. Soon, polygamy was introduced to increase the number of those marked for eternal life and he himself took fifteen wives. Setting up a throne in the marketplace, Bockelson announced that he had been anointed king of the whole world, chosen by God. Sunday was abolished, as was money. Gold pieces of merely ornamental function replaced it.

The Church – and the nobility – were outraged. Within months, the city was attacked by its neighbours and, after a lengthy siege, the heretics eradicated. Bockelson was captured and led about on a chain like a performing bear. In 1536 he was publicly tortured to death with red hot irons, making no sound throughout his ordeal. The cage that once contained his bones still hangs from the roof of the church in Münster.

Where such beliefs may lead is spelled out in an extraordinary psychological novel by the nineteenth-century Scot, James Hogg. *The Private Memoirs and Confessions of a Justified Sinner* is a tale of two half-brothers, John and Robert Colwan. Robert is the illegitimate child of a Calvinist preacher, the Reverend Wringhim. The preacher 'knew the elect as it were by instinct and could have told you of those in his own, and some neighbouring parishes, who were born within the boundaries of the covenant of promise, and who were not'. He persuades his son, who is racked by fear of damnation, that he is among the saved. Robert is transformed:

> I wept for joy to be thus assured of my freedom from all sin, and of the impossibility of my ever again falling away from my new state. I bounded away into the fields and woods, to pour out my spirit in prayer before the Almighty for his kindness to me: my whole frame seemed to be renewed; every nerve was buoyant with new life; I felt as if I could have flown in the air or leaped over the tops of the trees. An exaltation of spirit lifted me, as it were, far above the earth, and the sinful creatures crawling upon its surface; and I deemed myself an eagle among the children of men, soaring on high, and looking down with pity and contempt on the grovelling creatures below.
>
> As I thus wended my way, I beheld a young man of a mysterious appearance coming towards me . . .

That young man is, needless to say, the Devil. He persuades the Justified Sinner that he can do no wrong. Robert Colwan first slays a blameless old man. Then he tries to murder his brother and, returning home, falls into a trance during which he kills his mother. Realizing, at last, that he is possessed, he flees from the law (and from Satan, who, Colwan is now convinced, is Peter the Great of Russia). In the end he commits suicide in the hope of destroying his sinful self – and his other self, the Devil, who has by now taken his own form. The book is an astonishing insight into a divided mind; a description of schizophrenia a century before the term came into common use.

The idea that consumed Robert Colwan has returned, newly clothed in scientific language. Arguments about predestination, and the right of society to judge those whose fate is set at birth are at the centre of the dispute about genes and crime.

The law has, more or less, come to terms with the existence of rare genes (such as that for Huntington's disease) that increase the risk of offending. Now, though, it is having to accept that common mental illnesses long seen as grounds for mitigation are, in part, under genetic control. In medicine, too, genetics is no longer just a matter of rare diseases, but of the illnesses (such as heart disease) likely to strike almost everyone. Although they were once seen only as the result of a faulty environment, genetics shows that it is no longer enough to censure heart patients for failing to control their unhealthy impulses. For example, some patients with severe heart problems have a gene that prevents cholesterol being removed from the blood. Those who carry it are almost certain to become ill (although they may delay the onset of symptoms by changing their diet and taking drugs). Medicine is turning more and more to genetics to identify those who must be protected from the consequences of their birthright.

The biological arguments used by lawyers are becoming similarly sophisticated. They do not claim that some are predestined to offend whatever their circumstances; but that they are, because of their genes, less able to deal with the pressures that lead to crime. Like medicine when faced with disease, the law may have to face the fact that not just a few but many – perhaps most – criminals offend because their genes dispose them

The mutation responsible for the damage to the monoamine oxidase gene in a Dutch family. In this image, the DNA sequence of five people is spread out. Each DNA unit is shown in a different colour. The fourth individual from the left has a crucial change, from red to yellow. This marks an alteration in one of the building blocks of the DNA and causes fatal damage to the enzyme.

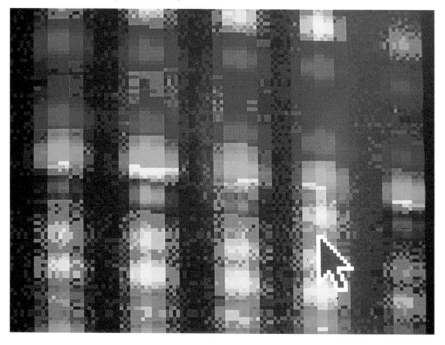

Crystals of serotonin, one of the nerve transmitters broken down by monoamine oxidase. Severe depression is associated with a shortage of serotonin, and the brains of some suicides have only half the normal amount of the substance.

to. Many of the thousands arrested for one crime or another carry genes that might alter their behaviour and, if the genetic defence is accepted, each will have at least the prospect of using them in mitigation. The loophole in the law's ability to judge identified by John Bockelson may lead to problems as great as those that oppressed the people of Münster.

There is plenty of evidence that genes are involved in crime. A man who has an identical twin with a criminal record is himself at a fifty per cent increased chance of being imprisoned. For non-identical twins (who share only half, not all their genes) the figure is about twenty per cent. Although this would be accepted as good evidence of biological pre-disposition for any other attribute, it did not impress those determined to deny any possibility of an association of genes with crime. Now, though, the evidence is becoming stronger.

About thirty years ago, a Dutchman began taking notes on a disturbing pattern of behaviour that had turned up in his family. Many of the young men had low intelligence and short tempers. Once annoyed, they became aggressive. Some forced their attention on women (one, indeed, raping his sister). Others committed arson. One, held in an institution, had stabbed his supervisor with a pitchfork. The problem was brought to a geneticist. The disease, which covered several generations, showed a classic pattern of inheritance, passed on through females but showing its effects in males. This is exactly what is expected for a gene carried on the X chromosome. Eight of the fourteen affected men then alive were examined. Their urine contained large amounts of certain chemicals involved in nerve transmission. These are normally broken down by an enzyme, monoamine oxidase, suggesting that this was at fault.

Quite what it does in the complicated business of transmitting messages between nerves is not clear. Monoamine oxidase is involved in metabolizing adrenaline, the 'fight or flight' hormone. It is also mixed up in the breakdown of another transmitter, serotonin (itself implicated in the effects of the drug LSD). One form of the enzyme does the minor job of digesting substances found in red wine, cheese and chocolate. Some people with low monamine oxidase activity have nightmares and may faint if they eat or drink too much of such things. Certain drugs that inhibit its action are used in treating depression but, again, how they work is not certain.

To the geneticists' delight, every patient in the Dutch study had an inherited defect in the gene that made monoamine oxidase. The mutation altered one DNA base and destroyed the enzyme's activity. Although the acts of those who carry that single change – out of three thousand million DNA bases – vary from arson and assault to unwanted gestures of affection, for much of the time their conduct is normal. Psychiatrists could not fit the behaviour of the affected men into any recognized mental illness. Most have committed no offence. One, indeed, is married with children and has a job. Perhaps the high levels of nerve transmitters that remain in the body make it hard for them to deal with stress and provoke them to sudden attacks of debilitating rage. The defective gene also has other effects. Those who have it suffer from dangerous attacks of high blood pressure, difficulty in sleeping, and agitation after eating certain foods such as soft cheese. Many of the men had died young, perhaps because – unknown to anyone at the time – they had inherited the damaged gene and had been unable to cope with environmental

A schizophrenic's vision of his illness.

stresses that are harmless to others. The gene has been searched for in other groups, mentally disturbed or not, but so far is confined to one family.

The discovery of such an apparently unequivocal link between a damaged gene and a pattern of antisocial behaviour led to predictable uproar. It was the beginning of the wave of newspaper reports dealing with 'criminal genes'. A member of the research team rapidly changed his mind about accepting a post in Germany when a German geneticist linked the Dutch work with that of biologists who had supported the Nazis. The version retailed to the public – that those with a particular gene all became criminals – was exaggerated, but it was a pointer to a wider problem that the law will soon begin to face; not confined – as in the Dutch mutation – to a single family, but of universal relevance.

Schizophrenia is a common affliction, with half a million cases in Britain alone. The illness, the divided self, was once seen as due to possession by demons. Evil voices commanding the poor sufferer to sin, whatever his better nature might wish, must – it seemed obvious – come from outside, and must be driven out. The disease is devastating: visions, voices, failures of logic and of emotion. Sometimes, the patient freezes almost solid; sometimes there are inescapable movements. Often there are streams of unconnected sentences. All this can begin in adolescence and continue throughout life – a life, all too often, ended by suicide.

A diagnosis of schizophrenia is often used by lawyers pleading that

Hallucinations are impressions that arise without external input. They can involve voices or visions. Positron Emission Tomography – PET – makes images of internal organs by bombarding them with rays from a cyclotron. These cause a chemical injected into the bloodstream to produce flashes of light when the organ is active. A computer-based scanner shows where the activity is centred.

This image shows the highlighted parts of the brain in one unfortunate schizophrenic who saw, in a brightly coloured landscape, rolling heads, separate from their bodies and mouthing instructions to him. Its colours are, of course, arbitrary and simply show levels of nervous activity. While sitting in the apparatus, he pressed a button whenever a vision appeared. During each visitation, small parts of his brain (many on the left side) showed up in colour as the nerve cells were activated. Some of the action was deep inside the brain, in the thalamus, the area that generates an inner image of reality, whether or not information is coming from

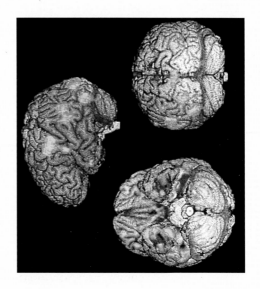

outside. The patient mistakes internal animation for an external signal, telling him, with what appears to be complete authenticity, what he should do.

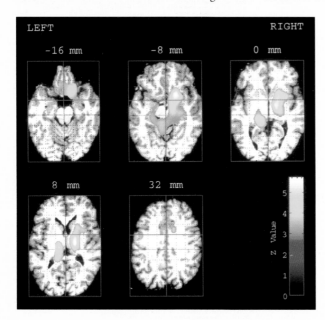

ABOVE AND LEFT:
Positron Emission Tomography (PET) scans of the brain of a schizophrenic during hallucinations. Active parts of the brain show up brightly. Their activity levels are sometimes so high as to produce mental images of overwhelming power.

their clients are not responsible for their actions. In recent years, several schizophrenics released from mental homes under a policy of treatment in the community have killed without warning. Their condition is always taken into account when deciding their fate. Instead of the imprisonment that awaits most of those who kill, they are likely to be sent to an institution and to be treated with drugs that may suppress the symptoms of the illness.

The disease runs in families. Only about one person in a hundred has the illness, but a tenth of children who have a schizophrenic parent will develop symptoms. This might show, of course, only that members of a family share the same stresses. Perhaps the household itself is at fault: to radical psychiatrists the 'dysfunctional family' was once as potent a cause of mental illness as is any piece of DNA. In the 1960s the romantic view was that schizophrenia is a sane response to an insane world.

That the illness is inherited does not prove the existence of genes. There is, though, every reason to expect that – as in heart disease or diabetes – they have some part to play in schizophrenia and other mental disorders. Psychiatrists have long been anxious to find them. Unfortunately, their field is littered with the corpses of genes for one illness or another (schizophrenia included) that have gone away when the work was done properly. There are many ways of searching for such genes. For schizophrenia, all have been tried. If one member of a pair of non-identical twins (sharing, as they do, half their genes) has schizophrenia, the other is at about a one-in-six risk of becoming ill. For identical twins (who have all their genes in common), the risk rises to one in two. Another clue that genes are involved comes from adopted children. Not only do they resemble their biological parents (who they may never have met) in the chance of becoming ill, but the biological relatives of adopted children with schizophrenia are at higher risk of showing its symptoms than are relatives of the family into which they were adopted.

The genetic basis of schizophrenia is not simple. The illness may – like breast cancer – be influenced by genes in some families, but not in others. It may not manifest itself even in all those with altered DNA. The environment is also important. Alcoholism, drug abuse and brain tumours can all produce its symptoms. Many mental disorders – depression, memory loss, agitation, anxiety – depend on this alloy of native inclination and difficult circumstance.

Now, though, there is evidence that schizophrenia is, at least in some people, associated with damaged DNA. Molecular biology hints at genes on two chromosomes that predispose to at least some cases. A very few people have a tiny piece of chromosome 22 missing. This causes all kinds of problems – heart disease, cleft palate, a characteristic face. One in ten of the patients develops schizophrenia. Studies of the families of other schizophrenics also suggest that genes on that chromosome (and on chromosome 6) are involved. One may code for an enzyme that breaks down nerve-transmitters such as adrenalin. Like monoamine oxidase, this varies in its ability to do its job and – perhaps – those with low levels of activity are predisposed to mental illness.

For people without a clear history of schizophrenia, a diagnosis (particularly in a legal setting) is not always easy. Quite soon, no doubt, a genetic test will be used and courts will consider this along with other evidence when assessing a defendant's mental state. This marks a further step towards acceptance of the idea that some people offend because of the genes they carry. Most schizophrenics, though, never get into trouble, and there remains plenty of room for discretion as to whether the illness is – or is not – behind a particular offence.

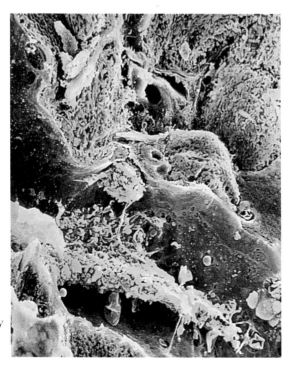

The liver of an alcoholic. Its cells are destroyed, and the patient may die as a result of bleeding from what remains. Genes, perhaps, play a part in increasing the risk of contracting the disease.

If – as sociologists have shown – criminal behaviour is so manifestly inherited and if DNA technology can be used as to diagnose illnesses that predispose to it why is there so much concern about genes that lead to crime? The issue returns to the ancient questions about free will. If science can identify genes whose main role is not to produce overt disease but to dispose to unacceptable behaviour then some may be able to define themselves, with more or less credibility, as destined to offend. Society then faces the problem raised by Calvin; that some people must be treated differently because their fate is set at birth. Although in its original form Calvinism had it that the elect were known only to God and that it was the duty of everyone, saved or not, to behave in a godly fashion, his doctrine was soon used to give certain people a special status because of their birthright. Now, genetics is, according to some, playing God (or at least the Reverend Wringhim) by claiming to identify – perhaps even at birth – who is elected to offend and who is not. How will the law deal with a generation of Justified Sinners?

In the United States, the problem is becoming apparent. The courts had little difficulty in dealing with those whose genes disposed them to severe mental illness, but in 1992 there was a case whose outcome had far-reaching implications.

John Baker is, or was, a successful California lawyer. He is also an alcoholic. Under the pressures of business he began to drink heavily. The practice sank into debt, and Baker embezzled money from a client's account. The crime was soon discovered, and he was hauled before the California Bar Association. Stealing clients' funds is a major offence. The punishment is automatic: to be thrown out of the profession. John Baker accepted his guilt, and assumed that his career would soon be over. Talking to his legal adviser, though, he mentioned that his father had North American Indian blood and was an alcoholic. The alcohol problem in Native American communities is well known. It arises in part because of genetics. American Indians – together with the Asian peoples from whom they derive – have a reduced ability to break down alcohol. This (like the Dutch change in monoamine oxidase and, perhaps, like the genes that incline towards schizophrenia) involves an enzyme, in this case one called alcohol dehydrogenase. The Indian form is less active than that in most Europeans and, as a result, those who carry it are more susceptible to the damaging effects of drink.

Baker's attorney suggested that he used his inherited inability to deal with the temptations of alcohol as a plea in mitigation. To their joint surprise, the defence worked. Instead of being disbarred, John Baker was merely suspended and could, had he wished, soon have returned to his profession. He now no longer drinks; but neither does he practise law. As he says, the stresses of the job might be enough to drive him back to the bottle. Instead, he runs a bingo supply company.

The case raises an issue that may, in the end, limit the use of genes in court. John Baker's defence was based not on a rare inherited disease but on a normal system of variation. Tens of millions of Americans – some with American Indian or Japanese ancestry, but many of European origin as well – have an inborn inability to deal with alcohol. Several genes are involved; some (like Baker's) concerned with changes in the machinery that breaks down the poison, but others with the ability to evade its addictive effects. Alcoholics of European origin are, some say, more likely to possess a particular variant of a nerve transmitter found in the brain's 'pleasure centre', a part of the body much appealed to by those favouring chemical theories of addiction. As many as seven out of ten alcoholics might carry this (the A1 variant of the Dopamine D2 receptor gene, as it is known). Most people who inherit genes such as these do not become alcoholics, and many of those who do remain within the law. However, in principle at least, each could ask that their genes be taken into consideration should they offend because of their drinking.

The law's most basic task is to identify and deal with individuals who stray from society's norms. Normality is also implicit in the idea of mitigation: only those few whose biology (or, perhaps, whose intolerable circumstances) are exceptional are held to be less than fully responsible. Genetics, too, was once largely restricted to genes that cause major deviations from the ordinary – albinism, cystic fibrosis, or schizophrenia. It was, until recently, a science of the extremes.

All this raises an obvious question: what, in society or in biology, *is* normal? The greatest shift in genetical thinking has been to realize that there is no 'standard' genotype. It is not true that everyone, apart from a few carriers of inherited disease, is the same. On the contrary, no two people are alike. There are three million sites in the DNA that vary from person to person. Most are in sections that have no apparent function, but there are thousands of functional genes (many of which affect behaviour) that differ from one individual to the next. There is, for example, variation of more than a hundred times in the activity of monoamine oxidase within the general population. Low activity may be associated with alcoholism, depression, and an abnormal desire for excitement. The enzyme whose failure in one Dutch family is much used by proponents of the 'criminal gene' theory is variable enough to be appealed to by thousands of potential offenders, should they wish to do so.

Such diversity means that a defence based on biology may soon be open to all. The A1 variant of the Dopamine D2 receptor gene (associated, as it is, to some degree with alcoholism) is carried by a fifth of the population. It may perhaps be a 'reward gene', favouring all forms of instant gratification. It is, for example, said to be frequent among cocaine addicts. Cocaine increases the production of dopamine itself – the substance that binds to the supposed receptor – in the pleasure centre. Some drug users might even be, quite unknowingly, treating themselves in a way appropriate for their genetic defect. It is also, according to some, unduly common among autistic children, those unable to cope with trauma, and even in people with relatively withdrawn personalities. Although many question whether a single gene could have such diverse effects, its presence in so many people is bound to alter the interaction between genetics and the law.

As it becomes increasingly clear that certain patterns of unwelcome conduct reflect (like many physical illnesses) an inherited inability to deal with difficult circumstances, there is a temptation to ascribe all bad behaviour to genes. Acts that would once have been thought of as merely anti-social, sparked off by poor upbringing or downright devilry, are more and more being blamed on inborn weakness. Children have always behaved badly, some disastrously so. All schools have pupils who cause trouble and do not concentrate. The problem is an old one, as are its conflicting explanations. Early reformers emphasized either the 'crust of sterility and rigidity' of schools, or certain pupils' 'inherited tendencies to vice' and 'lack of vital force'. The 1960s view that the system was to blame has, thirty years later, and with depressing symmetry, moved towards the idea that children themselves are the problem.

Once, children were seen as free spirits, to be controlled when necessary. Now, though, there is a disease known as attention deficit-hyperactivity disorder. Its symptoms include poor concentration, low tolerance of frustration and a general tendency to run riot. Since the condition was recognized a decade or so ago, it has reached epidemic proportions, affecting millions of American children. In some California classrooms, a quarter of the pupils have been diagnosed as having ADHD. Their parents are, naturally, concerned and often turn to psychiatrists for advice. Many see it as an organic disease and treat it with drugs. For some children at least this brings about a great improvement. With so many taking drugs, some argue that they are being used for control rather than treatment.

Why is the disease (if such it is) so common? Ideas range from dyes in soft drinks to computer games. Many psychiatrists, though, think that genes are involved and that the condition is part of a spectrum of behaviour that ranges from irritability to attacks of incapacitating rage. In its extreme manifestation it is known as Tourette's syndrome and involves bursts of swearing, spitting and disruptive behaviour. Those who have it may be, most of the time, witty and creative people. Suddenly, though, they burst into florid action – often alarming those around them. Some suggest that the gene responsible is, once again, the A1 variant of the D2 dopamine receptor gene. Perhaps having this variant increases the temptation to succumb to impulse common among all children and leads to a diagnosis of mental illness.

Children with ADHD have been shown to be much more at risk of drug or alcohol abuse when they grow up. It has long been known that an uncontrollable child is more likely to get into trouble with the law when adult. In Britain, a quarter of all juvenile crimes are carried out by a hard core of three per cent of all young offenders. Many of them continue their criminal careers into adult life. The Nixon Administration once thought of testing all children in the hope of detecting 'pre-delinquent' behaviour before they had a chance to offend. In the study of Camberwell children, too, the over-active and impulsive were shown to be at greater risk of arrest when they grew up. One young Californian robber who had been diagnosed as having Tourette's Syndrome has already claimed that his crime was a symptom of his disease, but his defence did not succeed.

It is, though, at least conceivable that childish bad behaviour and adult crime spring from the same source; a source that may, at least in part, be genetic. In the view of some American enthusiasts for the importance of ADHD, half of all prisoners are in jail because they carry the genes that predispose to it or to related disorders. If they are right, prisons are as much institutions for the genetically unfortunate as they are places of punishment. This is, so far, largely a transatlantic view. In Britain only one prisoner in twenty is defined as mentally disordered, and the number diagnosed as having a long-term (and perhaps inborn) condition is only a few hundred. However, the ADHD diagnosis – and the drugs used to treat it – are becoming more common in Britain and soon, no doubt, it will come into contact with the law.

The emerging work on ADHD, whatever its scientific merits, symbolizes the problems that emerge as genetic arguments are more and more used in court. If it is accepted that outrageous conduct in school should be excused (and, indeed, treated as an illness) because it reflects an inborn flaw, it is hard to argue that genetic predisposition should be ignored when considering the behaviour of the same person when he grows up. When, as in the United States, proportionately more children are diagnosed with ADHD than there are adult criminals then many, perhaps most, of those who offend may soon be able to appeal to their genes in mitigation.

The law cannot, it is clear, accept this. In the end, it is, whatever the philosophers may say, a pragmatic affair. Its central task is to ensure the smooth running of society and, as in theology, its doctrines will in time adapt to whatever science may discover. Calvin, in his vision of predestination, accepted that – although some were damned and some saved – it was essential that all behaved virtuously. In the same way, although the law may be obliged to admit that free will is constrained for many people because of the genes they carry, their actions must be treated as intentional simply because good order demands it. Even if it does emerge that most offenders do so because of an inborn weakness, the law will be forced to ignore the fact as its implications – like those so promptly noticed by John Bockelson and his antinomian fellows – are so damaging.

So far, Stephen Mobley, the Atlanta murderer, has not been put to the genetical test. His lawyers contacted those working on the Dutch family with a request that their client be examined for monoamine oxidase deficiency. Unlikely though he was to prove positive (after all, unlike the affected men in the Dutch family, his intelligence was normal) there was not much hope of any other defence; and, if execution was long enough delayed, other grounds for mitigation might emerge. The scientists offered to do the test for no more than the cost of the chemicals – around a thousand dollars. The American Bar Association, although they oppose the use of genetics in deciding guilt or innocence, have no problem with its use in sentencing. The judge, though, refused. In his view, 'the research is quite new and inconclusive at this time . . . the theory of genetic connection is not at the level of scientific acceptance that would justify its admission into court'. Stephen Mobley remains on Death Row. In a bizarre twist to the tale, his father has brought pressure to bear to

Albi Cathedral: the image of the Last Judgment, by an unknown master of the fourteenth century. Vivid though the portraits of torment are, the central figure is missing. The judging angel was destroyed when an arch was driven through the painting – a metaphor for science and the law today?

dismiss his son's lawyers, because of the slur a genetic defence casts on his own character. That defence is now in abeyance. Although the electric chair is ready, his son's damnation is deferred.

Early in the war of the Catholic Church against the heretics of Languedoc, both Cathars and Catholics were besieged by an army of the Church within the walls of Béziers. When the city fell, the commanding general was asked who to slaughter: heretics, his men assumed, must surely be separated from believers. Their leader's reply was simple: it presaged, in more brutal terms, what may become the attitude of the legal system. 'Kill them all,' he said, 'the Lord will know his own'; if there is any doubt about who has sinned, then all must be punished to ensure that the guilty do not escape. Killed they all were, some – perhaps – to be saved and some destined for damnation. The same Draconian logic may apply if, in time, genetics identifies more and more genes that predispose towards crime.

Albi Cathedral was built to celebrate the final victory of the Catholic Church over the Cathars. Its astonishing display of the tortures that the technology of the Middle Ages concocted for the doomed has a message for the law. Those awaiting judgement stand with open books in which their lives – and their sins – are recorded. One figure, though, is missing. Instead of an avenging angel deciding the fate of the resurrected there is, in the middle of the vast fresco, an elegant arch. It is a portal driven through the painting to give access to a chapel added in the seventeenth century, at a time when it seemed acceptable to mutilate a three-hundred year-old masterpiece. The building works destroyed the painting's central figure, who once held the scales of justice. Albi's triumphal statement of the Church's power is now a judgement without a judge.

Some hope to place genetics in the breach, to read the book of life at birth, not after death. To do so is to risk the process of justice, and to deny free will to everyone, good or evil. There can be no universal excuse for bad behaviour. If some are excused because of their genes, then others, with a different constitution, become relatively more culpable. Predisposition is a double-edged sword. If most criminals offend because of the genes they carry, the scope for mitigation becomes so all-embracing as to lose its meaning. For the law to survive it must ignore the defence of original sin, inherited frailty, in much the way as it ignores poverty, inborn or not. Society is not a product of genes but of people, and what they do must be judged by the law and not by science.

CHAPTER VI

Death Or Resurrection

So also is the resurrection of the dead. It is
sown in corruption; it is raised in incorruption.

I CORINTHIANS 15:42

LIFE IS AN UNLIKELY BUSINESS. That it has lasted for three billion years is surprising enough. What is astonishing is that living creatures can survive and make copies of themselves in the face of physical laws that should lead to immediate destruction. An animal is a chemical reaction so unstable that it is instantly reversed at death. How, then (to paraphrase *The Book of Common Prayer*) can our own vile bodies, bound as they are to return to dust, attain a resurrection to eternal life as one generation succeeds the last? How – almost miraculously – are young babies born to old parents?

Some creeds have a naive faith that those who die live on. Their bodies are merely removed, and may return. The dead speak to the living; Saul, the first king of Israel, consulted the Witch of Endor to find out their views and was much criticized for so doing by those who preferred God, rather than ancestors, to rule their affairs.

This literal version of a victory over death ignores the simple fact of corruption. All religions have, at their heart, renewal: the resurrection, in one form or another, of a body defiled by death. Plato realized that it can best be achieved by detaching the flesh from its essence, the soul. This can persist although the body decays. The same idea came to Mendel. His work disengaged the genetic message – a survivor until all life comes to an end – from the ephemeral existence of its carriers. The German embryologist August Weismann went further. He invoked a physical entity, the *germ plasm*, that transmits life but is insulated from the fate of the *soma*, the body. The paradox was that a decrepit soma produces, each generation, fresh germ plasm. How does it do it? What is the rejuvenating principle that has granted life a thousand million resurrections since it began? Weismann did not know.

In the *Symposium* the prophet Diotima addresses Socrates:

> The object of love, Socrates, is not, as you think, beauty . . . Its object
> . . . is to procreate . . . because procreation is the nearest thing to
> perpetuity and immortality that a mortal being can attain. It is in this
> way that everything mortal is preserved, not by remaining for ever the
> same, which is the prerogative of divinity, but by a process in which
> the losses caused by age are repaired by new acquisitions of a similar
> kind. It is in order to secure immortality that each individual is haunted
> by eager desire and love.

In other words, sex is the key to eternal life; it allows the body to be
born again and reverses the damage done by age.

Weismann disagreed. In his view, 'twice times nothing cannot make
one.' Why should two old and decayed individuals be better at making a
young one than a single elderly but asexual female? Mixing two degraded
sets of germ plasm together would not rejuvenate them. Sex alone was
not enough. Indeed, it was – if anything – a cause of decline. There is
plenty of evidence that he was right. Reproduction is expensive for both
males and females. In many creatures, males die in the act of mating
(occasionally sacrificing themselves as a nuptial meal to their mate). One
species of slug bites off its own penis after sex, leaving it as a plug to
ensure that the female can find no other partner. Even fruit flies live for
longer when celibate, and the same is true for men and women.

Sex, although it has long been known to connect life's beginnings to its
end, is usually seen as a source of debasement rather than salvation. It led
to the expulsion of Adam and Eve from the Garden of Eden, Eve the
more culpable as she tempted Adam towards immorality (a persistent
theme in the ideology of gender, in which sexual blame is usually placed
on females.)

The tie between sex and religion is, as a result, deeply ambiguous. Each
is an inner experience; each contains both threat and promise, and each
achieves some kind of victory over death. Sometimes the link between
them is embarrassingly clear. St Teresa of Ávila had a vision of Christ. 'In
his hands I saw a long golden spear . . . he seemed to pierce my heart
several times so that it penetrated to my entrails. When he drew it out . . .
he left me afire with a continual love of God. It is not bodily pain, but
spiritual, though the body has a share in it – indeed a great share. So

OPPOSITE: 'The Resurrection of Christ', by Matthias Grünewald , 1513–15, then court
painter at Mainz.

sweet are the colloquies of love that pass between the soul and God that if anyone thinks I am lying I beseech God, in his goodness, to give him the same experience.'

Genetics casts new light on the alliance of sex, age and death. It shows how all derive from errors, mutations, in copying the genetic message. They cause individuals to decay but genes to be preserved. Each generation, sex redeems the germ plasm and is the stuff of the evolutionary change that ensures its long-term survival. More and more it seems that this sexual renewal is paid for by somatic degeneration, in which mutations in body cells lead to the afflictions – cancer, heart disease, mental decline – that beset everyone who reaches old age.

To copy any message involves mistakes. For DNA, the task is (to use a hackneyed image) equivalent to rewriting an encyclopaedia again and again, one transcript after another. Before the advent of printing, monks had to do an equivalent job. Their error rate was huge. Sometimes, the copyists confused letters, sometimes they read straight across text set in columns, producing gibberish. Ancient maps of Germany showed the province of Suatutanda. It arose from a mistake made by the clerk who transcribed Tacitus' words that the tribes returned *ad sua tutanda* – to guard their own properties – but in so doing missed a space.

Some books were copied many times. If a scribe who was himself scarcely literate (and who was in any case forbidden to correct errors) received a corrupt version he would hand on the inaccuracies and add some of his own. Transcripts of popular works can be divided into families by making an evolutionary tree of accumulated errors. Those at the tip of the literary pedigree are almost unreadable because of repeated blunders. Two thousand years ago, Cicero complained that 'I no longer know where to turn for Latin books, the copies on the market are so inaccurate . . . They are books full of lies'.

The structure of the double helix suggests that, just because of its physical frailty, there should be one mistake in every few thousand attempts when copying one of its units, a DNA base. Decay at this rate would make the message incomprehensible within just a few divisions, and life would come to a stop. In practice, errors accumulate far more slowly than simple chemistry might predict. However, accumulate they do and, in time, the body's DNA document becomes unreadable, a book full of lies.

Life, though, is much more than a copying machine. It contains its own editors to correct mistakes as they happen – and even to use them to

A statue of a cloaked and smiling woman in St Sebaldus' Church in Nuremberg. She looks modestly towards the worshippers at her feet, a vision of purity. From behind, though, Madam World, as the statue is called, presents a different picture. Her naked back is covered with rotting flesh, an image not of chastity but of defilement.

improve the manuscript. Once, mutation was seen only as part of the apparatus of decline; a rare error in the workings of a finely tuned device. Like disease it seemed to result from malign external influences. Now it is admitted as an innate property of genes that assures their survival even as it damages their hosts. The story of mutation unites, as nothing else, scientific and spiritual views of the human condition. It gives the idea of resurrection – a corruptible body raised in incorruption – a new and precise meaning.

The facts of degeneration are obvious enough. Eight years ago I moved into my present house in north London. My hope of surviving another year is precisely half what it was on the day of the move. Whatever the levels of mortality, in third world or first, and whatever the age of the person at risk, individual expectations of death double with every eight years that pass. As a result, a sixteen year old has a one-in-two-thousand chance of dying each year, while for those who reach their centennial the prospect of celebrating the next birthday is only one in two. Unlike the wine-glasses in a restaurant (where the chance of breakage does not depend on the age of the glass) its customers do not die at a constant rate. Instead, their bodies are less able to maintain themselves as they grow old. Death, it seems, is a dynamic process.

Wear and tear play a part in averting immortality. During a lifetime, the heart pumps three hundred thousand tons of blood – enough to fill a decent-sized oil tanker. It is not surprising that it wears out. In the same way, joints deteriorate, and fat stops blood flowing through the arteries. Although simple mechanical failure plays a part, old age is also programmed into life itself. This is because some genes are advantageous when young but bring costs to the old. For example, young people who are good at converting food to fat survive when food is short, but pay the

Images of Decay: arthritis, a crippling disease of the joints, often due to the ageing immune system attacking the body's own cells, and atherosclerosis, deposits of fat that block arteries and can kill.

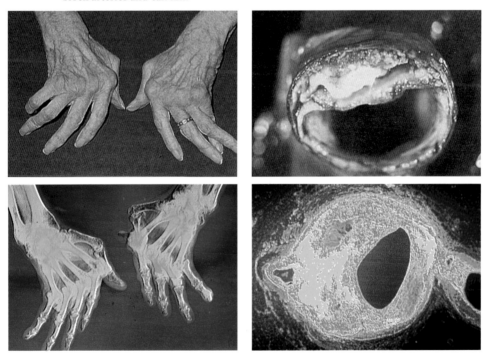

price as they become obese and die before their time. This philosophy of 'live now, pay later' is favoured when the benefits of helping the young to live long enough to pass on their genes outweigh the disadvantage – more or less irrelevant to evolution – that the same gene kills its carriers after they have had children.

Increasingly it seems, though, that age reflects a process of genetic decay; the accumulation of accidents in body cells as they divide. Mutations were once associated only with sperm and egg. Most of what is known about them still comes from such errors passed from parents to children. In today's genetics, the connection between mutations in soma and germ-plasm is beginning to reveal how the decline of one and the renewal of the other are close kin.

The best-known mutation of all was, by coincidence, and many years after its discovery, the first to show the closeness of the relationship between death and renewal. It was the tiny change in DNA that gave rise to the blood-clotting disease haemophilia in the descendants of Queen Victoria. In consort with the other great laboratory of human genetics, the cities of Hiroshima and Nagasaki, Queen Victoria's gene gave the crucial clue about what – and who – is responsible for the corruption of the genetic message.

In 1905, as part of every monarch's inborn duty to perpetuate his royal line, Alfonso XIII, the last of the Bourbon kings of Spain, went on a state visit to England in search of a bride. At a banquet he met Princess Victoria Eugénie, the granddaughter of Queen Victoria, who was known to her family as Ena. Tall, blonde and – apparently – the image of inherited perfection, her cold demeanour hid the truth about her feelings. In her old age, she wrote that 'I desired with all my heart to have this Spaniard who was as seductive as fire and as dangerous.' Soon, a holiday in Biarritz was arranged.

Ena became betrothed to Alfonso after having met him just five times. She was a popular choice: an opinion poll had put her at the top of a list of eight potential candidates for the position of next Queen of Spain. The press coverage – and the fate of the marriage – were curiously similar to that of the wedding of Victoria's great-great-great-grandson, Prince Charles. In Ena's case, much was made of the hope that an infusion of unpolluted blood might breathe life into what was universally seen as a decaying Spanish dynasty.

Alfonso's family, the Bourbons, had ruled Spain for two hundred years. Their heritage was one of madness and despair. The first in the line,

Philip V, suffered from melancholia. He became indifferent to time. The whole court was forced on to the night shift, sleeping during the day. The history of his line was once summarized as: Philip V – unbalanced, sensual; Ferdinand IV – mad and impotent; Charles III – less than normal; Charles IV – imbecile; Ferdinand VII – over-sensual, cruel, and sanguinary; Isabel II – nymphomaniac; Alfonso XII – tubercular. For good measure, the Bourbons were infected with syphilis and Alfonso XII died of the disease before his tuberculosis could kill him.

The family had one disastrous problem that appeared, in those pre-genetical days, to result from an inherited taint. They found it difficult to produce sons, the essential task of any monarch. Alfonso XIII was himself the only son of an only son, born King as his father had died at the age of twenty-eight, soon after conceiving him. As the Prime Minister of the time said at his birth, 'we have just about the smallest quantity of King we could possibly have.' It was clear that, if the Bourbons were to survive, the family needed a renewal: new blood or, in modern parlance, new genes.

Their last – failed – attempt to marry into a suitably flawless line uncovered a gene that was to play a vital part in understanding mutation. Alfonso XIII's choice helped to change Spain's history and to reveal, a century later, the surprising truth about how DNA is damaged. The secret turned out not to lie in Bourbon blood, but in that of his wife.

In May 1906, Ena was taken to the Pardo Palace, on an estate circled by a sixty-mile wall, just outside Madrid. She was married to Alfonso later that month. After the wedding, on the procession to the Royal Palace, an anarchist, Mateo Morral (described in newspaper reports as a syphilitic degenerate) hurled a bomb at their carriage and – in a chilling foretaste of the future – Ena was soaked in the blood of a decapitated guardsman.

Within a few weeks, she was pregnant and, to universal joy, gave birth to a son; Alfonso, Prince of Asturias, heir to the Spanish throne. The following day, in an elaborate ceremony, his father brought him to court on a silver salver. Soon there was concern. In the Spanish royal family boys were circumcised, perhaps because of the influence of Jewish advisers in the middle ages. When the new-born heir was operated on, he bled uncontrollably. He had, his father realized with horror, an inborn defect.

The response to what seemed to be a new hereditary taint was bitter and predictable. In an early example of gutter journalism, the *American Examiner* newspaper told the world of the secret of the Prince of Asturias. It blamed Alfonso. His son's condition was associated with the centuries of madness of the Bourbons. 'Knowing the burden of ancestral sins under which he laboured, his advisers chose for him a wife of unusual health and vigour, in the hope that she would put new strength into the Spanish royal family.' That choice, it was obvious, had failed.

Whether Alfonso knew the risk is not clear; after all, the pattern of inheritance of haemophilia was not worked out until five years after his wedding. Had he been aware of it, he certainly would not have chosen Ena. As he said, 'I cannot resign myself to the fact that my heir has contracted an infirmity which was carried by my wife's family and not mine. I know that I am unjust. I recognize it; but I cannot think in any other way . . .'

Queen Victoria – the Prince of Asturias' great-grandmother – had been brought up with the knowledge that her descendants would rule Europe. Not until her mid-thirties did she learn of the problem that was to make her family as important to science as to history. Her eighth child, Leopold, Duke of Albany, was a delicate infant. He had, as she wrote to Disraeli, 'been four or five times at death's door . . . never hardly a few months without being laid up'. Leopold married at the age of twenty-nine, but died a few years later. He suffered from the blood-clotting disease now known as haemophilia. At his birth, Victoria had been given, for the first time, chloroform as an anaesthetic. This caused controversy

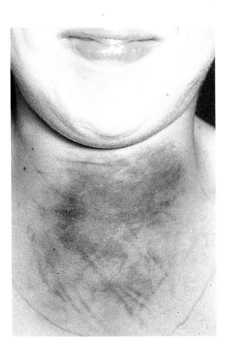

A haemophiliac with a blood-filled bruise caused by 'extravasated' blood that has leaked from the vessels into the tissue.

(one clergyman complaining that it 'robs God of the deep earnest cries which arise in time of trouble for help'). Needless to say, Leopold's condition was blamed on the unnatural use of pain-relief in childbirth. Now, though, we know that it was due to a mutation, one that was to reappear in many of her descendants although it had never been seen in the Royal Family before.

The symptoms are devastating. Bleeding after a cut is bad enough, but even without injury those affected suffer greatly as blood seeps into the tissues and joints. A copy of the gene that killed Leopold entered the Russian royal family through the marriage of Victoria's granddaughter Alexandra to Tsar Nicholas II. When their son, the young Tsarevitch Alexis, was on holiday with his family he was taken for a drive. Without warning, blood began to leak into his body from his arteries and veins. Their servant's account shows how harrowing is the disease. The drive was 'an experience in horror. Every movement of the carriage, every rough place in the road, caused the child the most exquisite torture, and by the time we reached home the boy was almost unconscious with pain.' His son's illness cast a shadow over much of the rest of Tsar Nicholas' reign.

Haemophilia had entered the Tsar's family – as it did that of Alfonso – through the female line. In the language of genetics, the condition is sex-linked: it is carried on the X chromosome. As males have but a single X, all boys with a copy of the gene show its effects. Girls, with two X chromosomes, must inherit two separate copies to become haemophiliac. To do so is very unusual. The pattern of inheritance was worked out in 1911, in one of the first publications of the Eugenics Society (the precursor of the Galton Laboratory at University College London). In a few families, the gene could be tracked for many years. One of their pedigrees, from the Swiss village of Tenna, goes back to the seventeenth century. Although the Royal Family was not discussed in print, their history, as recorded by the Eugenics Society, is preserved on two long handwritten scrolls bearing hundreds of names of the relatives and ancestors of Queen Victoria. She can be traced, through her mother, back for seventeen generations with no evidence of bleeding disorder (although one of her sixteenth-century ancestors was known, for reasons obscure, as Ludovicus the Skinless). Her family's mutation must have been new.

The copy that passed into the family of the Romanovs of Russia was obliterated by the slaughter at Ekaterinburg. That carried by her granddaughter Ena appeared not only in the Prince of Asturias, but in a later son, Gonzalo, who was also a haemophiliac. In spite of her family problem, the Queen continued to reproduce, with seven children in as many years. As a rhyme of the era had it: 'One month's pleasure, eight month's pain,/Three months leisure, at it again;/Oh what a life for the Queen of Spain!' Spanish historians still claim that the illness was concealed by the British in the interests of a marriage between the Spanish and the English royal houses. Ena's family, it seems clear, must have been aware of some kind of hereditary ailment. At the time of the engagement with Alfonso, two of her brothers, her uncle Leopold, and several cousins had already shown the symptoms of haemophilia. Whether, as some say, the Spanish ambassador was privately warned no-one can now be certain.

How was the heir to the Spanish throne to find a wife and ensure the survival of the monarchy? As the Prince grew up, he was weak and delicate and was sent to live in a small house in the grounds of the Pardo palace. Although he enlisted into the Army at the age of one, the last Alfonso was not even allowed to climb a tree. Rumours spread through the country. Some peasants believed that a soldier was sacrificed every day to provide blood for the young prince. With a certain genetical irony, he became interested in animal breeding; and, each year, on his birthday, his parents presented him with a pedigree pig.

Several attempts were made to introduce the Prince to suitable spouses from the minor aristocracy of Europe, but none wished to marry into so obviously debased a lineage. In a Swiss clinic he met and married a Cuban woman. He was at once forced by his father to renounce all rights of succession to the throne; allegedly as he had married a commoner, but really to remove the genetical stain from the royal line.

The young couple moved to the United States. Soon, their marriage collapsed. The Prince's next, to a Cuban model, lasted a mere six months. He began an affair with a Miami nightclub hostess, Mildred Gaydon. In 1938 she crashed her car. The rejected heir to the Spanish throne died of uncontrollable bleeding. With depressing symmetry, his haemophiliac brother Gonzalo was also killed in a crash, this time in a vehicle driven by his own sister. Those sisters themselves had a one-in-two chance of carrying the gene. Their father felt obliged to tell their suitors of the problem. Although both in the end married, for a time both felt doomed to be perpetual spinsters – and both married commoners.

The King and Queen of Spain began to quarrel. Their marriage was not helped by Alfonso's promiscuity. He took up the pseudonym of Monsieur Lamy on his frequent visits to Paris and had a lengthy affair

Edward, Duke of Kent by William Beechey, 1818.

Queen Victoria by Thomas Sulley, 1838.

ROYAL FAMILIES OF EUROPE

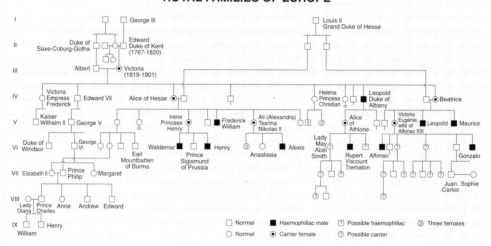

254

IN ROYAL BLOOD:
HAEMOPHILIA IN THE ROYAL FAMILIES OF EUROPE

The pedigree of haemophilia in the royal families of Europe, with some of the protagonists. The pedigree shows, quite clearly, sex-linked inheritance. Every affected child (blacked in) is male (the square symbol) and must have received the gene from his mother. All the carrier females (round symbol with spot in centre) are direct descendants, through the female line, of Queen Victoria. No unaffected male descendant of hers transmits the gene (see, for example, the British Royal Family, free of haemophilia for several generations).

Edward Duke of Kent – the probable originator of the mutation – and Queen Victoria are shown above the pedigree. To the right is Prince Leopold, the first child to reveal that the gene was indeed in the family; and below is the Spanish Royal Family – Alfonso and Ena, with the Prince of Asturias, looking tired and frail.

Prince Leopold by Edwin Landseer, 1860s.

BELOW: *King Alfonso and Queen Ena with the Prince of Asturias, dressed in the gowns of the Order of Santiago, June 1924.*

with an actress. Two illegitimate children were born and the fact that neither had haemophilia was seen by Alfonso as a private revenge against his wife. The couple became completely estranged after their expulsion from Spain following a ballot on the future of the monarchy in 1931. Alfonso is recorded as meeting a fellow Spaniard who spoke of his own English wife: Alfonso's response being 'My dear sir, how awful for you!'. Ena lived on in Lausanne until the 1960s; according to Noel Coward 'delightful but a great bore, poor dear'.

There is still a real – and understandable – reluctance among European royalty to publicize the history of haemophila. All attempts to investigate those who may still be at risk among the descendants of Victoria are resisted. In fact, the chance of the gene cropping up among today's royal houses is small. Every daughter of a woman who carries the gene has a one-in-two chance of being a carrier. If she has several sons, all of whom are healthy, that chance can, with hindsight, be reduced. Each generation that passes without an affected son reduces the likelihood that the gene is still lurking in the family.

As most of Victoria's descendants are now separated by several generations from the last recorded haemophiliac, the chance of the gene making an unexpected appearance is low. It may even be that her mutation is extinct. However, the fecundity that is part of the duties of any queen means that parts of Victoria's X chromosome are carried by well over a hundred people today, and the gene may still be concealed within one of her female descendants. One young boy, Paul Alexandre, whose mother was the daughter of the Prince of Asturias' sister, died at the age of five in 1975 of what was described as 'a problem with the blood'. He may have been a haemophiliac (although this is denied by his family). If he was, one or more of his five sisters is at real risk of transmitting Victoria's mutation to a new generation. All descendants of a healthy son even from a lineage known to carry haemophilia are free from it. As a result, today's British royalty (who descend from Victoria through her first-born son, Edward VII) do not carry the gene. The Spanish royal line has also lost it.

The life of those with the disease is much more hopeful than it was. In the early days, all kinds of eccentric remedies were tried. X-rays, adrenalin, female hormones and bromide extract of egg white were all said to help. The venom of Russell's Viper, which causes blood to coagulate, did some good, but not until transfusion, first of whole blood and later of the actual protein at fault, was there any real success. Now, many haemophiliacs lead normal lives.

256

Victoria could not understand where the illness came from. She insisted that it was 'not in our family' – that is, not in her father's Hanoverian lineage – and that it must have come from her mother's side, the Saxe-Coburgs. For many Spaniards, though, the cause was obvious; and, in an ancient tradition, a woman was to blame. Their own royal line, they knew, had been cursed by an angry female. Charlotte, wife of the Hapsburg Emperor Maximilian of Mexico (shot in 1867 after a failed attempt by the French to gain influence in the New World) had anathematized those who refused to help him. All suffered: the Empress Eugénie of France lost her throne, Pope Pius IX was deprived of his power. The son of Emperor Franz Josef of Austria died in a suicide pact, while his wife and nephew were assassinated at Sarajevo. Even the death of Alfonso XII's first wife was attributed to Charlotte's oath. It seemed natural to ascribe the new hereditary taint to the family curse. Ena, though, blamed herself and became obsessed with the idea that she had been bewitched by a Protestant seer because of her reluctant conversion to Catholicism.

In Victoria's, Ena's and Alfonso's view as well as in Spanish mythology the onus for inherited disease was placed on females; a link, no doubt, to the primitive concept of woman, from Eve onwards, as a source of corruption. That belief – and the social and moral pressures it places on women – is not confined to Christianity. The Japanese have a creation myth more robust than that of Adam and Eve but with a similar theme. On the Island Spontaneously Congealed, the Japanese Garden of Eden, the woman tempted the man and was punished for so doing. Their offspring was a hideous leech-child; a disaster altogether attributable to her having dared to take the lead. On a second try, in which the male set the pace, Japan and its gods were born. Izanami, their mother, was killed during the birth of the God of Fire and, when her husband Izanagi travelled to Hades in the hope of rescuing his mate, he found her corrupted, with maggots crawling from her genitals.

The Bourbons – and the ancestors of Queen Victoria – had believed in a divine right of kings stretching back to Adam himself; in the unique perfection of their own blood (fail them though it might where disease was involved). Hirohito, the last emperor of Japan to consider himself a god, went further in affirming his inherited majesty. He traced his bloodline directly from the sun goddess Amaterasu, founder of the Japanese nation. In an odd conjunction of fates, the loss of the Emperor's divinity and the deficiencies of European royal blood coincided to solve the mystery of mutation.

The Japanese Creation Myth.
The first man, Izanagi, and his sister
Izanami circled a gigantic phallic lance
before copulating and founding the family
line that led to the present Emporor of
Japan. Detail from a Meiji period silk
scroll (late nineteenth century).

On 6 August 1945 the *Enola Gay* took off from Tinian Island in the
Pacific. By 8.15 on a hot, clear morning it was above Hiroshima. The first
atom bomb to be used in anger, Little Boy, exploded half a kilometre above
the ground, with the force of fifteen thousand tons of TNT. Its effects
were devastating. Forty thousand buildings were destroyed, and eighty
thousand people killed at once or within a few weeks. The bombing has
been described both as the most cynical scientific experiment ever and –
according to President Truman – 'the greatest thing in history'.

Hiroshima had every reason to expect an attack. By July 1945 more
than a million Japanese had been killed in air-raids. Hiroshima was one of
the last cities to escape heavy bombing and hence provided an ideal
opportunity to show the new weapon's might. Before the war, it had been
a poverty-stricken industrial city. The eruption of Japan's military power
in the 1930s made it an important military base, headquarters of the

Second Imperial Army and departure point for the troops who poured into the new empire. In the last few months of the conflict, most of the city's population – children included – had been impressed into the military machine. The bombing made them the unwilling participants in the biggest of all surveys of human mutation.

To stand at the impact point today is an oddly superficial experience. In a very ordinary street, opposite a petrol station and in the wall of a multi-storey car park, is a granite slab marking the hypocentre. Nearby is a much-photographed ruin, its roof pushed inwards by the huge explosion overhead. The adjacent Peace Park has a mound made from the ashes of the thousands of corpses burned there and a display that acknowledges both the atrocities carried out by the Japanese and the ultimate military atrocity that ended the war. The city has become a focus of anti-nuclear protest, and for every test, the Mayor of Hiroshima writes in protest to the nation involved, but to no avail.

Even the suburbs have their memories. The Mitaki-ji temple, a few miles from the Peace Park, has a Japanese teashop which is, like an English pub, both more and less than what the tourist expects. The surroundings could not be finer: a rocky valley with hundreds of Buddhas,

Hiroshima after the bombing. The ruins of the domed building in the background remain as a memorial today.

each of which is, in winter, decorated with a red knitted cap to keep out the cold. Fifty years ago this was a scene of horror. Thousands of people struggled up its narrow paths – burned, scarred and suffering. Some came to get water, but many to die, as they knew they must, in a sacred place. They were the survivors of the bomb that had burst in the city below.

Now, Hiroshima has been rebuilt. Apart from the clean streets, efficient transport and air of a society at peace with itself, it could be any modern city in Britain. One of the oldest structures is a group of American military huts overlooking the site of the bomb. This is close to an ancient castle, Carp Castle, now reconstructed. The Japanese call the invader's citadel 'Fishcake Castle' after the resemblance of the bent corrugated-iron buildings to a local snack. Its history began just after the surrender in 1945. Once this was signed, the Japanese began to cooperate with their American occupiers. The Atomic Bomb Casualty Commission was set up to deal with the aftermath of the bombing. Initially its task was to restore order and to treat the wounded. The first headquarters were in three railway carriages, then in an abandoned military structure called, with a certain incongruity, 'The Triumphal Return Building'. It soon moved to Fishcake Castle.

The Radiation Effects Research Foundation building – Fishcake Castle, as it is known. Now one of the oldest structures in Hiroshima it overlooks the modern city below.

The Commission (now renamed the Radiation Effects Research Foundation) has, since 1947, been studying the effects of the bombing on survivors and their children. The physicists who designed the bomb had thought only of its explosive power. They were astonished by the thousands of casualties from a new and horrible sickness involving death from loss of body fluids that took place over the next year and more. As one said later, they had expected that 'Any person with radiation damage would have been killed by a brick first.'

The reports of delayed effects were at first seen as a Japanese attempt to gain sympathy. Soon, though, their accuracy was only too obvious. They brought alarming fears of an insidious new agent of destruction – atomic radiation. Many of the survivors had fallen victim to the ability of radiation to damage DNA. It does so by transferring its energy into living cells. When radiation of the right wavelength is absorbed, it breaks the DNA chain. In addition it interacts with water and constituents of the cell to produce electrically charged molecules that destroy the genetic material. Radiation can even shatter whole chromosomes. An intense dose quickly kills cells, particularly during the process of cell division when their DNA is most vulnerable. Should the cells of the gut die, the body loses the ability to retain water. In Hiroshima, vomiting and diarrhoea led to a massive loss of fluid and to death for thousands within a few days of the bomb. The survivors were still at risk. With the destruction of blood cells, the immune system begins to lose its power and death from infection happens within a month or so.

Cancer is an ancient disease (with tumours diagnosed in three-thousand year-old Egyptian mummies). With a third of the population in industrialized countries likely to suffer from it at some time, it is now a universal one. At the time of the bombs, it was already clear that external agents could spark it off. The effects of chemicals were discovered in London in 1775 when chimney sweeps were found to be liable to cancer of the scrotum, of tobacco in 1920s Germany as lung cancer became common among those who took up the new habit of smoking. Radiation – which was just becoming used in medical diagnosis at the time of the war – had killed several of the early X-ray workers. Marie Curie, who was in the habit of carrying a vial of radium in the pocket of her laboratory coat to show the curious how it glowed in the dark, herself died of cancer. The population of Hiroshima and the scientists sent to study them were well aware of the danger they faced.

Although thousands in Hiroshima died of radiation sickness (and many more, much later, would die of cancer) the survivors had another and even deeper fear; of effects delayed not for months or years, but for generations. Pregnant women were certainly at risk. Foetuses are very sensitive to radiation, and many babies whose pregnant mothers had survived the blast were born dead or deformed. If radiation damaged the germ line – the sperm and egg of the survivors – though, the price of the bombing would be paid by people born many years after it took place.

The American geneticist H. J. Muller had shown, in the 1930s, that X-rays caused mutations in fruit flies. Even a minute dose did the job. This meant, he thought, that a small increase in radiation would, if it went on long enough, have serious consequences for the genetic future. The nineteenth century's fears of hereditary degeneration had found a new and sharper focus. By 1945 there was an urgent need to assess the danger as estimates of the amount of radiation needed to double the human mutation rate varied by a hundred times. The bombed cities were an ideal opportunity to do so. One of the first tasks of the Radiation Effects Research Foundation was to check the children of survivors for genetic damage. The fear of a wave of new mutation turned out to be unfounded but, in the end (and as so often in science) the search produced an unexpected answer to quite a different question. In Hiroshima and Nagasaki it uncovered an agent of mutation more powerful and more inexorable than anything contrived by human ingenuity.

Thousands of people – some irradiated, some not – have been coming to Fishcake Castle for medical checks for most of their lives. Often, they are accompanied by their children. The survivors, the *hibakusha* as they are known, are now old, and are received with the deep bows customary in Japan. They deserve honorifics, for the Radiation Effects Research Foundation gives no treatment. It is, by treaty, strictly a research organization. Once, the survivors resented being treated as guinea-pigs, but now most have accepted the importance of the scientists' work.

Much of the research effort has been directed towards cancer in an irradiated population studied longer and harder than any other. Leukaemia appeared among the survivors within five years of the end of the war and reached a peak in 1968. Lung cancer, too, is relatively common, and the A-bomb survivors, smokers or not, are at increased risk. For some cancers (such as that of the thyroid) even a minute amount of radiation had an effect. So far, the effects, although real, are small, with an excess in deaths from cancer of less than five per cent compared to that in other Japanese cities. The survivors are reaching the age when cancer incidence shoots up – and when the full effects of the bombs may be ready to reveal themselves. The scientists hope to keep the programme going until 2015, when nearly all those who experienced the bomb will have died. However, a quarrel about who should pay (based largely on disagreements about trade between the United States and Japan) may mean that Fishcake Castle will close down long before then.

In 1946 six thousand three hundred and eighty-nine children were born in Hiroshima, many to survivors. By 1953, seventy thousand pregnancies had been logged in the bombed cities. The Japanese registration system recorded everyone in their *honseki* or ancestral home. In Hiroshima and Nagasaki, mothers were given ration books to ensure that they took part in the survey. The survival rate, number of birth defects and weight at birth were recorded for children whose parents had, and an equivalent group whose parents had not, been exposed to radiation.

At that time, human genetics had just begun. For the radiation scientists, only primitive tests for mutation (such as the birth of overtly damaged children) were available. Not until the 1950s was the number of human chromosomes established, and not until the mid-sixties was it possible to look at differences in proteins, the products of genes. As technology progressed, the Radiation Effects Research Foundation used it. First, they looked for failures of pregnancy, or for the birth of overtly damaged children. Excepting, of course, the children of mothers who were irradiated when actually pregnant they found no effect (although this work was one of the first to show that the children of related parents, such as cousins, were less healthy on average than were those who did not share a recent common ancestor). A search for damaged chromosomes in those whose parents were exposed to radiation gave equally negative results. For a time, there was talk of abandoning the research programme altogether as such enormous effort and expense was being directed to no apparent end. In spite of such criticisms – and of some continued resentment by the people of Hiroshima and Nagasaki themselves – the scientists continued (discovering, on the way, more about the genetic structure and evolutionary history of the Japanese population than of any other group). Finally, the first meaningful results began to emerge.

The most comprehensive survey, completed fifty years after the end of the war, involved the comparison of twenty-five thousand children with their parents for changes in blood proteins. A technique called two-dimensional electrophoresis, which picks up small differences in electrical charge brought about by gene mutation, was used. Thirty different

CANCER AS A GENETIC DISEASE OF CELLS

Cancer is not a single illness but many. All cancers, though, involve damage to DNA and, for most, this takes place as body cells divide. Like the manuscript copies of a blemished original it is sometimes possible to trace cancerous cells through the body by following an error as it spreads. In one form of leukaemia, for example, almost every white blood cell carries an unusually small chromosome 22 (a Philadelphia chromosome, as it is called after the city in which it was discovered). This suggests that all these cells descend from a single damaged progenitor, deep in the bone marrow. They are a *clone*, identical cells reproducing without sex. The cancer arises because malignant cells divide faster than normal and continue to divide when other cells are programmed to die.

The transformation of a normal into a cancerous cell may need many mutations. The more divisions a cell has been through, the more chance that the requisite number will accumulate. This is why cancer is so much a disease of old people. Cancer genetics is beginning to show how complicated the process can be and how many genes are involved. In leukaemia, for example, the reduction in size of chromosome 22 is because part of it is broken off and transferred to chromosome 9. The break is in a gene that controls the growth of the cell (a protooncogene, as it is known). When a fragment moves to its new chromosomal home, it fuses with a local gene on chromosome 9 and the two together produce a new and abnormal protein that speeds up cell division.

Other cancers are sparked off by viruses that damage the genes controlling cell growth, or by chemicals or radiation that do the same thing. Sometimes, susceptibility towards a particular cancer is inherited. This is true, for example, for the eye cancer *retinoblastoma*. It runs in families, but also needs a mutation in a body cell. When a child is unfortunate enough both to inherit one flawed copy of the appropriate gene and to have a body-cell mutation in its normal equivalent the cancer develops.

Cancer involves much more than this. Body cells have mechanisms that detect when DNA is damaged. They instruct the cell to stop dividing, or even commit suicide. However, these 'security-guard' genes can be harmed by mutation, so that cancer cells continue to spread. Chemicals – such as those in tobacco smoke – and radiation can sabotage these rescue systems; and heavy smokers often destroy the genes that have evolved to protect them.

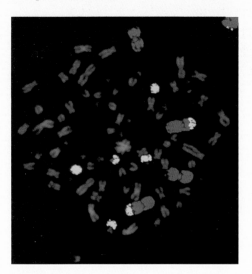

A cancer cell in the act of dividing. It contains seventy-nine rather than the usual forty-six chromosomes. Most of them are coloured in blue but Chromosome 1 is picked out in red (using special dyes called chromosome paints that bind only to specific chromosomes) and Chromosome 17 in yellow. Parts of the former have fused with the latter, adding to the genetic confusion in this severely damaged cell.

proteins were looked at in every individual; well over a million genes altogether.

The results were simple and reassuring. Just six mutations were found. At first they were thought to be equally distributed between the groups but, owing to a book-keeping error, the real result was that four were in children whose parents had not been exposed to radiation and two in the offspring of those close to the bomb. Although the number of mutations is too small to make it certain that radiation had absolutely no effect it is clear that fears of a race of mutated monsters were unfounded.

Now, with advances in technology, the search has shifted to the DNA itself. A few survivors and their children have achieved a sort of eternity by having their cells frozen in liquid nitrogen, waiting for a technical breakthrough that might uncover hidden genetic changes. Already, a stretch of six thousand DNA bases in the haemophilia gene has been compared in children and their irradiated parents and, again, no new mutations were found.

In those parts of the genome that produce protein, mutation is relatively rare (although it may vary in how common it is by a thousand times or more from gene to gene). For some parts of the genetic material, though, it is extraordinarily frequent, with a rate of one in a thousand or more when children are compared with their parents. This is particularly true in the DNA 'fingerprint' in which short blocks of DNA sequence are repeated many times. The actual number of repeats increases or decreases quite often, changing the pattern when DNA is cut on either side of the repeated segment – the longer the repeat is, the more slowly it moves into an electrophoretic gel. The auto-radiograph on the left and, alongside it, a simplified diagram shows a mother, a father and their three children, together with the number of repeats in a particular DNA segment in each one. The mother has 5 and 3 repeats; the father 2 and 5. The children have inherited, in turn, 3 and 2, 5 and 2, and 3 and 2 repeats. Any new mutation to – say – 6 repeats or 1 repeat in the children is immediately obvious.

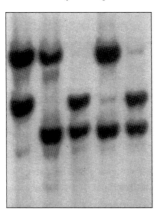
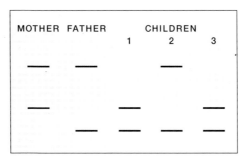

Some of the DNA – that of the famous 'fingerprint' for example – mutates at a much higher rate than does the small part of the genetic material that actually makes proteins. One child in a hundred may show, quite spontaneously, a small difference in fingerprint pattern from its parents. Once again, although several new mutations were uncovered, there was no increase in genetic damage that might be ascribed to the bombing.

Most scientists now accept that the alarmist prophecies of fifty years ago were wrong and that radiation is not a major force in harming genes. The Japanese were harder to convince. So terrifying were the immediate effects of the invisible killer that it seemed certain that those exposed would pass on its effects to their children. The fears were deepened by the publicity which followed the discovery of the structure of DNA in the 1950s.

The *hibakusha* began to suffer discrimination of the kind experienced by families (including royal families) in the West thought to carry inherited disease. Many had been children when the bomb fell. As they grew up they began to think of marriage. In Japan, then and now, parents have a say in who their son or daughter might choose. As do Orthodox Jews and many other groups, they use matchmakers to check the moral and financial health of a potential spouse. Any history of disease is carefully considered before two families are linked. So intensive is the scrutiny that the law has tried to limit it, with little success.

Perhaps, the rumour grew, those who had been irradiated were genetically injured. The Americans said that they were not; but, after all, claims about radiation sickness had been dismissed as a Japanese attempt to gain sympathy. To their dismay, the *hibakusha* found themselves shunned in the marriage market. Women found the stigma harder to avoid than did men. Fifteen years after the war, three-quarters of the male victims had found a mate, but half the irradiated women remained unmarried. For them, the ancient bias against women when sex meets blame was very much alive.

It is important not to be too calm about radiation. It may may do less harm to sperm and egg than once feared, but it certainly shortens lives. Sometimes its effects are immediate; sometimes, as in the cancer victims of Hiroshima, delayed. In mice, a lifetime of low-level radiation causes those exposed to it to age and die before their time, without obvious signs of disease. All this confirms that damage to the DNA is not confined to the germ line but affects all the cells of the body. Now, the study of

Mr and Mrs Okada
– two survivors who
married each other.
Mr Okada was rejected
by an earlier fiancée
when she saw his
radiation scars.

genetic changes in body cells, induced by radiation or not, is the most exciting area of genetics. Its theme is age and decay, but on the way it has shown what causes inherited mutations and – perhaps – has discovered how one small group of cells escapes the fate of all others.

The only difference between eggs, sperm and body cells is that the last are copied without benefit of sex. Apart from that, every cell is open to all the processes of genetics. Because these include mutation, everyone gains a new genetic identity as they age. Like it or not, we are each an evolving system on a pathway of genetic decline that begins with fertilization and ends at death.

Everyone starts from a single fertilized egg; from six feet of DNA. An adult, though, is made of a hundred thousand billion cells – one of those numbers so large as to be almost without meaning, ten with fourteen zeros after it – every one with its own copy of the DNA, deriving, after many rounds of duplication, from that in the egg. What is more, many body cells continue to divide, with ten followed by sixteen zeros cell divisions in an average lifetime. Some cause a minute egg to grow into an enormous adult, but many more renew the body as it wears out. The body makes tens of thousands of miles of DNA an hour (men more than women as they constantly produce new sperm – a hundred million a day, containing enough DNA to put a girdle twice round about the earth – while women use up a store of eggs made before puberty). It is, needless to say, a complicated chemical with some three thousand million units to be copied each time a cell divides. Mutations build up at every division.

As is inevitable in any copying process, the genetic message in cells and the people fashioned from them becomes corrupted. Just as can happen to cells exposed to radiation, old cells lose whole chromosomes. All the cells of a young boy have an X and a Y chromosome. In a fifty year old, one in two hundred has lost the Y (and, in women, one cell in twenty is missing an X). Genes, too, are destroyed. The first indication of how severe the effects of age may be came from mitochondria (whose genes are inherited down the female line). Now it seems that mutations in their DNA as mitochondria reside in body cells may be responsible for the universal afflictions of old age.

The initial clues came from inherited mitochondrial diseases. Unlike many of those involving the nuclear DNA these often show their symptoms late in life. This is, it transpires, because mitochondrial DNA (already flawed through faulty inheritance) suffers more and more muta- tions as the years pass. In one family, a young girl was unlucky enough receive ninety-five per cent of her mitochondria bearing a genetic abnor- mality. She died at six months old of a degenerative brain illness. Her sixteen year-old cousin, who had slightly fewer of her cell constituents in mutated form, still seemed healthy. That girl's sixty-five year-old mother, though (who had inherited just the same proportion of defective genes as her daughter), was deaf, demented, and crippled. As time went by the unfortunate lady's few working mitochondria had accumulated errors until they could no longer do their job.

These genes and their misfortunes have a royal link. The family of the Tsar (including his haemophiliac son) was executed after the 1917 Revolution. In 1992, their bones were exhumed, in part to test the false claim of one Anna Anderson to be Anastasia, his daughter, by comparing the DNA with that of their living relatives (including the present Duke of Edinburgh). The Tsar turned out to carry two types of mitochondria. One was identical to that borne by his relatives in the maternal line, and the other differed by a single DNA change. That mutation took place either in his own body or, perhaps, in that of his mother.

Mitochondria play a wider part in age and decay. Their main job is to generate energy. As their ability to do so decreases because of the accu- mulation of mutations with age, the body's powers decline. The harm done depends on the tissue that receives a corrupted copy of the message. If a mutation happens early in development it can spread, by descent, throughout the body. If late, it is confined to a few places. Parts of the brain in some old people with Alzheimer's disease or with Parkinsonism are full of mitochondria that have lost sections of DNA. The same is true of the heart muscle of patients with coronary heart disease. Everyone who lasts to old age has had their mitochondria so assailed by mutation that their vital furnaces, and their energies, burn low.

Every gene faces the same fate. As they are copied errors creep in. Sooner or later, the instructions become so garbled that the machinery goes wrong. The result may be disastrous: nearly every eighty year old, for example, has some form of cancer. This new insight into the role of mutation in destroying cells suggests that bodily decay is an inexorable process. It explains why attempts to increase the maximum length of life have had little success: there may be more eighty year olds than there once were, but there is still a notable shortage of those celebrating their one hundred and twentieth birthday. It also gave the first vital clue as to what – if not radiation – causes genetic damage in the cells that produce the next generation. Queen Victoria's gene provided part of the answer.

Victoria became Queen because George IV had failed to produce an heir. Several couples were competing in the ensuing race (known to wits of the time as Hymen's War Terrific) to have their genes occupy the throne of England. Three Dukes – Clarence, Cambridge and Kent, the brothers of King George – were potential winners. None was popular (and were described by Shelley as 'the dross of their dull race') and each had a chequered past. In the end, Edward, Duke of Kent, got there first.

Edward had been a martinet: stiff, upright and – according to a contemporary – ruled like a piece of music paper. His governorship of Gibraltar had been so strict as to provoke a mutiny and he was retired to live in splendour at Ealing. The Duke had kept, for many years, a mistress; a Frenchwoman called Thérèse Bernardine (who took the name Madame de St Laurent). Moving with her to Brussels, he met Victoire, Duchess of Leiningen. After much hesitation he proposed to her, never seeing Madame de St Laurent again. Soon after the marriage, Victoire became pregnant and the couple returned to England. Her daughter Victoria was born on 24 May 1819 at Kensington Palace. Within a year, her father was dead; his dynastic duties done, he entered a sphere where (at least according to his earthly contact Robert Owen) he lost his commission.

Because of the delay in persuading himself to carry out his obligations to the royal line, Edward was fifty-one by the time Victoria was conceived. The genes in his body cells – like those of the mitochondria in his relative Tsar Nicholas, who was exactly the same age when he was executed – had, without doubt, already been harmed by mutation. The same was certainly true of the genes in those cells that gave rise to his sperm, including the one that produced the next monarch. That single genetic accident, the mutation of the haemophilia gene in Victoria's elderly father, gave the first hint of the most powerful mutational agent of all. It is simple, inexorable and obvious: old age itself.

Evidence for its importance no longer rests on royal anecdote but on the latest discoveries of molecular biology. Like that in Queen Victoria's own family, most haemophilia mutations are fairly recent; as in the Hanoverians, they appear in families with no history of the disease. Tracing each back by looking at the DNA of lineages in which several generations are still alive allows its arrival to be pinned down. A haemophiliac son (or a carrier mother) each of whose parents lacks a copy of the gene must have inherited a new mutation. Many such families have been studied. By comparing them with families that have not suffered the mutation it is possible to detect what might be doing the damage.

The effects of age are clear. On the average, the parent within whom a new mutation to haemophilia took place is older by eight years than a typical – unmutated – parent in the population as a whole. Old age attacks the genes that make it to the next generation in just the same way as it harms the parents who produce them.

Its impact certainly outweighs that of radiation. Any change in parental age will alter the mutation rate. In Japan, as elsewhere, people have a new reluctance to have children. In 1970, only eighteen per cent of twenty-to-thirty year-old Japanese were unmarried. In 1990, the figure rose to forty per cent; the salaryman and salarywoman are so busy promoting the economic miracle that they have little time for sex. Later marriage may mean older parents and more mutations. How many is hard to say, as the tendency to complete families quickly and their small size (in Japan an average of 1.4 children) produces a shortage of very old parents, with their high mutation rate.

When reading the scientific publications about the children of Hiroshima and Nagasaki it is hard to avoid sensing the disappointment felt by their authors. Although, naturally, it was a relief to find that radiation had not caused many mutations in genes coding for proteins, scientists are only human and prefer positive results to negative. The feeling of frustration in the Radiation Effects Research Foundation evaporated as soon as DNA technology became available. Their work, it turned out, provided another crucial clue about mutation, and, quite by

DWARFS, DOMINANTS AND OLD PARENTS

Hereditary dwarfism has been known for thousands of years: it is recorded by the ancient Greeks, an Egyptian tomb has a memorial to a dwarf who played some prominent part in court life; and Velázquez painted several portraits of the dwarves in the Spanish royal household (including, famously, the dwarf Maribarbola in his masterpiece, *Las Meninas* where she has an important role as the handmaiden of the young Princess, Margarita).

Restricted growth can arise for many reasons. Sometimes, for example, there is an inherited failure to produce growth hormone. The commonest hereditary form of dwarfism, though, is *achondroplasia*: a failure of the long bones to develop properly. As a result, those with the condition have short arms and legs and characteristic facial features. Apart from that, their health is good. About one child in twenty-five thousand is born with achondroplastic dwarfism; eight out of every ten to parents of normal height. The gene involved in dominant; that is, only one copy is needed to manifest its effects. Dwarf children born to normal parents must hence represent new mutations. To estimate the mutation rate all that is needed is to count how many such births there are.

The gene itself was found during the long search for that causing Huntington's disease and is located close to it, near the tip of chromosome 4. Its normal job is to make a receptor molecule on the surface of cells that responds to a growth factor instructing them to divide. The genetic accident means that it fails to work properly in developing bone and collagen, leading to dwarfism. Everyone with the condition has a mutation in exactly the same place in the gene (which is in itself unusual: compare it with, for example, the situation for haemophilia). The mutation rate is – at around one in thirty thousand births – astonishingly high, suggesting that there is a region of instability within the gene. What is most remarkable, though, is the strength of association between that rate and the age of parents. It goes up by more than ten times in fathers of forty-five compared to those of twenty-five (and, presumably, is even higher in older fathers).

A 5th dynasty statue from a tomb at Giza (c.2500 – 2300BC). The dwarf Seneb sits with his wife. Their two children stand at their feet.

accident, an insight into the ancient and universal tendency to blame women for the corruption associated with sex.

The discovery turned on a new ability to identify changes in the DNA itself, particularly those parts (including the 'fingerprint') that have a very high natural rate of mutation. In Hiroshima, radiation had no effect on mutations in this segment of the genetic material, with its uniquely rapid rate of change. However, of the twenty-eight spontaneous fingerprint mutations (of fourteen hundred genes tested) found during the fruitless search for an effect of the bombs, twenty-five were contributed by the father. Mothers generated just three. In other words, for DNA finger-prints at least, mutation was overwhelmingly a male affair. The prejudice against female *hibakusha* was quite unfounded; most of the mutations – in working genes as much as in DNA fingerprints – happened in men. Old men like Edward Duke of Kent (incidentally, and rather depressingly, my own age when Victoria was conceived) are the most dangerous partners of all. From the Book of Genesis to the present day, the guilt for polluting the bloodline has been wrongly assigned.

Although males do most to damage the germ line its rejuvenation is largely a female responsibility. In spite of her aged and decrepit father Victoria, like every other child, was born young and full of life. What granted her – and her descendants – resurrection? The answer is, in spite of the Bible's certainties and Weismann's doubts, sex; and, in particular, woman's contribution to the process.

Sex must be important, simply because reproducing in this eccentric way is so expensive. By becoming involved with a male, a female dilutes her genes with those of someone else who does rather little to ensure that they survive. Even worse, she produces sons who go in for the same selfish behaviour. To balance this enormous cost, sex must have some hefty advantages for genes if not for their products – and it does: for a sexual world has conquered death.

The main task of sex is to undo the damage caused by mutation. It does so in many ways. The simplest is just a filter. In a sexual organism far more cells set out on the journey to convey genes through history than ever reach their destination. A woman makes her full complement of around a million egg cells before she is born and releases them at intervals throughout her reproductive life. At every cycle, thousands are released. Each time a man has sex, he produces enough sperm to fertilize the entire female population of Europe. He continues, tirelessly, to manufacture thousands of millions of sperm cells throughout his days.

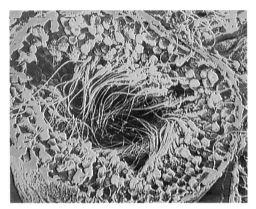
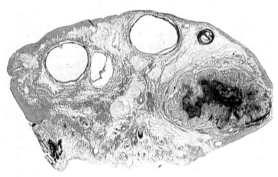

A section through testis and ovary. The testis is a mass of tubules (cut across here) containing cells that constantly divide to produce sperm. The ovary, in contrast, contains only about a hundred thousand potential egg cells, only about five hundred of which ever become mature.

In the modern world, a mere two or three of these billions are ever used.

Every egg and every sperm is at the end of a long chain of divisions of body cells. These separate it from its source in the fertilized egg that made the woman or man who generates it. Only a tiny proportion can hope to pass through this corporeal filter between one generation's eggs (or sperm) and those of the next. It sifts out cells carrying mutations that reduce their ability to compete in the somatic race through a man or woman to become a fully fledged germ cell.

This is natural selection of the Darwinian kind, but the opponents are cells, not organisms, and the theatre of battle is the body itself. The soma deals with the inevitability of decline by setting aside one lineage of body cells during early development that will, in the end, produce its sex cells. The lineage has the capacity to produce enormous numbers of cells, but only a select few are admitted to the next generation as sperm meets egg. This means that, from the genes' point of view, the body is an ecosystem, evolving within itself in a struggle for existence as bitter as that in the world outside. Only the best – that is, those least damaged by mutation – can win. The cellular conflict means that tissues (such as brain and muscle) whose cells do not divide much age more quickly through mutation than those (such as blood) with constant division and the chance for the best cell to prevail. Although the idea of the body as an evolving organization is unfamiliar it is central to its workings, most notably in the immune system.

THE IMMUNE SYSTEM AND NATURAL SELECTION
IN BODY CELLS

The body is under constant attack by a subtle and protean army. Whatever its enemy – bacteria, viruses, simple or complex chemicals – the immune system is able to respond. It can even react to chemicals synthesized in the laboratory that have never before been experienced by any living creature. It does so with amazing specificity, making antibodies, defensive proteins, fashioned to bind to and neutralize each invader. A second attack is met with the exact protein needed to repel it. The immune system shows the extraordinary power of evolution taking place not over the generations, but within a single body. Only recently has it become clear that much the same process is involved in the long chain of events leading to the formation of sperm and egg.

Antibodies are produced by specialized white cells called lymphocytes. Each antibody consists of four protein chains, two heavy and two light, arranged in a 'Y' shape. The stem of the Y is identical in all of them, but at the tips of the molecule are regions that vary from antibody to antibody and fit each to a specific antigen.

The variable and constant regions are coded for by two groups of genes located a long way apart. As each lymphocyte develops, there are mutations that delete lengths of DNA until the two regions are brought together. The light chain has about two hundred genes in the variable region, the heavy chain about the same number. Differing numbers are deleted in a developing family of cells and are spliced – using half a dozen or so different joining genes – to the constant part of the molecule. As well as the diversity generated by mixing combinations of genes in this way each variable gene has a high mutation rate. All this means that many millions of potential antibodies can be produced from only a few hundred genes.

Once a new antigen is encountered, any lymphocyte producing an approximately matched antibody begins to multiply. As it does so there are mutations that generate new variants. Those that best match the antigen continue to divide until there evolves, by natural selection, the family line of cells – the clone – that produces an antibody fitting it exactly. Once the first attack has been defeated, a few members of that clonal reserve ('memory cells') are held in reserve, ready should there be a second attack.

BELOW LEFT: *A lymphocyte, the cell that makes antibodies, with attached foreign red cells.*
BELOW RIGHT: *A computer-generated three-dimensional image, based on high power X-ray microscopy, of the recognition site of an antibody binding to its antigen.*

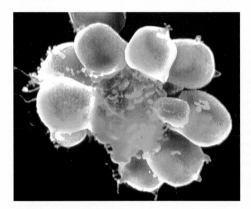
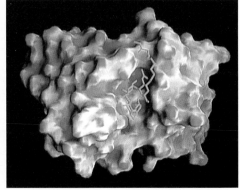

Even after sperm and egg are made there are plenty of chances for screening out those damaged by mutation. After all, just one can succeed on each try at fertilization; and millions die on the way. Most fertilized eggs die, too, giving another opportunity to cull the genetically imperfect before they have a chance to produce a new soma of their own.

The efficiency of the genetic filter is increased by the way in which sperm and egg are made. Unlike body cells, they are not just a slightly degraded copy of the cell that went before. Instead, their genes are reshuffled into new combinations in a complicated cellular event in which chromosomes of paternal and maternal origin line up side by side and exchange lengths of chromosome with each other. This ensures that some sex cells receive several damaged genes at once, while others have none. The death of those who draw an unlucky combination purges the germ line of many mutations at the cost of a single cell and makes the last lap of the biological race to enter the next generation the most competitive of all.

Sex means that only the finest cells make it to the finishing post. The older the parents, though, the more time there has been for mutation, and the less favourable the hand from which the choice can be made. The situation is worse for men as they produce new sperm by repeated cell division throughout life. They are hence exposed to a higher risk that their genetic heritage will be damaged before they can pass it on. From egg to egg, there are about twenty cell divisions, irrespective of the age of the mother. For a twenty-eight year-old father (the average age of reproduction in the West) there are about three hundred divisions in the somatic race to make a sperm. For a fifty-one year-old man such as the Duke of Kent there may be more than a thousand generations of division between his own germ cells and the sperm (in his case that of George III) that produced him; each one of which increases the chances of accident. The relationship between mutation and parental age is explained.

Whatever the age of an aspiring parent, there is more to sex than damage-limitation. By filtering out the best copy of the instructions in the genetic passage through the body from one fertilization to the next it acts only like an illiterate copyist whose job is not to understand what is written but to minimize chaos. All cells, sexual or not, do much more to ensure the accuracy of the hereditary message. They act as their own proof-readers, checking the DNA against a master-copy and correcting it before it is transmitted. This process is at its most active during sex

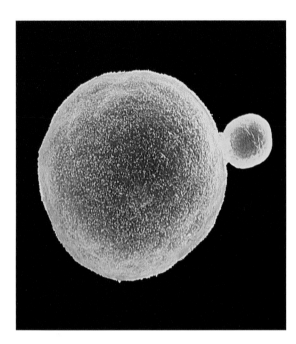

Sperm meets egg as the genetic race of the germ cells through the soma is at last completed.

and is most efficient in long-lived creatures such as ourselves, again emphasizing the link between DNA damage and age.

The first step in guarding the inherited message is to ensure that as little harm as possible takes place. A whole series of enzymes and protective proteins soaks up destructive chemicals in the cell. Injury to these guardians by, for example, tobacco smoke predisposes to cancer. A second line of defence ensures that cells unfortunate enough to suffer a mutation are persuaded to commit suicide by proteins that block cell division. By far the most important defence is the army of enzymes that ensures that mutated DNA can be patched up in many ways. Specialized enzymes reverse chemical changes to DNA bases, others cut out and repair lengths that contain a mutation. Yet more recognize and replace distorted pieces of the double helix as its mutated chains attempt to pair. All this elaborate machinery is itself harmed by mutation – and severe illness can then result. There is much interest among cancer biologists in the machinery of DNA repair as to understand it – and its failures – may be to understand the disease itself.

How did this complicated system of genetic proof-reading evolve? The answer lies, as it so often does, in sex. It might seem obvious that sex evolved for reproduction. It may, though, have begun more as a cooperative venture to repair disfigured DNA. Asexual cells, floating in a primaeval soup and containing only one copy of their genetic instructions were in danger of being bewildered by the build-up of mutations, with no clue as to what the correct DNA sequence might be. The easiest way to find out was to ask a neighbour: to check one's own instructions against a flawless copy. To do so inevitably involved getting together and comparing genes. Sex was born and those who were good at it survived for long enough to reproduce.

Sex provides every cell with the basic tool of the proof-reader, an uncorrupted version of a manuscript against which to check the one in front of him. It means that everyone has a back-up copy of each gene simply by virtue of receiving a duplicate from each parent. Should one be injured by mutation, the other is likely to remain unblemished. Sex makes the biological copyist, unlike his monastic equivalent, literate: it allows mistakes to be corrected against a fair copy before the message is handed on.

The process is most active when sperm and egg are formed. Then, members of each chromosome pair line up, the maternal version pairing with its paternal equivalent. The match is precise and entails a frenzy of DNA cutting and splicing. Sometimes, because the cut molecules rejoin in different arrangements, germ cell formation produces new combinations of genes in sperm or egg, differing from those in the individual who made them. This is manifest as recombination, new associations of characters in offspring compared to their parents. More often, though, mutations within each DNA molecule are repaired before it joins the race to participate in the next generation, without any obvious reshuffling of genes.

As the victims of Hiroshima were among the first to reveal, mutation itself is pretty much a male affair. Repair, though, may be more the province of females. There is more cutting and splicing of DNA (as evident in the formation of new gene combinations) during the formation of eggs than of sperm. Indeed, in some creatures such as fruit flies there is no recombination at all in males, suggesting that they have little or no DNA slicing, reshuffling and repair. For the average gene it seems that males do the damage and females reverse it. The conventional image of females as a source of defilement is wrong. Instead, they are the essence of resurrection.

DNA repair certainly plays a part in renewing the genetic message. However, the question of why babies are born young remains the most

THE BLIND PROOFREADER –
DNA REPAIR AND GENETIC DISEASE

This book – like most nowadays – was typed on a word processor. It has several tools to correct mistakes. Some are simple; backspace and delete. Others are more sophisticated. Hit the right keys and the document is compared with a dictionary and unfamiliar words highlighted. Soon there will be programs that recognize context; type 'there' instead of 'their' in the wrong place and the mistake will at once be put right. The days of correcting fluid are long gone.

The body's editing machine is even more effective. Just one letter in tens of millions is wrongly transcribed – a record that any typist, even with the finest word processor, would be proud of. We depend for our very survival on the ability to repair mutations. Xeroderma pigmentosum is a rare illness that is due to the absence of an enzyme for cutting out damaged DNA. Those with the gene are very sensitive to ultraviolet – and all develop skin cancer. Few live beyond thirty.

Ataxia telangiectasia is a related disease. Those – just one in fifty thousand – who inherit it are at risk of developing certain blood cancers and are very sensitive to X-rays. Radiotherapy may leave permanent wounds. The gene involved, in its normal form, makes a protein that recognizes DNA damage and blocks cell division until it is repaired. Only those with two copies of the mutated gene have the disease. However, women with a single copy – a quarter of a million in Britain alone – have a fivefold chance of developing breast cancer, making this gene the

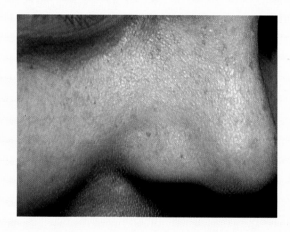

A patient with an early case of xeroderma pigmentosum. The dark spots will, in time, spread and may be fatal.

commonest single cause of the hereditary form of the disease. Even breast screening with X-rays may put some women at increased risk. The commonest cancer of the large intestine – with one person in two hundred bearing an inherited susceptibility to the disease – is also due to a defect in a repair gene.

The complexity – and the vital role – of DNA repair are manifest in the severe effects of a failure of just one of the body's many mechanisms for repairing the genetic material.

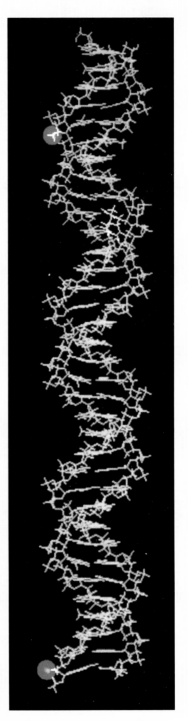

RIGHT: *Cutting out a wrongly paired duo of DNA bases (coloured in yellow) using a repair mechanism called excision repair. The orange blobs mark the sites in the DNA recognized by the repair enzyme, which has to cut out a lengthy section of the molecule – always twenty-eight base pairs long – to repair the single point of damage. The missing single-stranded piece is then replaced by copying the complementary DNA message carried in the matching strand. Xeroderma pigmentosum results from a failure of this machinery.*

BELOW: *A cluster of tumour cells from a rat embryo lacking the protective P53 tumour suppressor gene; damaged by placing the cells in contact with tobacco smoke.*

difficult in biology. To answer it would be to solve the central problem of sex and of mutation and might also help in understanding ageing and its afflictions. A hint about the explanation lies in one biological timer, reset each time a child is born. When it is in working order it rejuvenates genes. Should it go wrong, though, the result is disaster.

Cells grown in the laboratory in bottles of culture medium have a programmed existence of their own. After a set number of divisions they lose interest in copying DNA and become dormant or die. How many times they divide is related to the lifespan of the creature from which they come. Mouse cells abandon hope sooner than those from elephants.

Some cells, though, refuse to obey their instructions; they are indestructible, and continue to divide for as long as they are fed. Many of them come from cancers. One, the HeLa cell line, has lasted since the death of its progenitor – a black woman called either Helen Laing or Henrietta Lacks – from the disease more than fifty years ago. Cancer itself is the result of a cell's refusal to respond to a signal telling it to cease division. Instead it multiplies out of control, spreading through the body.

Much of today's cancer research is concerned with the genetics of cell mortality; the search for the agents of 'programmed cell death', as it is known. At least one of them has a close tie with the sexual rejuvenation of

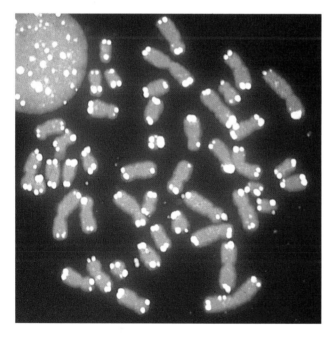

Chromosomes stained to reveal telomeres. Several cells have been squashed and the brightly stained spots are the telemeres at the end of each chromosome.

the genetic message. Chromosomes are a bit like shoelaces. At their ends are caps, made not of metal but of DNA bases. Just like laces, these 'telomeres' fray away with use; in this case by mutation. They are made from thousands of repeats of a simple six-part motif. In a typical lineage of dividing cells about a hundred DNA bases per division are lost. The telomeres act as a timer of mortality. Giving up cell division depends on how much of the protective telomere cap is left. Once the number has been chipped away by mutation to four thousand or so, the cell is no longer able to divide. The telomere is a clock that pilots the cell through its designed life-span. Counting the amount that remains is a good way to predict when it is likely to enter old age.

What is true of cells is also true of people. An eighty year old has fewer of these units than does a child because so many have been lost. Telomeres are a sort of genetic nemesis, waiting to catapult their carriers – cells or people – into senility. Just as Nemesis (the goddess who distributed bad and good fortune at whim) might have arranged, not everyone is born equal. The number in young children ranges from about six thousand to around twice that. Identical twins have chromosome caps of about the same length suggesting that telomere size is under genetic control. The smallest yet found was in a man of ninety-seven, who had fewer than five thousand repeats left at the end of each chromosome. Goethe's Faust, it may be recalled, died at the age of a hundred (his telomeres, no doubt, suitably reduced) having renounced immortality as he was bored with life. Goethe, biologist though he was, did not realize how much of that choice was already coded into his hero's genes.

The rate of fraying of telomeres means that some babies – those born with short chromosome ends – may fall below the crucial length earlier than others. Perhaps they will enter old age sooner than their more fortunate colleagues. How, or even whether, telomere mutations lead to decay is not known. A simple, simplistic, but sinister calculation suggests that a baby at the lower end of the telomere range is programmed to live for threescore years and ten while a child with a more generous endowment could linger on for another twenty years before he expires, sans eyes, sans teeth, sans telomeres, sans everything. It may soon be possible, by checking the genes, to guess whether a baby born in the year 2000 has any chance of seeing the first century of the new millennium almost to its end.

Sex resets the telomere clock. As the chromosomes pair up during the formation of sperm and egg they are revitalized by a enzyme that makes new chromosome ends. The gene – a veritable fountain of youth – produces an enzyme, telomerase (sometimes called, with the leaden humour of science, TLC or Telomere Lengthening Component). It is not active in tissues other than those producing germ cells; only sperm and egg can be rejuvenated.

There is, though, an exception to this rule. The TLC gene is switched on in cancer cells. It gives them renewed life. It may even be the gene that allows them to continue to divide and, in the end, to outrun cells which have obeyed the instructions to die. Its level of activity is at least a thousand times greater in cancer cells (and in the precursors of sperm and egg) than in others. Those whose cancerous tissues have found everlasting life are likely to die before those whose cells accept their predestined demise.

Telomeres show how close is the tie between mutation and age and how Faustian the bargain between sex and death. No doubt they are just a part, perhaps a small part, of the machinery of rejuvenation that works its magic each time a baby is born. They affirm, though, that – when the dead are metaphorically raised, in the shape of their offspring – their genes will be changed. St Paul himself described the conflict between the fate of the genetic message in the body and that in the cells which transmit it to the next generation in terms familiar to a biologist: 'For this corruptible must put on incorruption, and this mortal must put on immortality.' Biology shows how right he was: that, although the life of those who bear them is transient, the world of the genes will live for ever.

FURTHER READING

BECAUSE GENETICS and a belief in inborn destiny inform so much of what we believe about ourselves there is almost no limit to what can be read when exploring inheritance. It ranges from the Old Testament to the *Proceedings of the National Academy of Sciences*, taking in much of biology and philosophy (not to mention a healthy chunk of fiction, poetry and biography) on the way. Although the questions asked in this book were formulated long ago, the answers (even in their merely biological sense and incomplete though they are) are becoming obvious only now. I therefore, where possible, refer to the most recent publication in a particular field; but because human genetics advances so quickly these will themselves soon be overtaken. Journals such as *New Scientist* and *Scientific American* constantly produce reviews of the latest discoveries and, once the embellishments are removed, the press usually gets it more or less right.

GENERAL READING AND INTRODUCTION

There are many excellent texts on genetics. The best by far is *An Introduction to Genetic Analysis* by A. J. F. Griffiths et al (6th edn, W. H. Freeman, 1996). Foremost, when human genetics is concerned, are J. M. Connor and M. A. Ferguson-Smith, *Essential Medical Genetics* (4th edn, Blackwell, 1993) and R. F. Mueller and I. D. Young, *Emery's Elements of Medical Genetics* (9th edn, Churchill Livingstone, 1995). For a simple and more general treatment of its molecular aspects there is Paul Berg and Maxine Singer, *Dealing with Genes: The Language of Heredity* (Blackwell, 1993).

My own *The Language of the Genes* (2nd edn, Flamingo & Anchor, 1994) gives a broader and (inevitably) shallower treatment of what genetics means than does the present book. Richard Dawkins, in *River Out of Eden: A Darwinian View of Life* (Basic Books & Weidenfeld and Nicolson, 1995), gives, as ever, a brilliant insight into evolutionary thinking, using the Heraclitean metaphor of time as a river, always the same but always changing; a living stream never to be stepped in twice as genes flow from the past into the future. Alex Shoumatoff's *The Mountain of Names: A History of the Human Family* (Simon and Schuster, 1985; reissued, Kodansha, 1995) uses that analogy to trace the human pedigree with an extraordinary collection of anecdotes on pedigrees, relatedness and ancestry, built around the Mormon repository in Salt Lake City.

R. Cole-Turner, in *The New Genesis: Theology and the Genetic Revolution* (Westminster Press, 1993), gives the established Christian view of gene therapy, genetic screening and genetic engineering and asks how genes might alter views of the human relationship to God. For those not well versed in theology *The Oxford Companion to the Bible*, edited by B. M. Metzger and M. D. Coogan (Oxford University Press, 1994), and *The Oxford Illustrated History of Christianity*, edited by J. McManners (Oxford University Press, 1990), both do something to compensate for all those Sundays not spent in church.

The history of ideas about inheritance is discussed by R. C. Olby in the *Companion Encyclopedia of the History of Medicine*, eds W. F. Bynum and Roy Porter (Routledge, 1993). Alexander Graham Bell and deafness is in N. E. Groce, *Everyone Here Spoke Sign Language: Hereditary Deafness on Martha's Vineyard* (reissued, Harvard University Press, 1988); and a scientific review of the most recent work can be found in K. Steele and S. D. M. Brown, 'Genes and deafness', in *Trends in Genetics* 10, pp. 428–35 (1994).

CHAPTER I: THE PARADOX OF ARMAGEDDON

Adams, M. D., et al, 'Initial assessment of human gene diversity and expression patterns based on 83 million nucleotides of cDNA sequence', *Nature* 377 supp., 28 September 1995, pp. 3–174.

Bittles, A. H., and Neel, J. V., 'The cost of human inbreeding and their implications for variations at the DNA level', *Nature Genetics* 8, pp. 117–21 (1994).

Boyer, P., *When Time Shall Be No More: Prophecy Belief in Modern American Culture*, The Belknap Press of Harvard University Press, 1992.

Cannon-Albright, L. A., et al, 'Familiality of cancer in Utah', *Cancer Research* 54, pp. 2378–85 (1994).

De la Chapelle, A., 'Disease mapping in isolated human populations: the example of Finland', *Journal of Medical Genetics* 30, pp. 857–65 (1993).

Goody, J., *The Development of the Family and Marriage in Europe*, Cambridge University Press, 1983.

Morral, N., et al, 'The origin of the major cystic fibrosis mutation (DeltaF508) in European populations', *Nature Genetics* 7, pp. 169–75 (1994).

Newman, M., et al, 'Structure of Bam H1 endonuclease bound to DNA: partial folding and unfolding on DNA binding', *Science* 269, pp. 656–63 (1995).

Struewing, J. P., et al, 'Detection of eight BRCA1 mutations in 10 Breast /Ovarian Cancer families, including 1 family with male breast cancer', *American Journal of Human Genetics* 57, pp. 1–7 (1995).

Varilo, T., et al, 'The age of a human mutation: Genealogical and linkage disequilibrium analysis of the CLN5 mutation in the Finnish population', *American Journal of Human Genetics*, 58, pp. 506–12 (1996).

CHAPTER II: SEX AND TAXES

Dorit, R. L., et al, 'Absence of polymorphism at the ZFY locus on the human Y chromosome', *Science* 268, pp.1183–5 (1995).

Heyer, E., 'Mitochondrial and nuclear genetic contribution of female founders to a contemporary population in North-East Quebec', *American Journal of Human Genetics* 56, pp. 1450–5 (1995).

Jobling, M. A., and Tyler-Smith, C., 'Fathers and sons – the Y chromosome and human evolution', *Trends in Genetics* 11, pp. 449–56 (1995).

Torroni, A., et al, 'mtDA variation of aboriginal Siberians reveals distinct genetic affinities with native Americans', *American Journal of Human Genetics* 53, pp. 591–608 (1993).

Wallace, D. C., and Torroni, A., 'American Indian prehistory as written in the mitochondrial DNA: a review', *Human Biology* 64, pp. 403–16 (1992).

Wolff, G., et al, 'On the genetics of mandibular prognathism: analysis of large European noble families', *Journal of Medical Genetics* 30, pp. 112–16 (1993).

Wright, R., *Stolen Continents: The Indian Story*, Pimlico, 1993.

CHAPTER III: THE SEARCH FOR THE LOST TRIBES

Anonymous, *Beyond the Sambatyon: the Myth of the Ten Lost Tribes*, The Nahum Goldmann Museum of the Jewish Diaspora, 1991.

Bonné-Tamir, B., and Adam, A., eds, *Genetic Diversity among Jews: Disease and Markers at the DNA level*, Oxford University Press, 1992.

Cohn-Sherbok, L., and Cohn-Sherbok, D., *A Short History of Judaism*, Oneworld Publications, 1994.

Garlake, P. S., *Great Zimbabwe*. Thames and Hudson & Stein and Day, 1973.

Kerem, E., et al, 'Highly variable incidence of cystic fibrosis and different mutation distribution among different Jewish ethnic groups in Israel', *Human Genetics* 95, pp. 193–7, 1995.

MacDonald, K., *A People that Shall Dwell Alone: Judaism as a Group Evolutionary Strategy*, Praeger, 1994.

Parfitt, T., *Journey to the Vanished City: The Search for a Lost Tribe of Israel*, Hodder and Stoughton, 1992.

Risch, N., et al, 'Genetic analysis of idiopathic torsion dystonia in Ashkenazi Jews and their recent descent from a small founder population', *Nature Genetics* 9, pp. 152–9 (1995).

Ritte, U., et al, 'The differences among Jewish communites – Maternal and paternal contributions', *Journal of Molecular Evolution* 37, pp. 435–40 (1993).

Weingarten, M. A., *Changing Health and Changing Culture: The Yemenite Jews In Israel*, Praeger, 1992.

CHAPTER IV: THE SOUL BENEATH THE SKIN

Altick, R. D., *The Shows of London*, The Belknap Press of Harvard University Press, 1978.

Deacon, H. J., 'Southern Africa and modern human origins', *Proceedings of the Royal Society* Series B: 337, pp. 177–83 (1992).

Fraser, S., ed., *The Bell Curve Wars: Race, Intelligence and the Future of America*, Basic Books, 1995.

Gaston, R. S., et al, 'Racial equality in renal transplantation: the disparate impact of HLA-based allocation', *Journal of the American Medical Association* 270, pp. 1352–6 (1993).

Hacker, A., *Two Nations: Black and White, Separate, Hostile, Unequal*, Ballantine Books, 1995.

Hill, H. Z., 'The function of melanin: or six blind people examine an elephant', *BioEssays* 14, pp. 49–56 (1992).

Jorde, L. B. et al, 'Origins and affinities of modern humans: a comparison of mitochondrial and nuclear genetic data', *American Journal of Human Genetics* 57, pp. 523–38 (1995).

Lapping, B., *Apartheid: A History*, Grafton, 1986, & Braziller, 1990.

Malik, K., *The Meaning of Race: Race, History and Culture in Western Society*, Macmillan Press & NYU Press, 1996.

Ortiz de Montellano, B., 'Melanin, Afrocentricity and pseudoscience', *Yearbook of Physical Anthropology* 36, pp. 31–58 (1993).

Robins, A. H., ed., *Biological Perspectives on Human Pigmentation*, Cambridge University Press, 1991.

CHAPTER V: ORIGINAL SIN

Comings, D. E., et al, 'The Dopamine D2 receptor locus as a modifying gene in neuro-psychiatric disorders', *Journal of the American Medical Association* 266, pp. 1793–1800 (1991).

Chen, Z.-I., et al, 'Norrie disease and MAO genes: nearest neighbors', *Human Molecular Genetics* 4, pp. 1729–37 (1995).

Cohn, N., *The Pursuit of the Millennium: Revolutionary Millenarians and Mystical Anarchists of the Middle Ages*, reissued, Pimlico, 1993.

Craig, I., 'Misbehaving monoamine oxidase gene', *Current Biology* 4, pp. 175–7 (1994).

Dreyfuss, R. C., and Nelkin, D., 'The jurisprudence of genetics', *Vanderbilt Law Review* 45, pp. 313–48 (1992).

Farrington, D. P., 'Implications of criminal career research for the prevention of offending', *Journal of Adolescence* 13, pp. 93–113 (1990).

McGuffin, P., et al, 'Genetic basis of schizophrenia', *Lancet* 346, pp. 678–82 (1995).

Mullett, M., *Calvin*, Routledge, 1989.

Silbersweig, D. A., et al, 'A functional neuroanatomy of hallucinations in schizo-phrenia', *Nature* 378, pp. 176–9 (1995).

Thomson, O., *A History of Sin*, Canongate, 1993.

CHAPTER VI: DEATH OR RESURRECTION

Antonarakis, S. E., et al, 'Molecular etiology of Factor VIII deficiency in hemophilia A', *Human Mutation* 5, pp. 1–22 (1995).

Kim, N. W. et al, 'Specific association of human telomerase activity with immortal cells and cancer', *Science* 266, pp. 2011–2105 (1994).

Michod, R., *Eros and Evolution: A Natural Philosophy of Sex*, Addison-Wesley /Longman, 1995.

Neel, J. V., 'New approaches to evaluating the genetic effects of the atomic bombs', *American Journal of Human Genetics* 57, pp. 1263–6 (1995).

Noel, G., *Ena: Spain's English Queen*, Constable, 1984.

Nowak, R., 'Discovery of AT gene sparks off biomedical research bonanza', *Science* 268, pp. 1700–1 (1995).

Potts, D. M., and Potts, W. T. W., *Queen Victoria's Gene*, Alan Sutton, 1995.

Putnam, F. W., 'Hiroshima and Nagasaki revisited: the Atomic Bomb Casualty Commission and the Radiation Effects Research Foundation', *Perspectives in Biology and Medicine* 37, pp. 515–45 (1994).

Ricklefs, R. E., and Finch, C. E., *Aging, a Natural History*, Scientific American Books, 1995.

Wallace, D. C., 'Mitochondrial DNA sequence variation in human evolution and disease', *Proceedings of the National Academy of Science* 91, pp. 8739–46 (1994)

Zakian, V. A., 'Telomeres: beginning to understand the end', *Science* 270, pp. 1601–7 (1995).

PHOTOGRAPHIC CREDITS

Page ix *reproduced by courtesy of* Wellcome Institute Library, London; xi *Punch* Magazine; xii The Library, Academy of Natural Sciences of Philadelphia; xv British Film Institute; 3 AKG London; 4 David South; 7 Bibliothèque de la Ville de Colmar; 8 CNRI/SPL; 10 Prof. P. Motta/Dept of Anatomy, La Sapienza University, Rome/SPL; 11 *both* Biophoto Associates; 15 Range/Bettmann; 16 Image Select; 18 AKG London; 19 Mendelianum, Brno; 21 SCR Photo Library; 22 *top* Prof. Oscar Miller/SPL, *bottom* Biophoto Associates/SPL; 23 Oxford Molecular Biophysics Laboratory/SPL; 26 *left* Hulton Deutsch Collection, *right* NIH/SPL; 33 Alfred Pasieka/SPL; 34 *left* Dennis Stephenson, *right* Jane Burton/Bruce Coleman Ltd; 35 from *Clinical Genetics* 39, 1991 by I. Winship et al; 37 Zev Radovan, Jerusalem; 39 Bodleian Library/Robert Harding Picture Library; 41 Museum Pomorskie, Gdansk/AKG London; 44 Church of Jesus Christ of Latter-Day Saints. Used by permission; 46 from *The Conquest of Arid America* by William Ellsworth Smythe, 1899; 47 Robert Harding Picture Library; 48 Range/Bettmann; 50 Aneel K. Aggarwal & M. Newman; 55 British Library; 57 *top* James King-Holmes/SPL; *bottom* Kings College School of Medicine/SPL; 58 Yann Layme; 59 Church of Jesus Christ of Latter-Day Saints. Used by permission; 61 Steve Jones; 63 The *Independent*/Philip Meech; 66 Steve Jones; 68 *left* Hulton Deutsch Collection, *right* National Portrait Gallery; 69 The College of Arms; 73 Bibliothèque Municipale de Grenoble; 76 CNRI/SPL; 78–9 *all* Petit Format/Nestlé/Steiner/SPL; 85 J. D. A. Delhanty, University College London; 88–9 *background picture* H. Sander, Institute of Human Genetics, University of Freiburg; 88 *inset* Phillips, International Fine Art Auctioneers/Bridgeman Art Library, London; 89 *inset* Museo Real Academia de Bellas Artes, Madrid/Index/Bridgeman Art Library, London; 91 Musée Condé, Chantilly/Bridgeman Art Library, London; 93 K. R. Porter/SPL; 96 Peter Newark's Western Americana; 97 Culver Pictures; 102–3 *all* from *Monograph of the Land & Freshwater Mollusca of the British Isles* by J. W. Taylor 1907 & 1914/University College London; 105 Peter Newark's Western Americana; 106 Western History Collections, University of Oklahoma Library; 108 from *Newes from America* by John Underhill, 1638; 110 *both* Mashantucket Pequot Tribal Nation Public Relations; 113 Steve Jones; 115 David South; 116 Private collection/Bridgeman Art Library, London; 121 Tessa Livingstone; 122 Associated Press; 125 *both* Museum of Welsh Life; 128 Sonia Halliday Photographs; 129 Scala; 130–1 Reproduced by kind permission of the Lord Bishop of Durham & the Church Commissioners for England; 132 Colin Clark; 133 Garo Nalbandian/ASAP; 134 Giraudon; 137 British Museum, London; 138 from *Great Britain & the USA: Revealed as the New Order* by A. J. Ferris, 1941. Jewish National &

University Library/Beth Hatefutsoth Photo Archive; 140 Yivo Institute for Jewish Research; 141 BBC Television; 143 Associated Press; 144 Jewish National & University Library/Beth Hatefutsoth Photo Archive; 145 British Library; 146 Comstock; 148 National Archives of Zimbabwe; 149 Colin Clark; 155 Popperfoto; 162 Ashmolean Museum, Oxford; 164 from *Who are the Europeans?* by A. Piazza, *Science* 260, 1993, with permission of the author; 166 University of Cambridge Committee for Aerial Photography; 169 British Museum, London; 170 Musée de l'Homme, Paris; 171 South African Library, Cape Town; 174–5 London Topographical Society; 179 Omikro/SPL; 181 SPL; 182 *left* Bernard Vandermeersch, *right* Véronique Barriel; 184 H. L. Pierce Fund, courtesy Museum of Fine Arts, Boston; 186 Steve Jones; 188 Fitzwilliam Museum, University of Cambridge/Bridgeman Art Library, London; 189 *right* John Burbridge/SPL; *left* Astrid & Hanns-Frieder Michler/SPL; 191 Nancy Kedersha /Immunogen/SPL; 193 *left* Leonard Lee Rue/Bruce Coleman Ltd, *right* Johnny Johnson/Bruce Coleman Ltd; 194 Klaus Paysan; 195 Biophoto Associates/SPL; 200 *main picture top* Hugh Fears, *inset top* Johan Binnemann, *centre right* H. L. Deacon, *bottom right* South Africa Museum/H. L. Deacon; 202 Mary Evans Picture Library; 203 Steve Jones; 205 J.L. Dubin; 208 Charles Taylor; 210 Brown Brothers; 211 Chris Hale; 216 Visible Human Project, National Library of Medicine, USA; 218 *both* Museo di Psichiatria e Antropologia Criminale, Turin/Deutsches Hygiene-Museum, Dresden; 223 P. Thomas/Explorer; 225 National Museum, Stockholm/Bridgeman Art Library, London; 229 David South; 230 Alfred Pasieka/SPL; 232 Bethlem Royal Hospital Archives & Museum; 233 *both* D. A. Silbersweig MD & E. Stern MD; 235 Prof. P. M. Motta & T. Fujita/SPL; 241 David South; 244 Musée d'Unterlinden, Colmar /Bridgeman Art Library, London; 247 *both* Bildarchiv Photo Marburg; 248 *top left* Dr P. Marazzi/SPL, *top right* BSIP/SPL, *bottom left* CNRI/SPL, *bottom right* Custom Medical Stock Photo/SPL; 251 Biophoto Associates/SPL; 254 *left* National Portrait Gallery, London, *right* Wallace Collection, London/Bridgeman Art Library, London; 255 *top Forbes* Magazine Collection, New York/Bridgeman Art Library, London, *bottom* Hulton Deutsch Collection; 258 William Sturgis Bigelow Collection, courtesy Museum of Fine Arts, Boston; 259 Hulton Deutsch Collection; 260 Radiation Effects Research Foundation, Hiroshima; 264 Howard Hughes Medical Institute; 265 Mari-Wyn Barley; 267 David South; 271 Egyptian Museum, Cairo/Werner Forman Archive; 273 *left* J.C. Revy/SPL, *right* Secchi, Lecaque, Roussel, UCLAF, CNRI/SPL; 274 *left* BSIP PIR /SPL, *right* Steven Sheriff, Bristol-Myers Squibb Pharmaceutical Research Institute; 276 Prof. P. Motta/Dept of Anatomy, La Sapienza University, Rome/SPL; 278 National Medical Slide Bank; 279 *left* Philippe Plailly/Eurelios/SPL, *right* Aziz Sancar, University of North Carolina; 280 David Kipling, MRC Human Genetics Unit, Edinburgh.

The image used on the endpapers is a light micrograph of human blood, reproduced by permission of Andrew Syred/SPL.

Abbreviation: SPL = Science Photo Library

INDEX

Page numbers in *italic* refer to illustrations